ADVANCES IN ELECTRON TRANSFER CHEMISTRY

Volume 5 • 1996

ADVANCES IN ELECTRON TRANSFER CHEMISTRY

Editor: PATRICK S. MARIANO
Department of Chemistry and
Biochemistry
University of Maryland-College Park

VOLUME 5 • 1996

 JAI PRESS INC.

Greenwich, Connecticut   *London, England*

CONTENTS

LIST OF CONTRIBUTORS

Angelo Albini

Dipartimento di Chimica Organica
Università di Pavia
Pavia, Italy

Janine Cossy

Laboratoire de Chimie Organique
Associe au CNRS
Paris, France

Elisa Fasani

Dipartimento di Chimica Organica
Università di Pavia
Pavia, Italy

Mauro Freccero

Dipartimento di Chimica Organica
Università di Pavia
Pavia, Italy

Linda J. Johnston

Steacie Institute for Molecular Sciences
National Research Council Canada
Ottawa, Canada

Frederick D. Lewis

Department of Chemistry
Northwestern University
Evanston, Illinois

Jean-Pierre Pete

Laboratoire des Rearrangements
Thermiques et Photochemiques
Université de Reims
Champagne-Ardenne
Reims, France

Norman P. Schepp

Steacie Institute for Molecular Sciences
National Research Council Canada
Ottawa, Canada

PREFACE

The consideration of reaction mechanisms involving the movement of single electrons is now becoming quite common in the fields of chemistry and biochemistry. Studies conducted in recent years have uncovered a large number of chemical and enzymatic processes that proceed via single electron transfer pathways. Still numerous investigations are underway probing the operation of electron transfer reactions in organic, organometallic, biochemical, and excited state systems. In addition, theoretical and experimental studies are being conducted to gain information about the factors that govern the rates of single electron transfer. It is clear that electron transfer chemistry is now one of the most active areas of chemical study.

The series, *Advances in Electron Transfer Chemistry*, has been designed to allow scientists who are developing new knowledge in this rapidly expanding area to describe their most recent research findings. Each contribution is in a minireview format focusing on the individual author's own work as well as the studies of others that address related problems. Hopefully, *Advances in Electron Transfer Chemistry* will serve as a useful series for those interested in learning about current breakthroughs in this rapidly expanding area of chemical research.

Patrick S. Mariano
Series Editor

PHOTOADDITION REACTIONS OF AMINES WITH ARYL OLEFINS AND ARENES

Frederick D. Lewis

Advances in Electron Transfer Chemistry
Volume 5, pages 1–39.
Copyright © 1996 by JAI Press Inc.
All rights of reproduction in any form reserved.
ISBN: 0-7623-0062-0

1. INTRODUCTION

Irradiation of styrenes[1-3] and stilbenes[4,5] in the presence of aliphatic amines results in the formation of 1,2-addition products along with aryl olefin reduction products. Research in the author's laboratory during the 1970s led to a proposed mechanism for the reaction of stilbene with tertiary and secondary amines which is outlined in Scheme 1.[5] According to this mechanism, electron transfer quenching of singlet stilbene by ground state amine results in the formation of a singlet exciplex or radical ion pair. Transfer of an amine α-C–H (tertiary amines) or N–H (secondary amines) to stilbene results in the formation of a radical pair, which can combine to yield adducts, disproportionate, or undergo cage escape. This mechanism was supported by analogy to mechanisms proposed for 1,2- and 1,4-addition reactions of arenes with amines.[6,7] These mechanisms have stood the test of time, more or less intact. The intermolecular photoaddition reaction of arenes and aryl olefins with amines has been the subject of several review articles,[8-12] including a comprehensive review by Yoon et al.[12] in the preceding volume of this series.

Whereas addition reactions of singlet aryl olefins and arenes with secondary and tertiary amines are common, addition of ammonia has not been reported and addition of primary amines

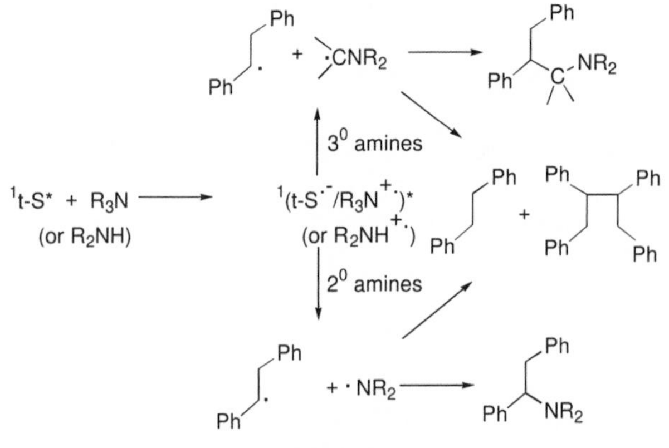

Scheme 1.

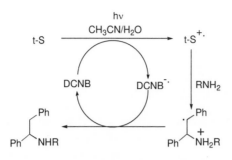

Scheme 2.

has been observed for styrene but not for stilbene or most arenes. Lack of reactivity with ammonia and primary amines is a consequence of their high oxidation potentials, which render the initial electron transfer process endergonic. Yasuda and Pac and their co-workers[13-16] have developed an efficient method for the addition of ammonia and primary amines to aryl olefins and arenes, employing the method of electron transfer sensitization. As outlined in Scheme 2 for the addition of stilbene with ammonia, photoinduced electron transfer from stilbene to dicyanobenzene (DCNB) generates the stilbene cation radical and the DCNB anion radical. Nucleophilic addition of the amine to the stilbene cation radical results in the formation of an intermediate which is converted to adducts via subsequent proton and electron transfer steps, which also serve to regenerate the sensitizer.

The 1980s witnessed a revival of interest in synthetic photochemistry, largely based on the successful application of intramolecular arene–olefin and enone–olefin photochemical cycloaddition reactions to the synthesis of polycyclic natural and unnatural products.[17] The potential application of intramolecular arene–amine addition to the synthesis of alkaloids was suggested in 1973 by Bryce-Smith et al.,[18] based on their observation of intramolecular photochemical 1,4-addition reaction of the (*N,N*-dimethylaminoalkyl)benzenes **1** and **2** to yield **3** and **4**, respectively. Intramolecular addition reactions have subsequently been observed for a large number of (aminoal-

1: n = 1
2: n = 2

3: n = 1
4: n = 2

kyl)arenes, (aminoalkyl)styrenes, and (aminoalkyl)stilbenes using both direct and electron transfer-sensitized irradiation conditions. Synthetic and mechanistic aspects of these reactions
are the subject of Part 3 of this review. Part 2 describes aspects
of direct and sensitized intermolecular photoamination reactions
of relevance to the discussion of intramolecular reactions and
is not intended to be a comprehensive review of this topic.
Photophysical aspects of intramolecular and intermolecular exciplex formation will not be covered in detail.

2. INTERMOLECULAR ADDITION REACTIONS

2.1. Direct Irradiation With Tertiary Amines

The initial step in the addition reactions of arenes and aryl
olefins with tertiary amines is electron transfer quenching of
the singlet arene or aryl olefin acceptor by a ground state amine
donor. The free energy of electron transfer can be calculated
using Weller's equation (Eq. 1);

$$\Delta G_{et} = E_{D^{ox}} - E_{A^{red}} - E_S + C \qquad (1)$$

where E_S is the singlet energy of the acceptor, $E_{A^{red}}$ the reduction
potential of the acceptor, $E_{D^{ox}}$ the oxidation potential of the
amine, and the final term is the solvent dependent Coulombic
attraction energy (–0.06 eV in acetonitrile and 0.54 eV in hex-
ane).[19] Values of E_s and E_{red} for some of the aryl olefins and
arenes discussed in this review are reported in Table 1.[20] Amine
gas phase ionization potentials and amine, aryl olefin, and arene
oxidation potentials are reported in Table 2. Quenching of the
aryl olefins and arenes in Table 1 by Et_3N in nonpolar solvents
is calculated to be exergonic and observed to occur with rate
constants near the rate of diffusion, except in the case of phen-

Table 1. Singlet Energies E_s, Ground State Reduction Potentials E_{red}, and Singlet State Reduction Potentials E^*_{red} for Selected Aryl Olefins and Arenes

Substrate	$E_s \, (eV)^a$	$E_{red} \, (V)^b$	$E^*_{red} \, (eV)^c$
styrene	4.22	−2.46	1.76
trans-stilbene	3.53	−2.15	1.38
naphthalene	3.97	−2.48	1.49
phenanthrene	3.58	−2.44	1.14
anthracene	3.28	−1.96	1.32
9-cyanoanthracene	3.42	−1.88	1.54
1,4-dicyanobenzene	4.2	−1.60	2.6

Notes: [a]From Refs. 9 and 20a.
[b]Half-wave reduction potentials in acetonitrile solution vs. SCE from Ref. 20b.
[c]Sum of singlet energy and reduction potential.

Table 2. Oxidation Potentials E_{ox} and Ionization Potentials of Amines, Aryl Olefins, and Arenes

Substrate	$E_{ox} \, (V)^a$	$IP \, (eV)^b$
N,N-dimethylaniline	0.52	7.1
triethylamine	0.79	7.50
diethylamine	1.01	8.01
ethylamine	1.60	8.86
ammonia		10.15
styrene	2.2	8.47
stilbene	1.50	7.95
naphthalene	1.62	8.16
phenanthrene	1.58	7.6
anthracene	1.16	7.43

Notes: [a]Half-wave oxidation potentials for amines and arenes from Ref. 15 and for aryl olefins from Ref. 9.
[b]Ionization potentials for amines from Ref. 20c and for arenes from Ref. 20d.

anthrene. The rate constant for endergonic quenching of phenanthrene by Et_3N (3.5×10^6 $M^{-1}s^{-1}$ in cyclohexane) increases with increasing solvent polarity or the use of the stronger electron donor, N,N-diethylaniline.[21] Rate constants are also dependent upon aromatic substituents which effect the singlet state reduction potential or singlet energy.[21,22]

Exciplex fluorescence is observed upon quenching of the singlet aryl olefins and arenes in Table 1 (except phenanthrene) by tertiary amines in nonpolar solvents.[5,9,21,22] Exciplex fluorescence has also recently been observed upon quenching of singlet fullerenes by tertiary amines.[23] The stability of the exciplex is dependent upon the redox properties of the donor and acceptor and the solvent polarity.[19,24] Increasing solvent polarity results in a red-shift of the exciplex emission maximum, indicative of the charge-transfer character of the exciplex. The exciplex lifetime also decreases in polar solvents, as a consequence of more rapid exciplex decay via return electron transfer or dissociation to radical ions. In the case of the stilbene–triethylamine system, formation of long-lived stilbene anion radicals has been observed by time-resolved resonance Raman spectroscopy in the polar solvent acetonitrile.[25] The process of dissociation to free radical ions in polar solvents is presumed to proceed via solvation of the initially formed exciplex or contact radical ion pair (CRIP) to yield a solvent-separated radical ion pair (SSRIP) which dissociates to free radical ions. For the purposes of this discussion, an exciplex can have varying degrees of electron transfer and is termed a CRIP in the limiting case of complete electron transfer.

The timing of the proton transfer process in Scheme 1 has proven to be the most difficult aspect of this mechanism to elucidate. The proton transfer process might occur via the singlet exciplex, CRIP, SSRIP, or free radical ions; or even be synchronous with electron transfer. Exciplex or radial ion pair intersystem crossing yields triplet stilbene, which does not react with amines.[26] The efficiency of addition of stilbene[5] and anthracene[6] with tertiary amines increases with increasing solvent polarity, in accord with the proposal that complete electron transfer must precede proton transfer in these reactions. On the basis of indirect kinetic evidence, we suggested that proton transfer in the stilbene–triethylamine system occurred via a relaxed CRIP[25]; however, Klaukien and Lehnig[27] have recently presented evidence, based on CIDNP spectroscopy, for the involvement of the SSRIP. Free radical ions have been excluded as a possible intermediate in the stilbene–triethylamine addition reaction, but may be involved in other addition and reduction processes.[25]

The addition reactions of styrenes with tertiary amines occur in nonpolar as well as polar solvents.[3] The enhanced reactivity of styrene vs. stilbene in nonpolar solvents may reflect either its larger singlet state reduction potential (Table 1) or increased kinetic basicity of its more localized anion radical. Addition reactions of singlet stilbene with "activated" tertiary amines (e.g. those with allyl or propargyl substituents) also occur in nonpolar solvents.[28] Hydrogen atom transfer (concerted electron and proton transfer) was proposed to account for highly selective hydrogen transfer in these reactions. Increased kinetic acidity of the poorly solvated amine cation radicals may also account for the selectivity of proton transfer. Donor–acceptor covalent bonding may, in some cases, precede proton transfer, as has been proposed for the reaction of anthracene with dimethylaniline in acetonitrile solution which yields the adduct **5**.[6,29]

The radical pairs formed upon proton transfer in the exciplex or radical ion pair intermediates can combine to form adducts, disproportionate, or diffuse apart (Scheme 1). Combination results in the formation of 1,2-adducts in the case of aryl olefins,[1–5] 1,4-adducts in the case of anthracene,[6] and mixtures of 1,2- and 1,4-adducts in the case of benzene and naphthalene.[7,30] Adduct formation has also been observed in the reactions of singlet fullerenes with tertiary amines; however, product structures have not as yet been reported.[23c] Radical pair disproportionation can result in regeneration of ground state reactants or reduced arene and oxidized amine. The former process would decrease the quantum yield of addition, whereas the latter process lowers the preparative yield. Dihydroaromatics are frequently isolated as by-products or even the major product of arene–amine reactions. Oxidized amines are generally unstable and not isolated; however, Klaukien and Lehnig[27] have identified the enamine formed in the reaction of stilbene with triethylamine in their CIDNP investigation. The cage-escaped 1,2-diphenylethyl radical formed in the reaction of stilbene with triethylamine has been trapped with a nitrosoalkane and the adduct detected by EPR.[31] Radical self-coupling accounts for the formation of tetraphenylbutane (Scheme 1) and related reductive dimers from styrenes and arenes.

The addition reactions of tertiary amines with nonsymmetric aryl olefins display varying degrees of regioselectivity. Regioselectivity is presumably determined in the proton transfer step of these additions. Addition of tertiary amines to styrenes normally occurs with bond formation at the styrene α-carbon[1–3]; however, the reaction of 1-(p-cyanophenyl)propene with trimethylamine yields a mixture of α- and β-adducts.[3] Additions of tertiary amines to stilbenes substituted on one aromatic ring are nonregioselective.[22a] In contrast, the photochemical addition of triethylamine and the electron-deficient cyclopropane 6 is highly regioselective, yielding the ring-opened adduct 7 along with the reduction product 8.[32]

Reactions of stilbene with nonsymmetrical tertiary amines also yields mixtures of adducts (Scheme 3).[8,33] The product ratios

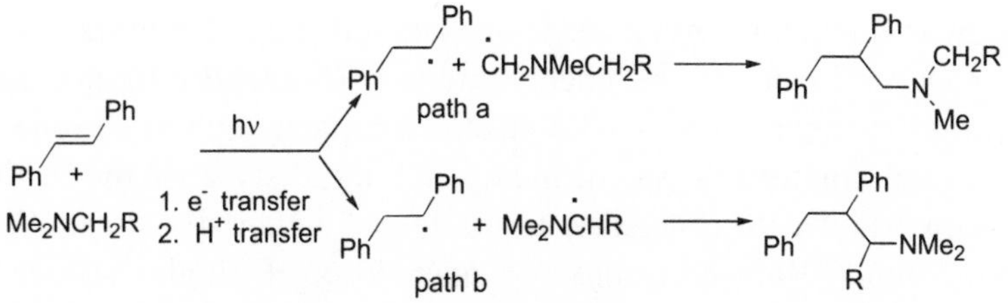

Scheme 3.

indicate that there is a slight preference for proton transfer from methyl (path a) vs. ethyl (path b, R = Me) and a large preference for methyl or ethyl vs. isopropyl proton transfer. Similar trends have been reported for other amine photooxidation processes; however, the selectivity appears to be dependent upon the identity of the basic species.[34,35] Selective proton transfer from the less substituted alkyl group has been attributed to steric inhibition of overlap between the nitrogen p-orbital and the α-C–H bond. Highly selective formation of the product derived from the more substituted radical (Scheme 3, path b) is observed in nonpolar solvents when R is a radical-stabilizing substituent (phenyl, vinyl, acetylene, methoxycarbonyl); however, the selectivity decreases with increasing solvent polarity.[8] These trends indicate that the transition state for deprotonation of amine cation radicals may be highly variable; the extent of bond breaking, and hence the selectivity, depending upon kinetic acidity of the α-protons and the nature of the basic species.

2.2. Direct Irradiation With Secondary and Primary Amines

The photochemical reactions of aryl olefins and arenes with secondary and primary amines are assumed to occur via a sequential electron transfer–proton transfer mechanism similar to that for tertiary amines (Scheme 1). Exciplex fluorescence is not observed in solution;[36] however, weak exciplex fluorescence has been reported for the styrene–diethylamine system in a supersonic jet.[37] Rate constants for quenching of strong acceptors such as stilbene[5] and styrene[36] by Et_2NH are diffusion controlled.

Slower quenching by Et_2NH is observed with the weaker acceptors anthracene[6] and phenanthrene.[21] Quenching by primary amines is observed only with strong acceptors such as styrene.[36] Detailed kinetic analysis of the quenching of styrenes by Et_2NH is consistent with reversible formation of a short-lived exciplex (<0.1 ns).[36] Rate constants for quenching of singlet stilbene[5] and 9-cyanophenanthrene[38] decrease in the order $Me_2NH >$ $Et_2NH > i\text{-}Pr_2NH$, even though α-alkylation decreases the amine ionization potential.[20c] No pronounced steric effect is observed for quenching of stilbene by tertiary amines.[8]

Okada et al.[39] have observed the formation of a charge-transfer stabilized exciplex upon quenching of singlet pyrene by N-methylaniline by means of picosecond laser flash photolysis. Decay of this exciplex via N–H proton transfer and intersystem crossing pathways is much more rapid than is the case for the N,N-dimethylaniline exciplex. This behavior was attributed to a N–H hydrogen-bonding interaction with the arene anion radical in the exciplex. A specific hydrogen-bonding interaction might account for the observed decrease in fluorescence quenching rates upon secondary amine α-alkylation.[5,38]

Exciplex N–H hydrogen bonding can also account for the selective formation of N–H vs. α-C–H adducts observed in most reactions of aryl olefins and arenes with secondary amines (Scheme 1). The absence of significant deuterium isotope effects for either fluorescence quenching or product formation in the reactions of secondary amines with anthracene[6] or 9-cyanophenanthrene[38] indicates that the barrier for N–H transfer must be very small. Quantum yields for stilbene[5] and anthracene[6] N–H adduct formation are larger in nonpolar vs. polar solvents and little addition is observed in hydroxylic solvents. Solvation of the exciplex may disrupt the exciplex hydrogen bond, creating a solvent-induced barrier for N–H transfer. Electron-withdrawing aryl substituents which stabilize the exciplex also decrease quantum yields for N–H addition to styrenes[3] and phenanthrenes.[38] In the case of 1,2-diphenylacetylene, N–H adduct formation with secondary amines competes with reduction to stilbene, but no reaction is observed with tertiary amines.[4]

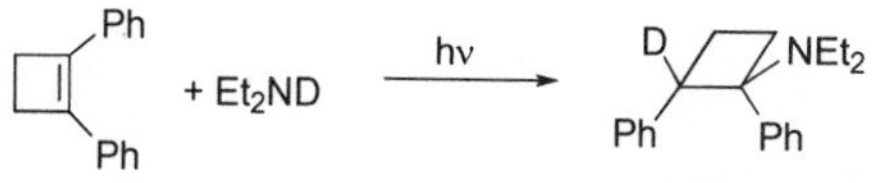

9

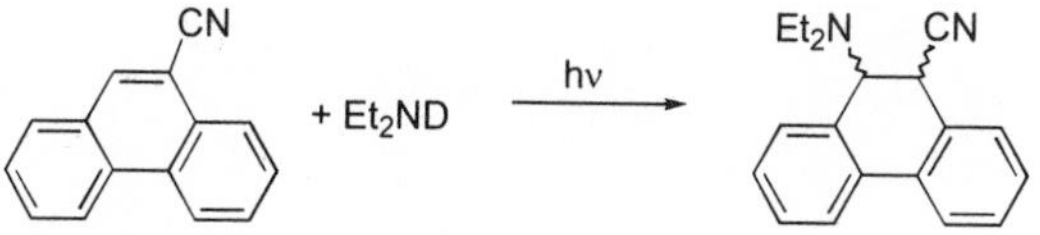

10

The radical pair resulting from N–H transfer can undergo combination, disproportionation, or cage escape (Scheme 1). Addition of Et_2NH to several ring-substituted styrenes occurs with bond formation at the styrene α-carbon.[3] Mixtures of regioisomers are formed in the addition of Et_2NH to stilbenes substituted on one benzene ring.[41] The two reported investigations of the stereochemistry of radical pair combination provide conflicting results. Stereospecific *syn* addition is reported for the formation of adduct **9** from the reaction of 1,2-diphenylcyclobutene with Et_2ND,[40] whereas a 2:1 ratio of *syn:anti* adducts **10** was obtained from the reaction of 9-cyanophenanthrene with Et_2ND.[38]

Whereas most reactions of singlet arenes and aryl olefins with secondary amines result in N–H addition, there are exceptions to this generalization. Cookson et al.[1] reported that irradiation of 1-phenylcyclohexene in isopropylamine yielded a mixture of N–H and α-C–H adducts. Gilbert and co-workers[30] found that the reaction of benzene with dimethylamine yields N–H adducts, whereas pyridine reacts with diethylamine to yield the substitution product **11**, which presumably is formed by aromatization of the α-C–H adduct. Irradiation of stilbene and indole in mixed crystals yields both N–H and C–H adducts, product ratios being dependent upon the reactant ratio.[42] Investigation of the reactions of 9-cyanophenanthrene with primary and secondary

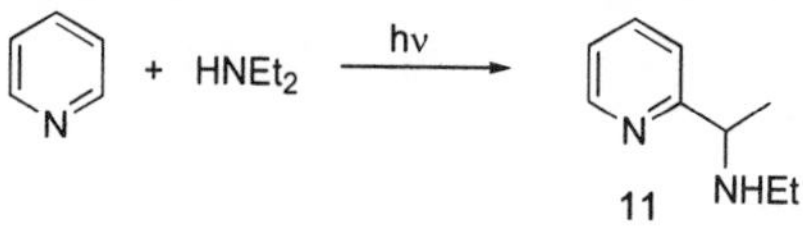

11

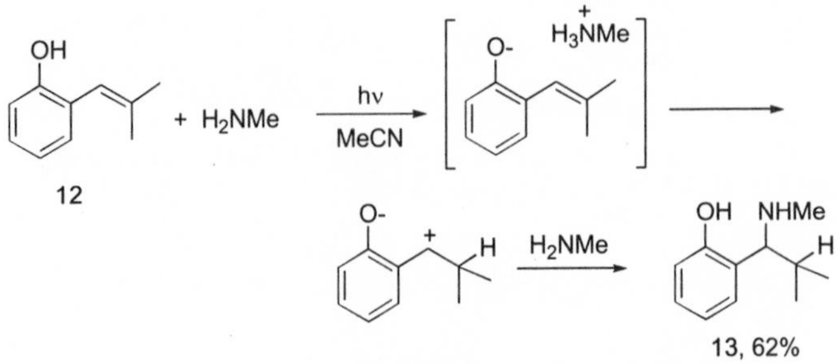

Scheme 4.

amines established that aminyl radical formation predominates in nonpolar solvents, but that aminoalkyl radical formation can be significant for α-alkylated amines in polar solvents. As noted above, α-alkylation may hinder N–H transfer while stabilizing the aminoalkyl radical formed via α-C–H transfer.

Yasuda et al.[43] have recently reported that irradiation of o-alkenylphenols and naphthols in the presence of primary or secondary amines results in Markovnikov addition of the amine. For example, irradiation of the alkenylphenol **12** with methylamine affords the adduct **13** (Scheme 4). The initial step in these reactions is proton transfer from the acidic phenol singlet state to the amine, which leads to the formation of the singlet phenolate anion and ammonium ion. Proton transfer from the ammonium ion to the phenolate anion yields a zwitterion, which undergoes nucleophilic addition of the amine. Thus the amine serves as a base in the initial step of this reaction and then as a nucleophile.

2.3. Electron Transfer-Sensitized Irradiation

The electron transfer (ET)-sensitized addition of nucleophiles to aryl olefins was initially reported by Arnold and co-workers.[44] A mechanism analogous to that in Scheme 2 was proposed for the p-cyanobenzoate-sensitized anti-Markovnikov addition of methanol to 1,1-diphenylethylene which yields the adduct **14**. Whereas terminal aryl olefins and indene were observed to undergo sensitized addition with a variety of nucleophiles (including water, acetic acid, and cyanide), 1,2-diarylolefins and arenes were found to be unreactive. Johnson and Schepp[45] have recently investigated the kinetics of reactions of styrene cation radicals with nucleophiles. Selected data for reactions of several styrenes with methanol in trifluoroethanol solution are reported in Table 3. Alkylation on the α-carbon has little effect on the rate of nucleophilic addition, whereas alkylation on the β-carbon significantly decreases the rate constant. Electron-donating aryl substituents which stabilize the styrene cation radical also significantly decrease the rate constant. Thus it is not surprising that stilbene and arenes fail to undergo ET-sensitized addition of methanol.

Yasuda and Pac and their co-workers[13–16] have significantly extended the scope of ET-sensitized addition in their studies of the photoamination reactions of arenes and aryl olefins (Scheme 2). DCNB is a powerful electron acceptor (Table 1) capable of oxidizing the singlet states of most arenes and aryl olefins (Table 2). Benzene does not undergo photoamination; however a dimethoxy derivative and biphenyl are reactive. Photoamination products are generally obtained in high preparative yield using ammonia or primary amines; however, secondary amines can only be used successfully with arenes such as anthracene which have oxidation potentials lower than those of secondary amines.[14] When the amine oxidation potential is comparable to

Table 3. Second Order Rate Constants k_{MeOH} for Addition of Methanol to Styrene Cation Radicals[a]

p–RC_6H–$CH=CHR'$	k_{MeOH}, $M^{-1}s^{-1}$	p–$RC_6H_4CH=CHR'$	k_{MeOH}, $M^{-1}s^{-1}$
R = H, R' = H	1.8×10^8	R = Me, R' = H	5.9×10^6
R = H, R' = Me	9.7×10^6	R = Me, R' = Me	5.6×10^6
R = F, R' = H	5.1×10^7	R = OMe, R' = H	3.0×10^4

Note: [a]From Ref. 45.

or lower than that of the arene, secondary electron transfer from the arene cation radical to the amine can compete with nucleophilic addition.

The initial step in the mechanism outlined in Scheme 2 is electron transfer quenching of the singlet arene by DCNB. Nucleophilic addition of the amine to the arene cation radical followed by proton and electron transfer steps yields the adduct and regenerates the sensitizer. Adduct formation requires the use of polar solvents, and yields are higher in aqueous vs. dry acetonitrile. Adduct formation is observed in moderately polar solvents (ethers) in the presence, but not in the absence, of an added salt, n-Bu$_4$NBF$_4$.[46] The solvent and salt effects were interpreted as evidence for C–N bond formation via the free arene radical cation, rather than via an ion pair (CRIP or SSRIP). However, Nieminen et al.[47] concluded that nucleophilic attack involves a radical ion pair on the basis of their laser flash photolysis investigation. In addition to this unresolved controversy, the timing of the subsequent proton transfer and electron transfer steps remains to be established.

Yasuda et al.[15] have used steady-state kinetics to investigate the reaction of the phenanthrene cation radical with ammonia and several primary amines. Rate constants were observed to increase from 0.3×10^8 M^{-1}s^{-1} for ammonia to 8.9×10^{-8} M^{-1}s^{-1} for t-butylamine. Correlation of these rates with the Taft σ^* parameter (Table 4) indicates that there is substantial development of positive charge on nitrogen in the transition state for bond formation.

Table 4. Second Order Rate Constants k_N for Addition of Amines to Phenanthrene Cation Radical and Taft σ^* Values[a]

Amine	Taft σ^*	$10^{-8} k_N$, M^{-1}s^{-1}
NH$_3$	0.49	0.3
MeNH$_2$	0.0	2.0
EtNH$_2$	−0.10	4.0
i-PrNH$_2$	−0.19	7.9
t-BuNH$_2$	−0.30	9.0

Note: [a]From Ref. 15.

Workentin et al.[48] have recently reported the results of an extensive laser flash photolysis investigation of the reactions of the cation radicals of 9-phenyl- and 9,10-diphenylanthracene (PA$^{+\bullet}$ and DPA$^{+\bullet}$, respectively) with amines. Primary amines react with both cation radicals via nucleophilic addition with rate constants which reflect both the amine basicity and a steric requirement for bond formation. Steric effects are more pronounced for addition of DPA$^{+\bullet}$ vs. PA$^{+\bullet}$, presumably due to the presence of substituents at both the 9- and 10-position. Tertiary amines and anilines react with PA$^{+\bullet}$ and DPA$^{+\bullet}$ via electron transfer with rate constants which correlate with amine ionization potentials. Rate constants for nucleophilic addition of primary amines are faster in acetonitrile than in acetonitrile/water solution. The rate-retarding effect of water is attributed to an equilibrium between the free amine (reactive) and hydrated amine (unreactive). The beneficial effect of water on preparative ET-sensitized photoamination may reflect its role as a catalyst for the proton transfer processes which follow C–N bond formation (Scheme 2). Hydration of the amine also should render it less reactive in primary and secondary electron transfer processes which can compete with the formation of the arene cation radical.

The ET-sensitized photoamination of 1,1-diarylethylenes with ammonia and most primary amines yields the anti-Markovnikov adducts.[16] Photoamination of unsymmetrically substituted stilbenes yields mixtures of regioisomers **15** and **16**.[17] Modest regioselectivity is observed for *p*-methyl or *p*-chloro substituents; however, highly selective formation of adduct **15** is observed for the *p*-methoxy substituent (Table 5). Selective formation of **15** was attributed to the effect of the methoxy substituent on the charge distribution in the stilbene cation radical. This regioselectivity has been exploited in the synthesis of intermediates in the preparation of isoquinolines and other alkaloids.[49] Photoamination of 1-phenyl-3,4-dihydronaphthalene yields a mixture of *syn* and *anti* adducts **17** and **18** (Scheme 5).[16] Use of bulky primary amines favors formation of the *syn* adduct (Table 5), presumably as a consequence of selective *anti* protonation of the intermediate carbanion.

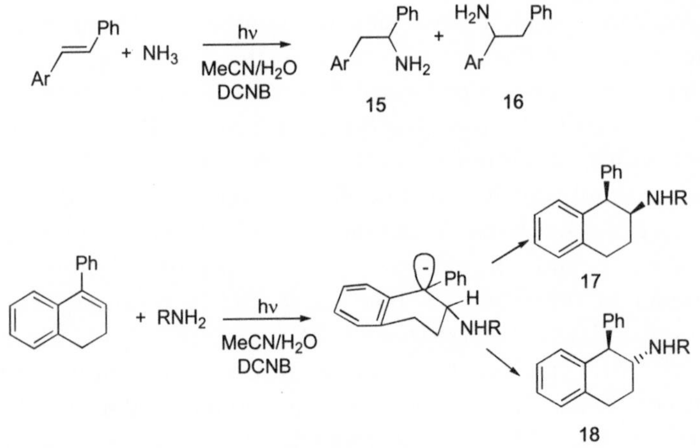

Scheme 5.

Mariano and co-workers[12,50] have employed the ET-sensitized irradiation of tertiary α-silylamines in the presence of silophiles to generate α-aminoalkyl radicals which can add to enones and other reactive olefins (Scheme 6). In these reactions the initial step is quenching of an excited acceptor such as DCA by the ground state tertiary amine. This methodology might prove applicable to arene–amine and aryl olefin–amine addition reactions. An example of an intramolecular addition to phenanthrene using this strategy is described in Part 3.3.

Table 5. Product Ratios Obtained for ET-Sensitized Addition of Ammonia to Substituted Stilbenes **15/16** and for Addition of Amines to 1-Phenyldihydronaphthalene **17/18**

Stilbene Substituent	15/16[a]	Amine	17/18[b]
p-Cl	1:0.9	NH_3	1:1.04
p-Me	1:0.6	i-PrNH$_2$	1:0.33
m-OMe	1:0.7	t-BuNH$_2$	1:0.27
p-OMe	1:0		

Notes: [a]From Ref. 17.
[b]From Ref. 16.

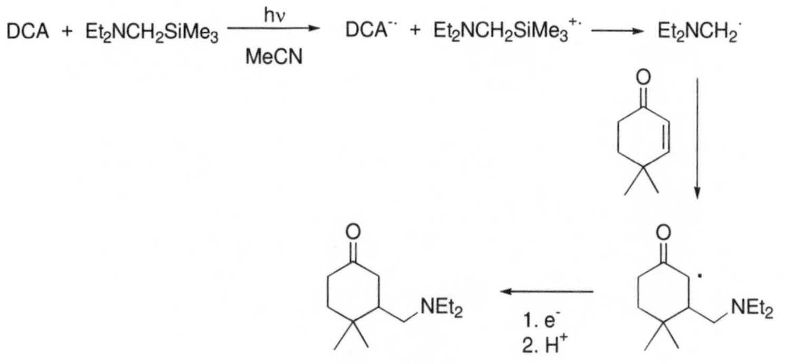

$$DCA + Et_2NCH_2SiMe_3 \xrightarrow[\text{MeCN}]{h\nu} DCA^{\cdot -} + Et_2NCH_2SiMe_3^{\cdot +} \longrightarrow Et_2NCH_2^{\cdot}$$

Scheme 6.

3. INTRAMOLECULAR ADDITION REACTIONS

3.1. Direct Irradiation With Tertiary Amines

The initial report of intramolecular benzene–tertiary amine addition by Bryce-Smith et al.[18] might have been expected to trigger a flurry of research activity similar to that generated by intramolecular benzene–olefin photoaddition reactions.[17] However, a detailed account of the formation of adducts **3** and **4**, including isolated yields and complete structural characterization, never appeared. Neither have additional examples of arene–tertiary amine addition reactions been reported.

This seemingly promising area of research languished until the mid-1980s when Aoyama and co-workers[51–56] initiated their studies of the intramolecular reactions of linked styrylamides and styrylamines. The *N,N*-dibenzylamide **19** yields a mixture of diastereomeric adducts **20** and **21** upon irradiation in methanol or acetonitrile solution.[51,52] The *N,N*-diallylamide forms analogous products, whereas the *N,N*-diethylamide and *N,N*-diisopropylamide fail to undergo intramolecular addition. Similar selectivity for benzyl vs. alkyl α-C–H addition was observed in the reactions of styrylamides in which the styrene is substituted at the β-carbon.[53] The *N*-benzyl-*N*-methyl amide **22** yields adducts **23** and **24** which are formed via selective transfer of a benzyl vs. methyl hydrogen. Styrylureas also undergo intra-

19   **20**, 51%   **21**, 7%

22   **23**, 45%   **24**, 17%

25   **26**, 49%   **27**, 14%

molecular addition, the N-benzylurea **25** forming adducts **26** and **27**.[54] Unlike the N-alkyl amides which fail to yield intramolecular adducts, irradiation of the N-alkylureas provides adducts analogous to **26** and **27**.

These intramolecular addition reactions are remarkable in that they have no intermolecular counterpart. In fact, N,N-dialkylamides and tetraalkyl ureas fail to quench styrene fluorescence. However, photoaddition of some 1,1-diarylethylenes and tetramethylurea has been reported.[57] The intramolecular reactions are proposed to occur via weakly bound nonfluorescent singlet exciplex intermediates, which undergo α-C–H transfer to yield the biradical precursors of the observed products.[51–54] A triplet mechanism was excluded based on the failure of sensitization by xanthone or quenching by 1,3-pentadiene. The involvement of charge transfer is consistent with the requirement of polar solvents for these reactions. The quantum yields for adduct formation from **19** and **25** are much higher than those of their p-methoxy derivatives, in which the styrene is a much weaker electron acceptor.[52,54]

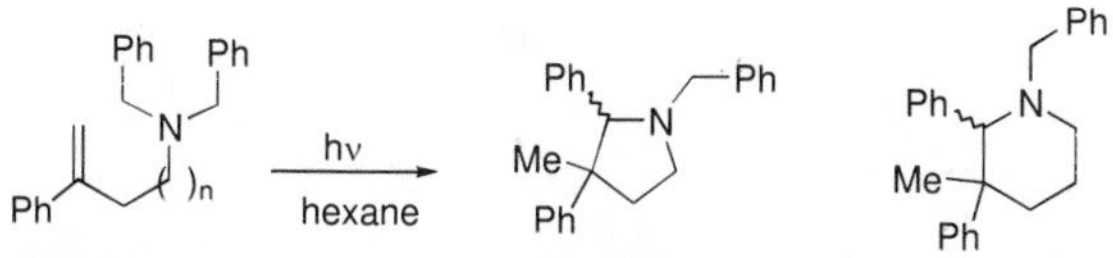

28: n = 1
29: n = 2

30, 35%

31, 20%

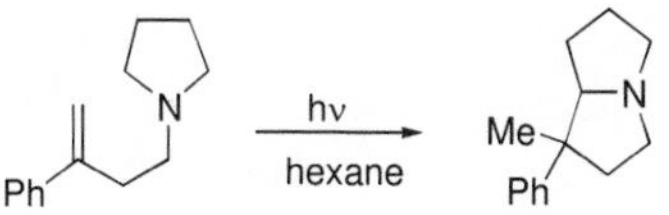

32

33, 73%

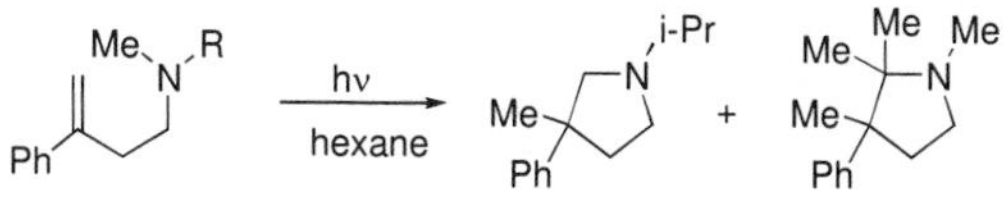

34: R = i-Pr
37: R = Me

35, 46%

36, 42%

Aoyama and co-workers[55,56] have also investigated the intramolecular photoamination reactions of several tertiary (aminoalkyl)styrenes. Irradiation of the (dibenzylaminoalkyl)styrenes **28** and **29** results, respectively, in the formation of the pyrrolidine **30** and the piperidine **31** as mixtures of diastereomeric adducts. Irradiation of the (aminoalkyl)styrene **32** provides the bicyclic adduct **33** in good yield. Unlike the highly regioselective intramolecular addition of **22** and intermolecular addition reaction of stilbene with *N,N*-dimethylisopropylamine (Scheme 3),[8] the intramolecular reaction of the *N*-methyl-*N*-isopropylamine **34** yields a mixture of adducts **35** and **36** which result from *N*-methyl and *N*-isopropyl hydrogen abstraction, respectively.

Exciplex fluorescence is observed for the (*N,N*-dimethylaminoethyl)styrene **37** and several of its *p*-substituted derivatives; however, Aoyama et al.[56] have questioned the involvement of exciplexes as intermediates in the photoaddition process. *p*-Cyano and *p*-methoxy substituents shift the exciplex fluorescence to a longer and shorter wavelength, respectively, as observed for the analogous intermolecular exciplexes.[22b] Increasing solvent polarity results in the usual shift of the exciplex fluorescence maximum to a longer wavelength and a decrease in the quantum yield for photoamination. An interesting substituent effect on intramolecular addition was noted for *p*-substituted derivatives of **37**.[56] The *p*-methoxy substituent has little effect upon the efficiency of addition, whereas the *p*-cyano substituent totally inhibits addition. Thus the system forming the most stable exciplex is least reactive. The opposite effect is observed for the intermolecular reactions of 1-arylpropenes with trimethylamine.[3] The low yield of adduct from 1-(*p*-methoxyphenyl)-propene was attributed to inefficient intermolecular quenching by trimethylamine.

The photochemical and photophysical behavior of the (*N,N*-dimethylaminoalkyl)styrenes **37–42**, in which the amino group is attached to the styrene α- or β-carbon by an ethyl, propyl, or butyl polymethylene linker, has been investigated in the author's laboratory.[58,59] The preparative results are summarized in Scheme 7 and display remarkable dependence upon the chain length and point of attachment to styrene. Whereas formation of the intramolecular adduct **43** upon irradiation of **37** requires α-C–H transfer from a *N*-methyl to the styrene β-carbon, formation of adduct **45** upon irradiation of **40** requires α-C–H transfer from a *N*-methyl to the styrene α-carbon. The latter process results in formation of a secondary alkyl radical rather than the more stable benzyl radical intermediate. The (aminopropyl)styrenes **38** and **41** both fail to undergo intramolecular photoaddition. The (aminobutyl)styrenes **39** and **42** form adducts which result from α-C–H transfer from a *N*-methylene to the styrene β-carbon, the former reaction leading to a mixture of diastereomeric aminocyclopentanes **44** and the later reaction to aminocyclohexanes **46**.

Our investigation of the mechanism of intramolecular adduct formation employed the technique of arene–amine exciplex quenching by primary amines, which had been developed in earlier investigations of exciplex quenching.[60] These experiments provided evidence for the occurrence of adduct formation via proton transfer in the fluorescent exciplex. In the case of **39**, activation parameters for exciplex formation and proton

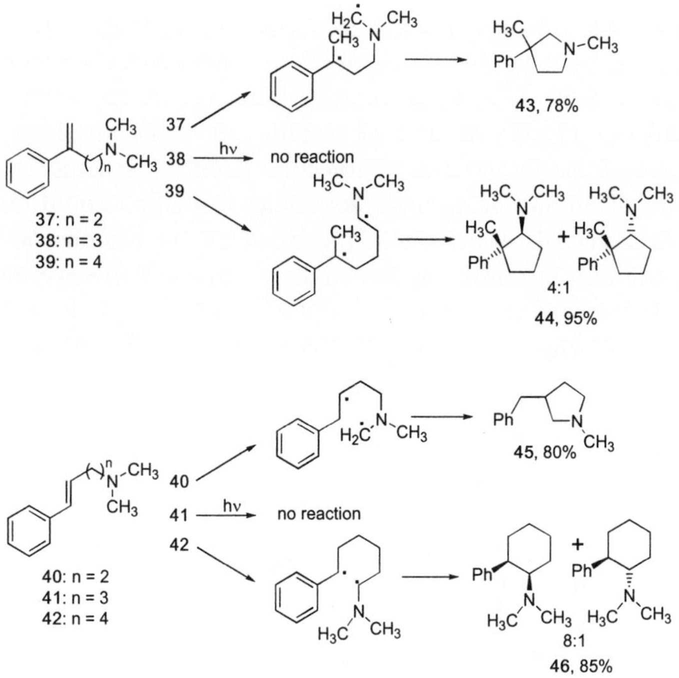

Scheme 7.

transfer were determined from the temperature dependence of the styrene locally excited and exciplex fluorescence lifetimes and quantum yields for adduct formation. Values of E_{act} = 3.7 kcal/mole and $\Delta S^{\ddagger}$ = −5.6 eu for exciplex formation are similar to those reported for formation of the (*N,N*-dimethylaminobutyl)benzene exciplex.[61] The activation energy for exciplex proton transfer is similar to that for valerophenone triplet hydrogen abstraction (E_{act} = 3.5 vs. 3.3 kcal/mole); however, the entropy of activation is substantially smaller for exciplex proton transfer (−14 vs. −24 eu).[62] Presumably intramolecular exciplex formation results in a folded geometry which reduces the entropic requirement of the subsequent proton transfer process.

The unusual dependence of product formation upon (aminoalkyl)styrene structure (Scheme 7) can be correlated with the folded conformation preferred by the intramolecular exciplexes in nonpolar solvents. Folded conformations analogous to those proposed by Van der Auweraer[63] for (aminoalkyl)arenes are shown in Scheme 8. Least motion pathways for α-C–H proton transfer in **37**, **39**, **40**, and **42** would lead to the biradical precursors of the observed intramolecular adducts (Scheme 7). The failure of **38** and **41** to undergo adduct formation could reflect a less favorable trajectory for intramolecular proton transfer. The exciplex lifetimes of the (aminopropyl)styrenes are longer than those of their aminoethyl and aminobutyl homologs, indicating that slow proton transfer is responsible for the absence

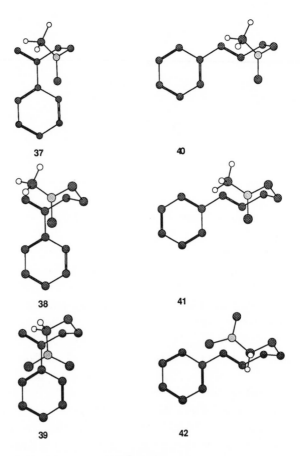

37   **40**

38   **41**

39   **42**

Scheme 8.

of adduct formation. Rate constants for proton transfer decrease precipitously with increasing solvent polarity. This decrease is attributed to a change in exciplex conformation from compact in nonpolar solvents to relaxed or extended in polar solvents, resulting in a less favorable trajectory for proton transfer in polar solvents. The exciplex formed by the *p*-cyano derivative of **37** might also have a relaxed structure in nonpolar solvents, accounting for its failure to undergo intramolecular addition.[56]

Intramolecular photoamination of styrene has also been observed for amide-linked styrene–tertiary amines including **47** and **48**, which yield the medium-ring lactams **49** and **50**.[64a] Considering the large separation between styrene and amine in the ground state, intramolecular quenching of singlet styrene is surprisingly efficient in these molecules. Exciplex fluorescence is observed in nonpolar solvents. The amide group serves both as a convenient linker in the synthesis of the styrene–amines and also as a conformational control element which facilitates intramolecular quenching. Extensions of this methodology for the formation of larger rings and the use of other linkers are currently under investigation.

47: n = m = 1
48: n = m = 2

49: n = m = 1, 48%
50: n = m = 2, 30%

Whereas intermolecular addition of tertiary amines has been observed for a large number of singlet arenes and aryl olefins, intramolecular addition has been observed only for benzene and styrenes. Intramolecular electron transfer quenching and exciplex formation has been observed for (*N*,*N*-dimethylaminoalkyl)arenes and aryl olefins with chain lengths ranging from 1 to 11 methylenes appended to benzene,[61] naphthalene,[65] phenanthrene,[66] anthracene,[67] pyrene,[68] stilbene,[41] and phenylacetylene.[64b] Thus the absence of intramolecular arene–amine addition is not due to the absence of electron transfer. Whereas the formation and photophysical behavior of these intramolecu-

lar exciplexes have been extensively investigated, we are un-
aware of reports of intramolecular photoamination other than
the initial report of Bryce-Smith, et al.[18] It is possible that inefficient photoamination might have been overlooked in some
of these studies; however, we have failed to detect the formation
of intramolecular adducts from (*N*,*N*-dimethylaminoalkyl)stil-
benes,[41] phenylacetylenes,[64b] phenanthrenes,[66] and phenan-
threne-9-carboxamides[69] in both polar and nonpolar solvents.
Sugimoto et al.[70] also noted the failure of some tertiary ami-
nophenanthrenes to undergo intramolecular addition.

The failure of tertiary (*N*,*N*-dimethylaminoalkyl)arenes and
stilbenes to undergo intramolecular addition may reflect structural differences between inter- vs. intramolecular exciplexes.
Polar solvents are generally required for the observation of intermolecular addition reactions of tertiary amine exciplexes.
Equilibration between solvent-separated and radical ion pairs
may be necessary in order to achieve an appropriate reaction
trajectory for α-C–H proton transfer. In the case of intramolecular exciplexes with short chain linkers, electron transfer in polar
solvents may occur in extended geometries which are inappro-
priate for proton transfer and chain folding may not compete
effectively with exciplex decay. The exceptions to these gener-
alizations, benzene and styrene, form more localized anion radicals which undergo both inter- and intramolecular reactions with
tertiary amine cation radicals in nonpolar solvents.

3.2. Direct Irradiation With Secondary and Primary Amines

Intramolecular addition reactions of arenes and aryl olefins
with secondary and primary amines have proven to be of broader
scope than the analogous reactions with tertiary amines. The
intramolecular addition of nonconjugated *o*-allylanilines **51** to
yield the 2-methylindolines **52** was reported by Koch-Pomeranz
et al.[71] in 1977. Intramolecular electron transfer from the singlet
aniline to the ground state alkene followed by N–H proton transfer to the alkene terminal carbon was proposed to account for
the regioselective formation of indolines. Proton transfer to the
internal carbon would yield tetrahydroquinolines, which were

a: R = H, 40%
b: R = Me, 75%
c: R = Ph, 80%

51   52

formed only in trace amounts. The lower yields observed for primary vs. secondary anilines might reflect less favorable electron transfer.

Sugimoto and co-workers[70,72–74] have reported that a number of covalently linked phenanthrene–secondary amine systems undergo intramolecular N–H addition. The 9-(2-(aminomethyl)-1-naphthyl)phenanthrenes **53a–c** were found to undergo intramolecular addition in benzene solution to yield **54a–c**.[70] No exciplex fluorescence is observed for these or other linked arene–secondary amine systems; however, the locally excited fluorescence of **53a–c** is much weaker than that of 9-methylphenanthrene. The analogous tertiary amines form fluorescent exciplexes but fail to form intramolecular adducts. The N-deuterated analog of **53a** exclusively forms the *syn* N–D adduct. Adduct yields are generally lower in acetonitrile or methanol solution. The magnitude of the solvent effect is dependent upon the bulk of the *N*-alkyl substituent, the use of methanol as solvent causing a much larger reduction in yield for the *N*-methylamine **53a** than the *N-t*-butylamine **53b**. Evidently, steric hindrance to solvation in the case of **53b** attenuates the normal inhibitory effect of solvent hydrogen bonding on the N–H proton transfer process.

Sugimoto and co-workers[72,73] have also investigated the photochemical reactions of a series of 9-(*N*-phenylaminoalkyl)phenanthrenes **55–58**. Irradiation of the aminoethyl compound **55** results in formation of the elimination product **59**, plausibly

a: R = Me, 30%
b: R = t-Bu, 84%
c: R = Ph, 93%

53   54

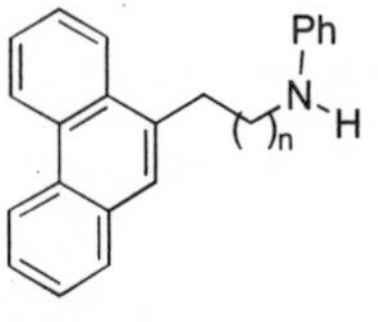

55: n = 1
56: n = 2
57: n = 3
58: n = 5

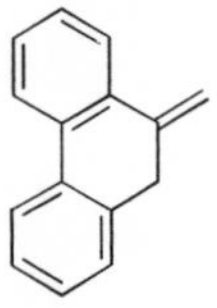

59, 60%

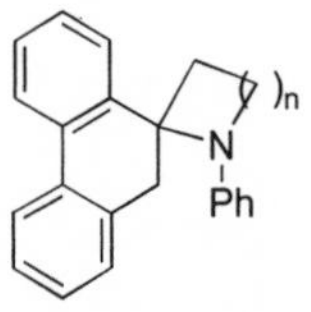

60: n = 2, 76%
61: n = 3, 31%

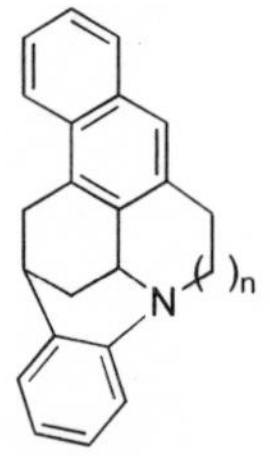

62: n = 5, 21%

via cleavage of the 1,4-biradical intermediate formed upon N–H transfer.[72a] Irradiation of aminopropyl and aminobutyl homologs **56** and **57** in either benzene or acetonitrile solution results in formation of the intramolecular N–H adducts **60** and **61**, respectively.[72b] The aminopentyl compound failed to yield an intramolecular adduct even though it displayed significant quenching of the locally excited phenanthrene fluorescence. Most remarkable is the reaction of **58** which yields the polycyclic adduct **62** in 21% yield upon irradiation in benzene solution.[73a] Several longer chain homologs of **58** form products analogous to **62**; however, the preparative yields are much lower than that reported for **62**.[73b]

The photochemistry of several 9-bromo-10-aminoalkylphenanthrenes has also been investigated.[74] The aminopropyl and aminobutyl compounds **63** and **64** undergo cyclization with loss of HBr to yield the fused adducts **65** and **66**, respectively, in modest yield. These products are accompanied by the debrominated phenanthrenes **56** and **57** and their photocyclization products **60** and **61**. Formation of **65** and **66** is proposed to occur via intramolecular electron transfer followed by loss of HBr to yield a biradical which cyclizes to yield the adducts. Improved yields are obtained in the presence of added Et_2NH or Et_3N,

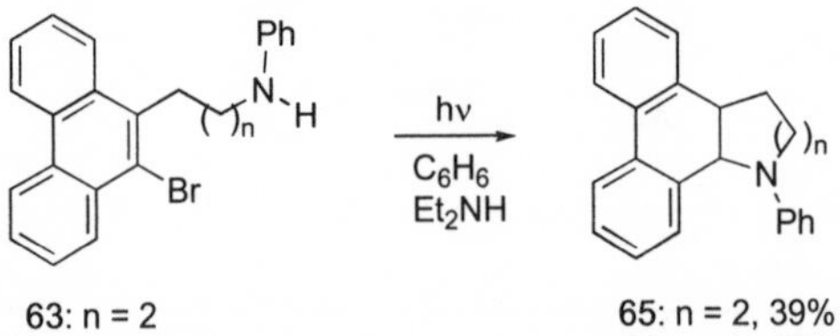

63: n = 2
64: n = 3

$\xrightarrow{h\nu}$
C_6H_6
Et_2NH

65: n = 2, 39%
66: n = 3, 12%

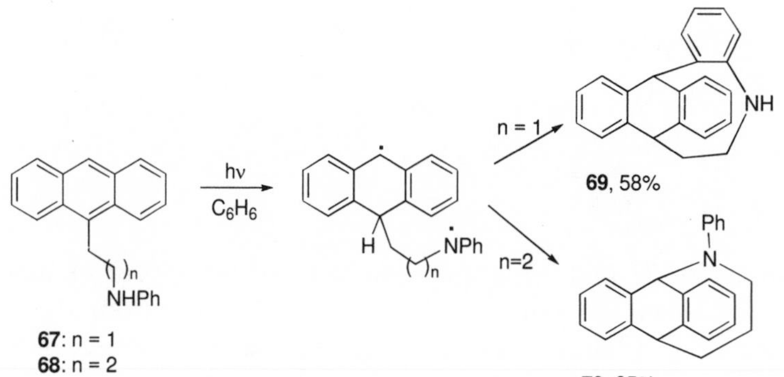

Scheme 9.

which are presumed to serve as scavengers of HBr. Homologs of **64** with longer polymethylene linkers fail to yield intramolecular adducts analogous to **66**.

The 9-(aminoalkyl)anthracenes **67** and **68** also undergo intramolecular addition upon irradiation in benzene solution to yield the 1,4-adducts **69** and **70**, respectively.[75] The formation of these adducts is proposed to occur via photoinduced electron transfer followed by N–H proton transfer to yield 10-anthryl-anilino biradical intermediates (Scheme 9). In the case of the biradical from **68**, C–N bond formation affords adduct **70**. The biradical from **67** undergoes C–C bond formation at the *ortho* position of the anilino radical, followed by hydrogen transfer to yield **69**, rather than C–N bond formation to form the highly strained lower homolog of **70**. The formation of **62** from the intramolecular reaction of **58** and of **5** from the intermolecular reaction of anthracene and dimethylaniline[29] may also occur via C–C bond formation in the biradical or radical pair intermediates.

The photochemical behavior of several families of (*N*-methylaminoalkyl)arenes and arylolefins have been investigated in the author's laboratory. No quenching of locally excited phenanthrene fluorescence is observed for the 1-(*N*-methylaminoalkyl)phenanthrenes **71** and **72** and no intramolecular adducts are formed.[76] The occurrence of electron transfer quenching for the secondary anilines in **55** and **56** but not the secondary aliphatic

71: n = 1
72: n = 2
73
74

amines in **71** and **72** is a consequence of the higher oxidation potential of the aliphatic amines (Table 2). Intramolecular quenching of locally excited naphthalene fluorescence is observed for the 1-(N-methylaminopropyl)naphthalene **73**[76] and the aminoalkyne **74**[64b]; however the primary photoproducts are unstable and complex product mixtures were obtained. In both cases the primary products are (aminoalkyl)styrenes, which are expected to be more reactive than the initial reactants.

Our investigation of the photochemical behavior of primary and secondary (aminoalkyl)styrenes has proven more rewarding.[36,76–80] The β-linked (N-methylaminoalkyl)styrenes **75–79** undergo intramolecular N–H addition to yield mixtures of regioisomeric adducts in which C–N bond formation occurs at either styrene C-β (β-adducts) or at C-α (α-adducts).[76–79] Quantum yields, preparative yields, and adduct ratios are summarized in Table 6. Selective formation of the α-adducts is observed for **75**, **76**, and **79**, as is the case for intramolecular styrene–amine addition reactions.[3] In the reactions of **76–78**, the regioselectivity increases with increasing solvent polarity: both for **76** and **77** which yield more of the α-adduct and for **78** which forms more of the β-adduct. In the case of **77** decreasing the temperature results in an increase in regioselectivity but a decrease in quantum yield. The N-deuterated analog of **77** undergoes stereospecific *syn* addition to yield an α-adduct in which the deuterium is *cis* to phenyl.

The locally excited styrene fluorescence lifetime is extensively quenched by the secondary aminoalkyl groups in **75–79**. The

75: n = 1
76: n = 2
77: n = 3
78: n = 4
79: n = 5

α-adduct   β-adduct

Table 6. Quantum Yield Φ_{add}, Isolated Yield, and Ratio of α/β Adducts from (*N*-methylaminoalkyl)styrenes[a]

Styrylamine	Φ_{add}	Yield, %	α/β Adduct Ratio
75		15	>10
76	0.024	63	14
77	0.11	57	2.4
78	0.05	82	0.15
79		30	>10

Note: [a]From Ref. 36.

formation of a mixture of regioisomers from the β-(amino-propyl)styrene **77** can be rationalized by the formation of a singlet exciplex with a compact folded chair-like conformation in which the N–H is either pseudoaxial or pseudoequatorial (Scheme 10).[36,79] Least-motion N–H proton transfer in these two conformers would result in formation of the biradical precursors of the observed adducts. In support of this proposal, replacing the *N*-methyl group in **77a** with a hydrogen in **77b** results in the formation of a 1:1 ratio of adducts **80b** and **81b**, whereas the *N*-isopropylamine **77c** yields exclusively adduct **81c**. The transition state for proton transfer leading to **80c** presumably is destabilized by a bulky pseudoaxial *N*-isopropyl group. The rate constant for quenching of locally excited styrene fluorescence by the primary amine in **77b** is smaller than that for the secondary amine **77a** (0.2 vs. 1.8×10^9 s^{-1}), in accord with the

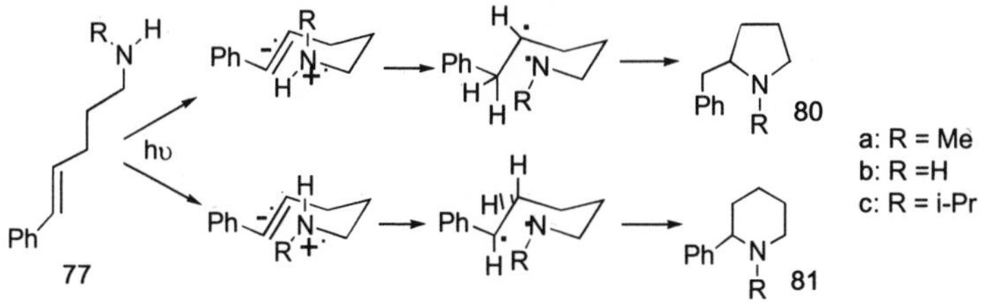

Scheme 10.

higher oxidation potentials of primary vs. secondary amines (Table 2).[79]

The α-(aminoalkyl)styrenes **82** and **83** undergo regioselective N–H intramolecular addition to yield the adducts **84** and **85**, respectively.[81] As in the case of the β-(aminoalkyl)styrenes, addition is presumed to occur via a short-lived nonfluorescent exciplex intermediate which undergoes regioselective N–H transfer to yield a benzyl–aminyl biradical. In the case of **83**, folding of the exciplex with maximum overlap between styrene C-α and nitrogen would place the N–H above either styrene C-β or the phenyl ipso carbon. A least-motion pathway for proton transfer is available in the former conformation, but not in the latter. Thus regioselective proton transfer to C-β may reflect exciplex conformational control as well as the energetic preference for formation of a benzyl vs. primary alkyl radical.

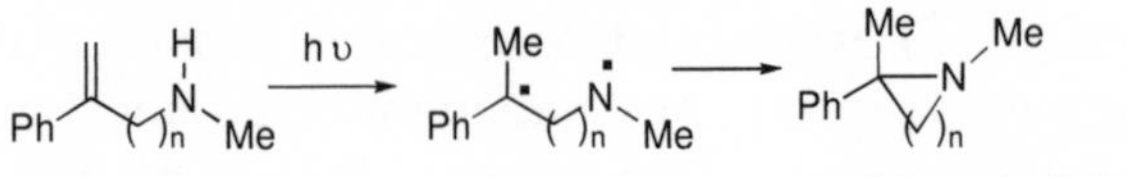

82: n = 3
83: n = 4

84: n = 3, 80%
85: n = 4, 75%

Intramolecular additions of secondary (aminoalkyl)styrenes provide an efficient method of preparing common- and medium-ring heterocycles. We are currently investigating the extension of this methodology to larger rings using amide-linked (aminoalkyl)styrenes such as **86**, which yields the azalactam **87** upon irradiation. Intramolecular photoamination of secondary (aminoalkyl)styrenes and stilbenes can also be utilized for the con-

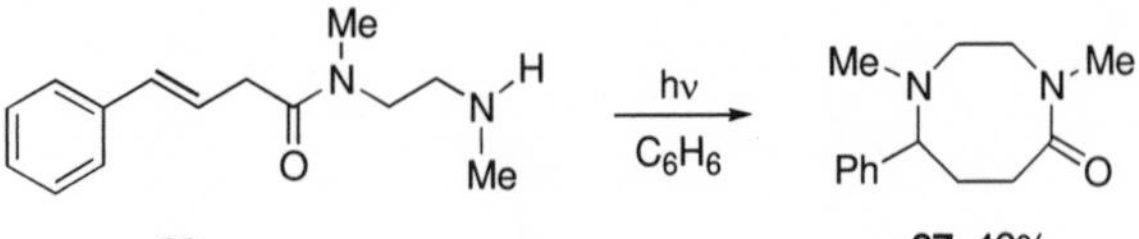

86

87, 42%

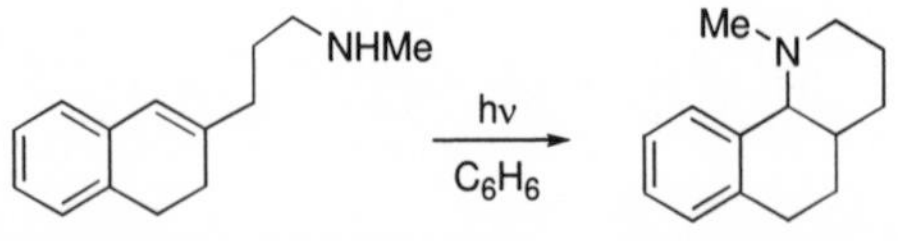

88

89

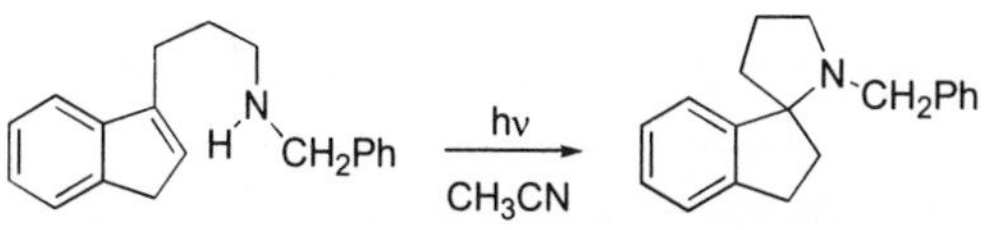

90   91, 70%

struction of polycyclic nitrogen-containing molecules. For example, irradiation of the (aminopropyl)dihydronaphthalene **88** provides the 4-azaphenanthrene **89**,[76] while the (aminopropyl)indene **90** yields the spiropyrrolidine **91**.[81] In both cases, intramolecular addition is presumed to occur via electron transfer followed by regioselective proton transfer to the aryl olefin C-β and coupling of the resulting singlet biradical.

The photochemical behavior of the *ortho*-(aminoalkyl)stilbenes **92–94** is also dependent upon the polymethylene linker (Scheme 11). Irradiation of **93** and **94** results in formation of the benzazepines **96** and **97**.[41,82] These adducts are presumably formed by regioselective N–H transfer to the proximal end of the stilbene double bond in **93** and the distal end in **94**, in both cases resulting in the formation of a 1,7-biradical intermediate. Since intramolecular stilbene–amine addition reactions are nonregioselective, the regioselectivity of N–H transfer must be subject to exciplex conformational control. The biradical inter-

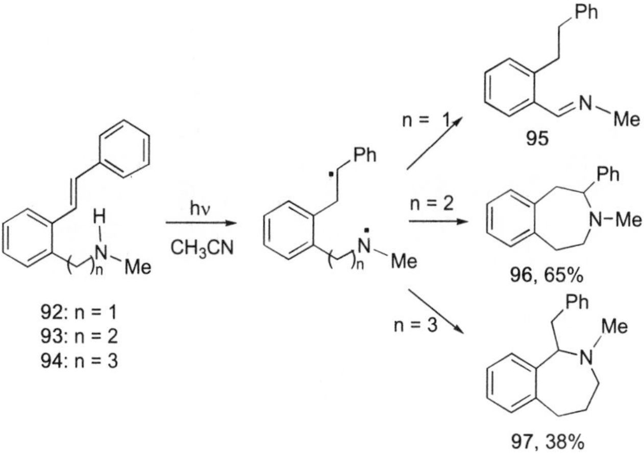

92: n = 1
93: n = 2
94: n = 3

95

96, 65%

97, 38%

Scheme 11.

mediate from **92** undergoes disproportionation to yield the imine **95** rather than cyclization to the isoquinoline. Closure of the 1,6-biradical intermediate may be unfavorable due to the presence of two adjacent sp^2 hybridized carbons between the radical centers.

3.3. Electron Transfer-Sensitized Irradiation

The regioselective ET-sensitized addition of primary amines has been cleverly employed by Yasuda and co-workers[49] in the synthesis of isoquinolines and related alkaloids. For example, the DCNB-sensitized photoamination of stilbene with 2-hydoxypropylamine in an acetonitrile–water solution yields the adduct **98**, which is converted to the benzylisoquinoline **99** upon treatment with CF_3SO_3H.[49a] The β-hydroxyl group of ethanolamine can be replaced with acetal or vinyl groups which also can serve as precursors of the carbocation required for the acid-catalyzed ring-forming reaction. Analogous reaction sequences have been used to convert phenanthrene to aporphines.[49b]

Intramolecular photoamination via the ET-sensitized irradiation of primary (aminoethyl)arenes has been employed by Pandey et al.[83] as a method for the synthesis of dihydroindoles. For example, the methoxybenzenes **100** and **101** provide the dihydroindoles **102** and **103**, respectively, upon irradiation in methanol or acetonitrile solution using dicyanonaphthalene (DCN) as the sensitizer.

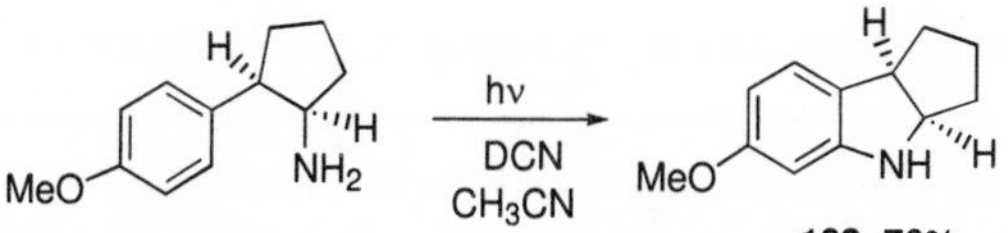

101   **103, 76%**

ET-sensitized irradiation of the primary *ortho*-(aminoalkyl)stilbenes **104** and **105** in an acetonitrile–water solution results in the formation of the isoquinoline **106** and the benzazepine **107**, respectively (Scheme 12).[41,82] By analogy to the mechanism proposed for intermolecular ET-sensitized addition (Scheme 2), C–N bond formation is proposed to occur via intramolecular nucleophilic attack on the stilbene cation radical by the primary amine to yield the distonic cation radical intermediates shown in Scheme 12. In both reactions, nucleophilic attack occurs at the proximal end of the C=C bond. These ring-forming reactions can be described in terms of Baldwin's rules[84] as 6-*exo*-trig and 7-*exo*-trig processes. The absence of products from the alternative 7-*endo*-trig or 8-*endo*-trig ring closures might be the consequence of either kinetic or thermodynamic control of amine nucleophilic addition to the stilbene cation radical. It is interesting to note that the regioselectivity of addition for **104** is opposite to that obtained for direct irradiation of the secondary (aminoethyl)stilbene **93**, whereas the same regioselectivity is observed for direct irradiation of **94** and ET-sensitized irradiation of **105**.

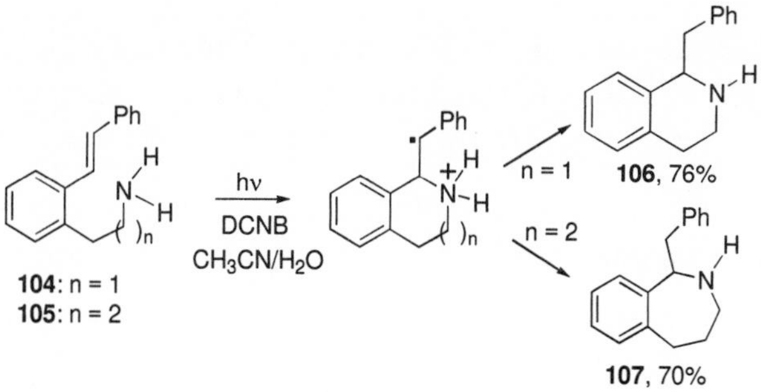

104: n = 1
105: n = 2

106, 76%

107, 70%

Scheme 12.

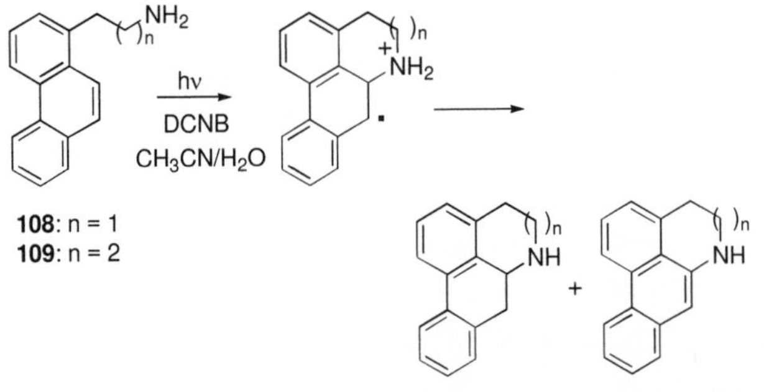

108: n = 1
109: n = 2

110: n = 1, 70%   **112**: n = 1, 15%
111: n = 2, 68%   **113**: n = 2, 12%

Scheme 13.

We have also investigated the ET-sensitized photoamination reactions of several primary (aminoalkyl)phenanthrenes.[85] The 1-(aminoalkyl)phenanthrenes **108** and **109** afforded good yields of the aporphine **110** and azepine **111**, respectively, along with small amounts of aromatized products **112** and **113** (Scheme 13). The 9-(aminoalkyl)phenanthrenes **114** and **115** provided lower yields of intramolecular adducts. In the case of the (aminoethyl)phenanthrene **114**, formation of **116** via ring closure occurs at C8 rather than C10, possibly reflecting an inherent preference for the formation of six- vs. five-membered rings in the nucleophilic addition step. The (aminopropyl)phenanthrene **115** yields a mixture of the phenanthropiperidines **117** and **118**, which are also formed via nucleophilic addition to form a six-membered ring.

An alternate approach to ET-sensitized intramolecular arene–amine addition is being explored by Jung and Mariano.[86] Dicyanoanthracene (DCA)-sensitized irradiation of the

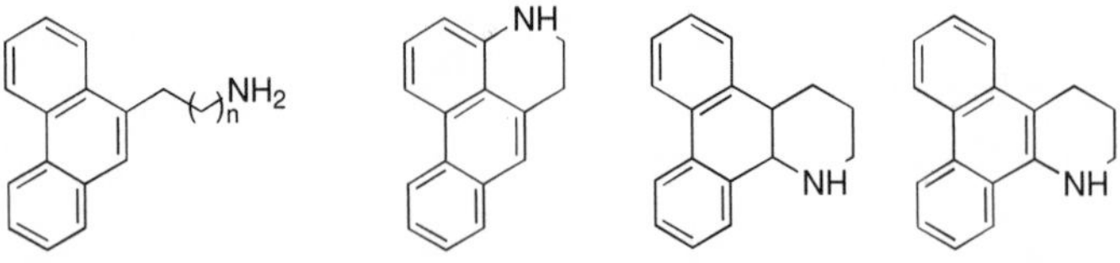

114: n = 1
115: n = 2

116, 30%   **117**, 13%   **118**, 22%

119   120

α-silylamide **119** in acetonitrile solution affords the adduct **120**. In this reaction, the silylamide serves as the precursor of an α-amido radical intermediate which adds to the phenanthrene. Reduction of the resulting α-keto radical and stereoselective protonation yields the adduct **120**. This reaction provides an attractive alternative to intramolecular α-C–H addition of tertiary (aminoalkyl)arenes (section 3.1), a reaction of limited scope.

4. CONCLUDING REMARKS

The direct and ET-sensitized reactions of aryl olefins and arenes with amines provide complementary methods for the synthesis of photoamination products. The formation of intermolecular adducts upon direct irradiation of aryl olefins or arenes in the presence of amines is limited by the requirement of exergonic electron transfer quenching and by competition of addition with products formed via cage escape of radical pair intermediates. Reactions of tertiary amines proceed via α-C–H addition, often via fluorescent exciplex intermediates. Both the stability of the exciplex intermediate and the adduct yield are highly solvent-sensitive. Reactions of secondary or primary amines normally proceed via N–H addition and display modest solvent dependence. Intermolecular ET sensitization requires the use of highly polar solvents and is restricted to the use of ammonia and primary amines by the requirement that the amine oxidation potential be higher than that of the aryl olefin or arene. However, the preparative yields are generally much higher than those for direct irradiation.

Intramolecular photoamination of (aminoalkyl)arenes and aryl olefins provides a versatile method for the synthesis of nitrogen heterocycles with a variety of ring sizes. Intramolecular addition of tertiary amines has been observed only in the case of (aminoalkyl)styrenes. Tertiary (aminoalkyl)stilbenes and arenes form fluorescent exciplexes which fail to undergo intramolecular addition. The occurrence of inter- but not intramolecular addition of tertiary amines suggests that exciplex conformation may be a crucial factor in these reactions. Intramolecular reactions of secondary amines are far broader in scope. The yields of adducts are often far superior to those in intermolecular addition reactions, presumably due to the absence of cage escape as a competing process for the biradical intermediate. ET sensitization of primary (aminoalkyl)stilbenes and arenes has also been successfully applied to the synthesis of polycyclic nitrogen heterocycles. Since different factors govern the regioselectivity of C–N bond formation in direct vs. ET-sensitized irradiation, the two methods can provide different regioisomers.

ACKNOWLEDGMENTS

The contributions of many collaborators are gratefully acknowledged, especially those of T.-I. Ho and G. D. Reddy who initiated our studies of inter- and intramolecular photoamination reactions, and members of the research group of Professor Sigfried Schneider in Erlangen, Germany, who have investigated photophysical aspects of these reactions. Financial support for the research performed at Northwestern University has been provided by the National Science Foundation.

REFERENCES

1. Cookson, R. C.; Costa, S. M. de B.; Hudec, J. *Chem. Commun.* **1969**, 753.
2. Toki, S.; Hida, S.; Takamuku, S.; Sakurai, H. *Nippon Kagaku Kaishi* **1984**, 152.
3. Lewis, F. D.; Bassani, D. *J. Photochem. Photobiol. A.* **1994**, *81*, 13.
4. Kawanisi, M.; Matsunaga, K. *J. Chem. Soc., Chem. Commun.* **1972**, 313.
5. Lewis, F. D.; Ho, T.-I. *J. Am. Chem. Soc.* **1977**, *99*, 7991.
6. Yang, N. C.; Libman, J. *J. Am. Chem. Soc.* **1973**, *95*, 5783.
7. Barltrop, J. A. *Pure Appl. Chem.* **1973**, *33*, 179.
8. (a) Lewis, F. D. *Adv. Photochem.* **1986**, *13*, 165. (b) Lewis, F. D. *Acc. Chem. Res.* **1986**, *19*, 401.
9. Lewis, F. D. In *Photoinduced Electron Transfer*; Chanon, M.; Fox, M. A., Eds.; Elsevier: Amsterdam, 1988, Part C, p. 1.

10. Pienta, N. J. In *Photoinduced Electron Transfer*; Chanon, M.; Fox, M. A., Eds.; Elsevier: Amsterdam, 1988, Part C, p. 421.

11. Bunce, N. J. In *Handbook of Organic Photochemistry and Photobiology*; Horspool, W. M.; Song, P.-S., Eds.; CRC Press: Boca Raton, FL, 1995, p. 266.

12. Yoon, U. C.; Mariano, P. S.; Givens, R. S.; Atwater, B. W. In *Advances in Electron Transfer Chemistry*; Mariano, P. S., Ed.; JAI Press: Greenwich, CT, 1994, Vol. 4, p. 117.

13. (a) Yasuda, M.; Yamashita, T.; Matsumoto, T.; Shima, K.; Pac, C. *J. Org. Chem.* **1985**, *50*, 3667; (b) Yasuda, M.; Yamashita, T.; Shima, K.; Pac, C. *J. Org. Chem.* **1987**, *52*, 753.

14. Yasuda, M.; Matsuzaki, Y.; Shima, K.; Pac, C. *J. Chem. Soc., Perkin Trans. 2* **1988**, *45*, 745.

15. Yamashita, T.; Shiomori, K.; Yasuda, M.; Shima, K. *Bull. Chem. Soc. Jpn.* **1991**, *64*, 366.

16. (a) Yasuda, M.; Isami, T.; Kubo, J.; Mizutani, M.; Yamashita, T.; Shima, K. *J. Org. Chem.* **1992**, *57*, 1351. (b) Yamashita, T.; Yasuda, M.; Isami, T.; Nakano, S.; Tanabe, K.; Shima, K. *Tetrahedron Lett.* **1993**, *34*, 5131.

17. (a) Wender, P. A.; von Gelden, T. W. In *Synthetic Organic Photochemistry*; Horspool, W. M., Ed.; Plenum: New York, 1984, p. 226; (b) Wender, P. A.; Dore, T. M. In *Handbook of Organic Photochemistry and Photobiology*; Horspool, W. M.; Song, P.-S., Eds.; CRC Press: Boca Raton, FL, 1995, p. 280.

18. Bryce-Smith, D.; Gilbert, A.; Klunklin, G. *J. Chem. Soc., Chem. Commun.* **1973**, 330.

19. Weller, A. *Z. Phys. Chem. (Wiesbaden)* **1982**, *133*, 93.

20. (a) Mattes, S. L.; Farid, S. In *Organic Photochemistry*; Padwa, A., Ed.; Marcel Dekker: New York, 1983, Vol. 6, Ch. 4; (b) Briegleb, G. *Angew. Chem. Internat. Edit.* **1964**, *3*, 617; (c) Watanabe, K.; Mottl, R. *J. Chem. Phys.* **1957**, *26*, 1773; (d) Turner, D. W. *Molecular Photoelectron Spectroscopy*; Wiley-Interscience: London, 1970.

21. Chen, J.-M.; Ho, T.-I.; Mou, C.-Y. *J. Phys. Chem.* **1990**, *94*, 2889.

22. (a) Mai, J.-C.; Lin, Y.-C.; Ho, T.-I. *J. Photochem. Photobiol., A* **1990**, *54*, 299; (b) Mai, J.-C.; Lin, Y.-C.; Hseu, T.-M.; Ho, T.-I. *J. Photochem. Photobiol., A* **1993**, *71*, 237.

23. (a) Sun, Y.-P.; Bunker, C. E.; Ma, B. *J. Am. Chem. Soc.* **1984**, *116*, 9692; (b) Sun, Y.-P.; Ma, B.; Larson, G. E. *Chem. Phys. Lett.* **1995**, *233*, 57; (c) Sun, Y.-P.; Ma, B. *Chem. Phys. Lett.* **1995**, *236*, 285.

24. Kavarnos, G. J. *Photoinduced Electron Transfer*; VCH: New York, 1993.

25. Hub, W.; Schneider, S.; Dörr, F.; Oxman, J. D.; Lewis, F. D. *J. Am. Chem. Soc.* **1984**, *106*, 708.

26. Lewis, F. D.; Simpson, J. T. *J. Phys. Chem.* **1979**, *83*, 2015.

27. Klaukien, H.; Lehnig, M. *J. Photochem. Photobiol., A* **1994**, *84*, 221.

28. Lewis, F. D.; Ho, T.-I.; Simpson, J. T. *J. Am. Chem. Soc.* **1982**, *104*, 1924.

29. Yasuda, M.; Pac, C.; Sakurai, H. *Bull. Chem. Soc. Jpn.* **1981**, *54*, 2352.

30. Bryce-Smith, D.; Gilbert, A. *Tetrahedron* **1977**, *33*, 2459.

31. Ho, T.-I.; Nozaki, K.; Naito, A.; Okazaki, S.; Hatano, H. *J. Chem. Soc., Chem. Commun.* **1989**, 206.
32. Tomioka, H.; Miyagawa, H. *J. Chem. Soc., Chem. Commun.* **1988**, 1183.
33. Lewis, F. D.; Ho, T.-I.; Simpson, J. T. *J. Org. Chem.* **1981**, *46*, 1077.
34. Goez, M.; Frisch, I. *J. Photochem. Photobiol., A* **1994**, *84*, 1.
35. Zhang, X.; Yeh, S.-R.; Hong, S.; Freccero, M.; Albini, A.; Falvey, D. E.; Mariano, P. S. *J. Am. Chem. Soc.* **1994**, *116*, 4211.
36. (a) Lewis, F. D.; Reddy, G. D.; Bassani, D.; Schneider, S.; Gahr, M. *J. Photochem. Photobiol., A* **1992**, *65*, 205. (b) Lewis, F. D.; Bassani, D. *J. Photochem. Photobiol., A* **1992**, *66*, 43.
37. Drescher, W.; Kendler, S.; Zingher, E.; Haas, Y. *Chem. Phys. Lett.* **1994**, *224*, 391.
38. (a) Lewis, F. D.; Zebrowski, B. E.; Correa, P. E. *J. Am. Chem. Soc.* **1984**, *106*, 187; (b) Lewis, F. D.; Correa, P. E. *J. Am. Chem. Soc.* **1984**, *106*, 194.
39. Okada, T.; Karaki, I.; Mataga, N. *J. Am. Chem. Soc.* **1982**, *104*, 7191.
40. Sakuragi, M.; Sakurai, H. *Bull. Chem. Soc. Jpn.* **1977**, *50*, 1802.
41. Lewis, F. D.; Bassani, D.; Burch, E. L.; Cohen, B. E.; Engelman, J. A.; Reddy, G. D.; Schneider, S.; Jaeger, W.; Gedeck, P.; Gahr, M. *J. Am. Chem. Soc.* **1995**, *117*, 660.
42. Koshima, H.; Ichimura, H.; Hirotsu, K.; Miyahara, I.; Wang, Y.; Matsuura, T. *J. Photochem. Photobiol., A* **1995**, *85*, 225.
43. (a) Yasuda, M.; Sone, T.; Tanabe, K.; Shima, K. *Chem. Lett.* **1994**, 453; (b) Yasuda, M.; Sone, T.; Tanabe, K.; Shima, K. *J. Chem. Soc., Perkin Trans. 1* **1995**, 459.
44. Maroulis, A. J.; Shigemitsu, Y.; Arnold, D. R. *J. Am. Chem. Soc.* **1978**, *100*, 535.
45. Johnston, L. J.; Schepp, N. P. *J. Am. Chem. Soc.* **1993**, *115*, 6564.
46. Yasuda, M.; Matsuzaki, Y.; Yamashita, T.; Shima, K. *Chem. Lett.* **1989**, 551.
47. Nieminen, K.; Niiranen, J.; Lemmetyinen, H.; Sychtchikova, I. *J. Photochem. Photobiol., A* **1991**, *61*, 235.
48. Workentin, M. S.; Johnston, L. J.; Wayner, D. D. M.; Parker, V. D. *J. Am. Chem. Soc.* **1994**, *116*, 8279.
49. (a) Yasuda, M.; Kubo, J.; Shima, K. *Heterocycles* **1990**, *31*, 1007; (b) Yasuda, M.; Hamasuna, S.; Yamano, K.; Kubo, J.; Shima, K. *Heterocycles* **1992**, *34*, 965.
50. Yoon, U. C.; Mariano, P. S. *Acc. Chem. Res.* **1992**, *25*, 233.
51. Aoyama, H.; Inoue, Y.; Omote, Y. *J. Org. Chem.* **1991**, *46*, 1965.
52. Aoyama, H.; Arata, Y.; Omote, Y. *J. Chem. Soc., Perkin Trans. 1* **1986**, 1165.
53. Aoyama, H.; Arata, Y.; Omote, Y. *J. Org. Chem.* **1987**, *52*, 4639.
54. Aoyama, H.; Tomohiro, T.; Arata, Y.; Omote, Y. *J. Phys. Org. Chem.* **1988**, *1*, 123.
55. Aoyama, H.; Arata, Y.; Omote, Y. *J. Chem. Soc., Chem. Commun.* **1985**, 1381.
56. Aoyama, H.; Sugiyama, J.; Yoshida, M.; Hatori, H.; Hosomi, A. *J. Org. Chem.* **1992**, *57*, 3037.
57. Miyamoto, T.; Tsujimoto, Y.; Tsuchinaga, T.; Nishimura, Y.; Odaira, Y. *Tetrahedron Lett.* **1978**, 2155.
58. Lewis, F. D.; Reddy, G. D.; Bassani, D. *J. Am. Chem. Soc.* **1993**, *115*, 6468.
59. Lewis, F. D.; Reddy, G. D.; Bassani, D.; Schneider, S.; Gahr, M. *J. Am. Chem. Soc.* **1994**, *116*, 597.

60. Hub, W.; Schneider, S.; Dörr, F.; Oxman, J. D.; Lewis, F. D. *J. Am. Chem. Soc.* **1984**, *106*, 701.
61. Van der Auweraer, M.; Gilbert, A.; De Schryver, F. C. *J. Am. Chem. Soc.* **1980**, *102*, 4007.
62. Lewis, F. D.; Johnson, R. W.; Kory, D. R. *J. Am. Chem. Soc.* **1974**, *96*, 6100.
63. (a) Van der Auweraer, M. *Acad. Anal.* **1986**, *48*, 27; (b) Van der Auweraer, M.; Grabowski, Z. R.; Rettig, W. *J. Phys. Chem.* **1991**, *95*, 2083.
64. (a) Lewis, F. D.; Denari, J. M., unpublished results; (b) Lewis, F. D.; Miller, A. M., unpublished results.
65. (a) Davidson, R. S.; Trethewey, K. R. *J. Chem. Soc., Chem. Commun.* **1976**, 827; (b) Swinnen, A. M.; Van der Auweraer, M.; De Schryver, F. C. *J. Photochem.* **1985**, *28*, 315.
66. Lewis, F. D.; Cohen, B. E. *J. Phys. Chem.* **1994**, *98*, 10591.
67. Yang, N. C.; Neoh, S. B.; Naito, T.; Ng, L.-K.; Chernoff, D. A.; McDonald, D. B. *J. Am. Chem. Soc.* **1980**, *102*, 2806.
68. Swinnen, A. M.; Van der Auweraer, M.; De Schryver, F. C.; Nakatani, K.; Okada, T.; Mataga, N. *J. Am. Chem. Soc.* **1987**, *109*, 321.
69. Lewis, F. D.; Burch, E. L. *J. Am. Chem. Soc.* **1994**, *116*, 1159.
70. Sugimoto, A.; Sumida, R.; Tamai, N.; Inoue, H.; Otsuji, Y. *Bull. Chem. Soc. Jpn.* **1981**, *54*, 3500.
71. Koch-Pomeranz, U.; Schmid, H.; Hansen, H.-J. *Helv. Chim. Acta* **1977**, *60*, 768.
72. (a) Sugimoto, A.; Yoneda, S. *J. Chem. Soc., Chem. Commun.* **1982**, 376; (b) Sugimoto, A.; Sumi, K.; Urakawa, K.; Ikemura, M.; Sakamoto, S.; Yoneda, S.; Otsuji, Y. *Bull. Chem. Soc. Jpn.* **1983**, *56*, 3118.
73. (a) Sugimoto, A.; Hiraoka, R.; Inoue, H.; Adachi, T. *J. Chem. Soc., Perkin Trans. 1* **1992**, 1559; (b) Sugimoto, A.; Fukada, N.; Adachi, T.; Inoue, H. *J. Chem. Soc., Perkin Trans. 1* **1995**, 1597.
74. Sugimoto, A.; Hiraoka, R.; Fukuda, N.; Kosaka, H.; Inoue, H. *J. Chem. Soc., Perkin Trans. 1* **1992**, 2871.
75. Sugimoto, A.; Yamano, J.; Suyama, K.; Yoneda, S. *J. Chem. Soc., Perkin Trans. 1* **1989**, 483.
76. Lewis, F. D.; Reddy, G. D., unpublished results.
77. Lewis, F. D.; Reddy, G. D.; Schneider, S.; Gahr, M. *J. Am. Chem. Soc.* **1989**, *111*, 6465.
78. Lewis, F. D.; Reddy, G. D. *Tetrahedron Lett.* **1990**, *31*, 5293.
79. Lewis, F. D.; Reddy, G. D.; Schneider, S.; Gahr, M. *J. Am. Chem. Soc.* **1991**, *113*, 3498.
80. Lewis, F. D.; Bassani, D. M.; Reddy, G. D. *Pure Appl. Chem.* **1992**, *64*, 1271.
81. Lewis, F. D.; Bassani, D. M.; Reddy, G. D. *J. Org. Chem.* **1993**, *58*, 6390.
82. Lewis, F. D.; Reddy, G. D. *Tetrahedron Lett.* **1992**, *33*, 4249.
83. Pandey, G.; Sridhar, M.; Bhalerao, U. T. *Tetrahedron Lett.* **1990**, *31*, 5373.
84. Baldwin, J. E. *J. Chem. Soc., Chem. Commun.* **1976**, 734.
85. Lewis, F. D.; Reddy, G. D.; Cohen, B. E. *Tetrahedron Lett.* **1994**, *35*, 535.
86. Jung, Y. S.; Mariano, P. S., unpublished results quoted in Ref. 12.

KINETICS AND MECHANISMS FOR THE REACTIONS OF ALKENE RADICAL CATIONS*

Linda J. Johnston and Norman P. Schepp

*Reference 1.

Advances in Electron Transfer Chemistry
Volume 5, pages 41–102.
Copyright © 1996 by JAI Press Inc.
All rights of reproduction in any form reserved.
ISBN: 0-7623-0062-0

1. INTRODUCTION

The widespread importance of electron transfer reactions in chemistry and biology has led to increasing interest in the chemistry of radical ions.[2] Radical cations, in particular, have been the subject of a number of mechanistic studies and are becoming increasingly important intermediates in synthetic methodologies.[3-10] Alkene radical cations have attracted a large amount of attention since they undergo a variety of different reactions including addition of neutral and anionic nucleophiles, deprotonation, electron transfer, *cis-trans* isomerization, and cycloaddition reactions. This rich chemistry makes them particularly interesting substrates for studying the factors that control the competition between various reaction pathways. Such studies are essential in order to develop a detailed understanding of radical cation reactivity that will allow one to predict and control the chemistry of these important intermediates.

A number of alkene radical cations have been generated in matrices at low temperature[11] and have also been studied by ESR, CIDNP, and electrochemical methods. However, until recently very little absolute kinetic data have been available for the reactions of these important reactive intermediates in solution under conditions comparable to those used in mechanistic or synthetic studies. In a few cases, competitive kinetic techniques have been used to estimate rates for nucleophilic additions or radical cation/alkene cycloaddition reactions.[3,4] In addition, pulse radiolysis has been used to provide rate constants for some of the radical cation chemistry relevant to the photopolymerization of styrenes.[12,13] More recently, we and others have used laser flash photolysis to generate and characterize a variety of alkene radical cations.[14-21] This method has been extensively applied to the study of other reactive intermediates such as radicals, carbenes, and carbenium ions and is particularly well-suited for kinetic measurements of species that have lifetimes in the tens of nanoseconds range and up and that have at least moderate extinction coefficients in the UV–visible region.

This review summarizes the generation and spectroscopic characterization of alkene radical cations and kinetic and mechanistic studies of their reactions with nucleophiles and cycloaddition chemistry. Most of the data have been obtained using laser flash photolysis techniques, but comparisons with kinetic data obtained using other methods and with steady-state experiments are presented where appropriate. To date most kinetic measurements using laser flash photolysis techniques have focused on arylalkene radical cations since these are relatively easy to generate and have spectroscopic and kinetic behavior that is commensurate with nanosecond laser flash photolysis techniques.

2. GENERATION OF ALKENE RADICAL CATIONS

Most time-resolved studies of radical cations in solution have been carried out using nanosecond laser flash photolysis, although pulse radiolysis and picosecond laser flash photolysis have also been used in a few cases. The use of laser flash photolysis for kinetic studies requires a rapid photochemical source for the reactive intermediate of interest. The species to be studied should have a reasonably strong UV or visible absorption and a lifetime that is approximately an order of magnitude longer than the pulse duration of the excitation laser. The latter requirement is particularly important in cases where bimolecular quenching studies are to be carried out. There are a variety of photochemical methods for generating radical cations in solution. Among these, the most general is a photoinduced electron transfer reaction between a donor and an excited state acceptor (the photosensitizer) such as a cyanoaromatic or quinone to generate a radical cation/radical anion pair (Eq. 1). The same radical ion pair can in principle be produced by reaction of the excited donor with a ground state acceptor, although in practice this route is much less frequently used. The yield of free radical cation from the original geminate radical ion pair is determined by the competition between back electron transfer and cage escape (Eq. 2).

$$\text{Acceptor} \xrightarrow{h\nu} \text{Acceptor}^* \xrightarrow{\text{Donor}} [\text{Acceptor}^{-\bullet} \text{ Donor}^{+\bullet}] \quad (1)$$

$$[\text{Acceptor}^{-\bullet} \text{ Donor}^{+\bullet}] \begin{array}{c} \xrightarrow{\text{back electron transfer}} \text{Acceptor} + \text{Donor} \\ \\ \xrightarrow[\text{cage escape}]{} \text{Acceptor}^{-\bullet} + \text{Donor}^{+\bullet} \end{array} \quad (2)$$

Photoinduced electron transfer (PET) has been widely used for synthetic and mechanistic studies of radical cation chemistry in solution, usually in relatively polar solvents such as acetonitrile, alcohols, or dichloromethane. The energetic requirements for the electron transfer reaction are governed by the Rehm–Weller equation (Eq. 3) which expresses the free energy for the electron transfer in terms of the available excited state energy (E_{oo}), the redox potentials of the donor and acceptor (E_{ox} and E_{red}), and the Coulombic attraction energy ($e^2/\alpha\varepsilon$) gained by bringing the two radical ions to the encounter distance α in a solvent of dielectric constant ε.[22] As a general rule electron transfer reactions that are exergonic by ~5 kcal/mol will occur at the diffusion controlled r? in a given solvent.

$$\Delta G_{et} = 23.06[E_{ox}(D/D^{+\bullet}) + E_{red}(A/A^{-\bullet}) - e^2/\alpha\varepsilon] - E_{oo} \quad (3)$$

Both singlet and triplet state sensitizers have been used to generate radical cations and compilations of their excited state energies and redox potentials are available.[23] Commonly used singlet sensitizers include 1,4-dicyanobenzene, 1,4-dicyanonaphthalene, and 9,10-dicyanoanthracene. Although the singlet energies and reduction potentials of the cyanoaromatics are such that they can be used to oxidize a wide range of substrates, their utility for kinetic measurements is limited by two potential problems. The first of these is the fact that their singlet lifetimes are in the 10–20-ns range and the observation of efficient quenching of their excited states requires high concentrations of the donor; this can result in prohibitively short lifetimes for radical cations that react with their precursor. Another more serious drawback of the cyanoaromatic sensitizers is the fact that back electron transfer in a singlet radical ion pair typically occurs with rate constants on the order of 5×10^8 s^{-1} and thus competes efficiently with cage escape to yield free ions in solution (Eq. 2).[24] The low yield of radical ions obtained for many singlet sensitizers is a considerable limitation for the detection of these species using laser flash photolysis and results in low quantum yields in preparative experiments. This problem can be overcome by generating a radical ion pair for which back electron transfer is sufficiently exergonic to fall in the Marcus-inverted region; in this region the rate of back electron transfer decreases with increasing exergonicity.[24,25] For example, it has been demonstrated that the yield of free radical ions using 9,10-dicyanoanthracene as a photosensitizer is 8% for hexamethylbenzene but ~83% for biphenyl.[24,25] Thus, in general the use of the weakest possible acceptor is a useful approach for maximizing the yield of cage escape since stronger acceptors will lead to faster back electron transfer and may also favor ground state complex formation.

Cosensitization using a codonor such as biphenyl is another approach that has been widely used to maximize the efficiency of cage escape using singlet acceptors. This method takes advantage of the fact that efficient cage escape for a cyanoaromatic/biphenyl radical ion pair gives a high yield of the biphenyl radical cation which then serves as a secondary oxidant (codonor) to generate the donor radical cation, as illustrated in Eqs. 4 and 5.[26,27] The cosensitization method is now widely used for the generation of radical cations in both preparative and time-resolved experiments and has also been used in cases

$$\text{(4)}$$

$$\text{(5)}$$

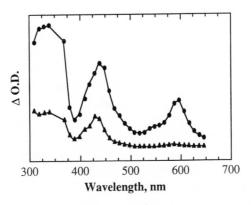

Figure 1. Absorption spectra of the 4-methoxystyrene radical cation and the chloranil radical anion recorded 100 ns (●) and 50 μs (▲) after 355-nm laser irradiation of chloranil in acetonitrile with 0.001 M 4-methoxystyrene.

for which the oxidation potential of the donor is comparable to or slightly higher than that of biphenyl.[28]

The problems associated with low cage escape yields using singlet sensitizers can also be overcome by using triplet sensitizers such as quinones. In this case electron transfer generates a triplet radical ion pair which must undergo intersystem crossing to the singlet ion pair prior to back electron transfer to regenerate the ground state donor and acceptor. As a result, diffusive separation of the ion pair usually competes efficiently with back electron transfer. For high-energy triplet radical ion pairs, back electron transfer to generate the triplet excited state of the donor or acceptor is also a possibility.

The spectrum shown in Figure 1 illustrates the results obtained by using triplet chloranil to generate the 4-methoxystyrene radical cation (Eqs. 6, 7).[15] The observed transients are readily identified as the chloranil radical anion (λ_{max} 450 nm)[29] and the 4-methoxystyrene radical cation (λ_{max} 600 nm), both of which contribute to the absorption below 400 nm. The results obtained demonstrate that good yields of radical ions are obtained using the triplet sensitizer. By contrast, the yield of styrene radical cations is quite low using 9,10-dicyanoanthracene as a sensitizer, although the yield can be dramatically improved by adding biphenyl as the cosensitizer. However, the use of triplet chloranil does suffer from the drawback that the chloranil radical anion cannot be removed by oxygen-purging as can cyanoaromatic radical anions, the difference being the relative reduction potentials of the two sensitizers as compared to oxygen. Cycloadduct formation, exciplex chemistry and the formation of ground state complexes are other potential limitations to the use of quinones as photosensitizers for electron transfer reactions.[30]

$$(6)$$

$$(7)$$

Polar solvents such as acetonitrile and alcohols are commonly used for PET reactions between neutral donors and acceptors in order to minimize the Coulombic barrier to charge separation in the initial radical anion/radical cation pair. The use of charged sensitizers has been examined as an alternative method of maximizing the yield of free ions in less polar solvents. For example, electron transfer to the excited state of a cationic sensitizer from a neutral donor generates a neutral radical/radical cation pair in which there is no Coulombic barrier to separation. The use of singlet states of *N*-alkylacridinium salts as sensitizers has been demonstrated to result in high yields of free radical cations from biphenyl in a variety of nonpolar solvents, including methylene chloride, chloroform, and benzene.[31] The radical cation yields in these solvents were considerably higher than those obtained for 2,6,9,10-tetracyanoanthracene, a neutral singlet sensitizer with comparable ground state reduction potential and excited state energy and lifetime. However, charged and neutral acceptors gave similar radical cation yields in acetonitrile.[27,31] 2,4,6-Triphenylpyrylium tetrafluoroborate is another commonly used cationic acceptor for both time-resolved and preparative PET reactions.[32–35] In this case both singlet and triplet states act as efficient oxidants, permitting the use of a wide range of donor concentrations, and allowing a direct comparison of the effects of changing the sensitizer multiplicity.

Several procedures that are analogous to the traditional photoinduced electron transfer reaction have been used to generate radical cations in aqueous solution where sensitizers such as dicyanoaromatics and quinones are sparingly soluble.[20,36] In one method, peroxydisulfate is photochemically cleaved to give the ground state sulfate radical anion (Eq. 8). This species is a good oxidant and undergoes diffusion controlled electron transfer with a variety of styrenes to generate the styrene radical cation and the sulfate ion (Eq. 9).

$$S_2O_8^{2-} \xrightarrow{h\nu} 2\ SO_4^{-\bullet} \tag{8}$$

$$SO_4^{-\bullet} + \underset{R}{\underset{\text{electron transfer}}{\bigcirc}} \xrightarrow{\text{electron transfer}} \left[\underset{R}{\bigcirc} \right]^{+\bullet} + SO_4^{2-} \tag{9}$$

In a related example, the photolysis of cerium(IV) ammonium nitrate generates the $NO_3^\bullet$ radical (Eq. 10) which has recently been demonstrated to react with alkylbenzenes via an electron transfer reaction.[37] This particular oxidant is able to generate radical cations of substituted benzenes with ionization potentials less than that of p-xylene (8.44 eV).

$$(NH_4)_2Ce^{IV}(NO_3)_6 \xrightarrow{h\nu} (NH_4)_2Ce^{III}(NO_3)_5{}_\bullet + NO_3\bullet \tag{10}$$

Photoionization provides an alternative photochemical method for generating radical cations in laser experiments. Laser excitation of a wide range of easily oxidized substrates (usually aromatic compounds) has been demonstrated to result in direct electron ejection to give a radical cation and the solvated electron.[14,15,38,39] In most cases photoionization occurs from an upper excited state produced either directly by absorption of a single high-energy photon or, more commonly, by sequential two-photon absorption. As a result the method is not of general use for preparative experiments. This method has been used to generate styrene (Eq. 11) and a variety of other radical cations for time-resolved studies.[14,15,36] Examples of the transient absorption spectra for several styrene radical cations generated by photoionization in polar solvents are shown in Figure 2.

$$ \underset{R}{\bigcirc}\!\!=\quad \xrightarrow{\;n h\nu\;}\quad \left[\underset{R}{\bigcirc}\!\!=\right]^{+\bullet}\; +\;\; e^{-}\,(solv) \qquad (11) $$

There are a number of advantages of the photoionization method for generating radical cations for kinetic studies. For

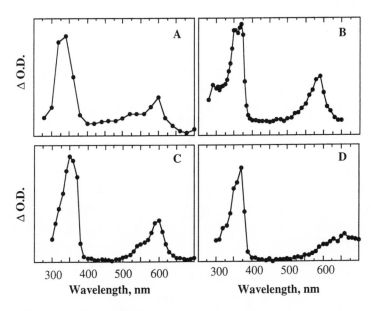

Figure 2. Absorption spectra of (**A**) styrene radical cation in 2,2,2-trifluoroethanol (TFE), (**B**) β-methylstyrene radical cation in TFE, (**C**) 4-methoxystyrene radical cation in acetonitrile, and (**D**) α-methyl-4-methoxystyrene radical cation in acetonitrile. Each radical cation was generated by 266-nm laser irradiation of the corresponding styrene.

example, photoionization of the substrate yields a transient spectrum that is not complicated by absorptions due to a sensitizer
radical anion. The solvated electron is not readily detectable in
acetonitrile where it exists as an equilibrium mixture of monomer and dimer radical anions that have very broad, weak absorptions between 500 and 1500 nm;[40] in alcohols or aqueous
solution the solvated electron has a characteristic visible absorption band at relatively long wavelength (~700 nm).[41] The
photoionization method also permits the use of relatively low
substrate concentrations, thus minimizing reactions between the
radical cation and its precursor. Similarly, bimolecular quenching studies are not complicated by reaction of potential radical
cation quenchers with the excited state of the sensitizer, leading
to lower radical cation yields. The use of most radical cation
scavengers does not interfere with substrate photoionization, although there are cases where the solvated electron may be
trapped by either substrate or quencher to give a radical anion.
Despite these advantages, the photoionization method is somewhat less general than the photosensitization route in that it
requires relatively easily oxidized substrates and polar solvents.
In cases where photoionization is biphotonic it is also essential
that the substrate excited state have an appropriate lifetime and
extinction coefficient at the excitation wavelength for absorption
of a second photon. Nevertheless, it has been our experience
that photoionization (where applicable) is the method of choice
for the generation of radical cations for kinetic studies.[15,21,39]

Excitation of charge transfer complexes (D--A, Eq. 12) is well
known to result in the formation of contact radical ion pairs.

$$D - - - A \xrightarrow{h\nu} D - - - A^* \rightarrow [D^{+\bullet} \, A^{-\bullet}] \qquad (12)$$

However, the dominant decay route for the contact ion pair is
back electron transfer and this method is not of general utility
as a source of radical ions for kinetic or spectroscopic characterization on a nanosecond timescale.[42] It has been used in some
picosecond studies and can provide useful chemical yields for

radical ion derived products in cases for which either the radical anion or cation has a rapid chemical decay route (e.g., bond cleavage) that can compete with back electron transfer.[43-45] It is also a suitable method for generating long-lived radical ions in organized assemblies.[46,47]

Pulse radiolysis has been used to generate alkene radical cations for kinetic studies.[20,48-50] In this case ionizing radiation produces radical cations of the solvent which, in the case of alkanes and chloroalkanes, have lifetimes that are sufficient to be scavenged by mM concentrations of an appropriate donor. The method has been used to generate styrene radical cations in nonpolar solvents, as indicated in Eq. 13 (RH = cyclohexane).[12,13,20,48] It has also been used in polar solvents, in which case the alkene is oxidized by a strong transient oxidant such as $SO_4^{-\bullet}$ or Tl^{2+} produced by pulse radiolysis.[20]

$$RH^{+\bullet} + Styrene \rightarrow RH + Styrene^{+\bullet} \qquad (13)$$

3. CHARACTERIZATION OF ALKENE RADICAL CATIONS

As noted above, most kinetic studies of alkene radical cations in solution have focused on aryl-substituted systems since they have convenient optical properties and have been extensively studied by other techniques. Radical cations are frequently identified on the basis of their characteristic UV–visible absorptions and the comparison of their spectra to those obtained in matrices at low temperature.[11] However, a number of other diagnostic tests are also commonly employed to identify these intermediates. For example, their kinetic behavior as a function of solvent nucleophilicity or added nucleophiles is analogous to that of other electrophilic species. Thus, reaction with nucleophiles such as azide and halide ions provides support for the assignment of a transient to a radical cation, although it will not serve to eliminate a carbocation intermediate. More useful in the latter respect is the method of generation of the transient since PET does not in general lead to the formation of carbocations. Quenching of the observed transient with a more easily oxidized donor to give a well-characterized and detectable radical cation can also provide strong support for a radical cation assignment. It is straightforward to distinguish between cationic species and neutral radicals or triplet excited states since the latter generally react with oxygen with rate constants in excess of 10^9 $M^{-1}s^{-1}$. Radical cations are substantially less reactive to oxygen; the limited amount of experimental data available for this reaction indicates that rate constants are typically substantially less than 10^8 $M^{-1}s^{-1}$.[15,51–53] This means that most radical cations will react with solvent or added nucleophiles rather than with the amount of oxygen present in aerated or oxygenated samples. Therefore, most kinetic measurements can be performed with oxygenated samples which serve to eliminate a variety of other species (radicals, triplets, or radical anions) that may overlap spectrally with the radical cation of interest.

A large number of alkene radical cations with a single aryl substitutent have now been generated in solution by either laser flash photolysis or pulse radiolysis and characterized using time-resolved UV–visible spectroscopy.[12,13,15,19,20] These styrene radical cations all have a typical transient absorption spectrum with a strong UV band at ~360 nm and a second weaker and broader band between 590 and 650 nm. The spectra in solution are in good agreement with those previously reported in matrices at low temperature.[11,54] Typical absorption spectra are shown in Figure 2 for four styrene radical cations generated by photoionization in acetonitrile or 2,2,2-trifluoroethanol (TFE). Solution absorption data obtained by time-resolved experiments are also compiled in Table 1. Although all styrene radical cations have both UV and visible absorption bands, the λ_{max} values are sub-stituent-dependent. Most dramatic is the hypsochromic shift of the long wavelength band with the addition of α-methyl groups in polar solvents such as acetonitrile or aqueous acetonitrile. For example, the long wavelength absorption shifts from 600 nm for 4-methoxystyrene to 650 nm for α-methyl-4-methoxystyrene and similar shifts are observed for styrene and α-methylstyrene. By contrast, β-methyl groups have little ef-fect on the visible band but do cause a red-shift of the UV band. For example, the absorption maxima of styrene and β,β-

Table 1. Absorption Maxima of Aryl and Diarylalkene Radical
Cations Generated by Pulse Radiolysis or Laser Flash Photolysis in
Solution

Alkene	λ_{max}/nm	Solvent
4-chlorostyrene	375, 650	cyclohexane[a]
4-fluorostyrene	350, 585	TFE[b]
styrene	350, 620	cyclohexane[a]
	350, 600	TFE[b]
4-methylstyrene	360, 600	cyclohexane[a]
	360, 600	TFE[b]
4-methoxystyrene	360, 610	cyclohexane[a]
	350, 600	TFE[b]
	350, 600	aq. acetonitrile[b]
β-methylstyrene	370, 590	cyclohexane[a]
	355, 370, 590	TFE[b]
β,β-dimethylstyrene	380, 590	TFE[b]
α-methylstyrene	350, 620	cyclohexane[a]
	350, 650	TFE[b]
trans-β-methyl-4-methoxystyrene	385, 620	cyclohexane[a]
	380, 600	acetonitrile[b]
	380, 600	aq. acetonitrile[b]
cis-β-methyl-4-methoxystyrene	380, 620	acetonitrile[c]
1,1-diphenyl-2-methylpropene	760–800	acetonitrile[d]
1,1-di-(4-methoxyphenyl)-2-methyl-propene	760–800	acetonitrile[d]
1,1-di-(4-methoxyphenyl)-2-propene	400	1,2-dichloroethane[e]
1,1-di-(4-methoxyphenyl)ethene	390	butyl chloride[f]
trans-stilbene	472	acetonitrile[g]
cis-stilbene	508	acetonitrile[g]
trans-4,4'-dimethoxystilbene	530	acetonitrile[g]
trans-4-methoxystilbene	485	acetonitrile[g]
cis-4-methoxystilbene	520	acetonitrile[g]
trans-4-cyanostilbene	480	acetonitrile[g]

Notes: [a]Ref. 20.
[b]Ref. 15.
[c]Ref. 55.
[d]Ref. 53.
[e]Ref. 56.
[f]Ref. 57.
[g]Ref. 27.

dimethylstyrene radical cations are at 350 and 380 nm, respectively. The shifts in the visible absorption band are consistent with the photoelectron spectra for styrene and its α- and β-methyl derivatives. The lower energy transition observed for α-methylstyrene in these experiments has been rationalized on the basis of an increase in the dihedral angle between the aromatic ring and the double bond due to the steric effect of the α-methyl group.[54] Similar shifts in the absorption maxima as a function of structure have been observed for styrene radical cations in cyclohexane solution.[13] However, it should be noted that a more recent study suggests that shifts in the absorption maxima upon α-methyl substitution may be less pronounced in cyclohexane than in polar solvents such as acetonitrile.[20]

In the absence of added nucleophiles or strong reducing agents, the lifetimes of styrene radical cations in solution depend strongly on the nature of the solvent and the concentration of the neutral precursor styrene. Reactive radical cations such as those derived from styrene, 4-methylstyrene, and 4-fluorostyrene are too short-lived to be observed with nanosecond resolution in nucleophilic solvents such as aqueous acetonitrile, or even in dry acetonitrile. That these radical cations are indeed produced by photoionization of the corresponding neutral styrene in these solvents has been shown from picosecond laser photolysis experiments in which the 4-methylstyrene radical cation was detected with a lifetime of 3 ns in acetonitrile.[15] In less nucleophilic solvents such as trifluoroethanol, or the hydrocarbon cyclohexane, these radical cations are sufficiently long-lived to be readily detected and studied using nanosecond techniques. On the other hand, styrene radical cations stabilized by a 4-methoxy group are much longer-lived, and can be readily detected in both acetonitrile and aqueous acetonitrile.

In addition to the effect of solvent, the decays of the styrene radical cations are often strongly dependent on the concentration of the neutral precursor. This is typically exhibited by an increase in the rate constant for the decay of the radical cations with increasing concentration of the precursor, and is due to addition of the radical cation to the neutral styrene to generate a dimer radical cation, as discussed in detail in Section 5. As

Table 2. Lifetimes of Substituted Styrene Radical Cations in Solution[a]

Styrene	τ	Solvent
4-fluorostyrene	170 ns	TFE
styrene	37 ns	TFE
4-methylstyrene	2.9 μs	TFE
	3.3 ns	acetonitrile
4-methoxystyrene	7.7 μs	acetonitrile
	9.1 μs	aq. acetonitrile
	13 μs	aq. 2-propanol[b]
β-methylstyrene	4.5 μs	TFE
β,β-dimethylstyrene	8.3 μs	TFE
α-methylstyrene	83 ns	TFE
β-methyl-4-methoxystyrene	25 μs	acetonitrile
	18 μs	aq. 2-propanol[b]
α-methyl-4-methoxystyrene	2.5 μs	acetonitrile
	2.5 μs	aq. acetonitrile

Notes: [a]Data taken from Ref. 15 unless otherwise noted.
[b]Ref. 20.

a result, the lifetimes of the radical cations in various solvents can only be compared directly by measuring the observed rate constant at different concentrations of precursor styrene and then extrapolating to zero precursor concentration. Extrapolated lifetimes for some styrene radical cations are summarized in Table 2. While quantitative conclusions about the effect of structure on the lifetimes of styrene radical cations are complicated by the different solvents used, a number of qualitative conclusions have been discussed.[15] For example, the aromatic ring substituent has a large effect on the reactivity of the radical cation. The strong stabilizing effect of the 4-methoxy group is evident from the fact that the lifetime of the 4-methoxystyrene radical cation in acetonitrile is over 3 orders of magnitude longer than that of the 4-methylstyrene radical cation in the same solvent. The latter is in turn almost 2 orders of magnitude less reactive than the parent styrene radical cation.

The other structural feature that plays a dominant role in determining radical cation lifetimes is the presence or absence of methyl groups at the β-position. For example, the β-methylstyrene radical cation has a lifetime that is 100-fold longer than that of the parent styrene radical cation and the addition of the methyl group to the β-position of the 4-methoxystyrene radical cation results in a further threefold increase. Conversely, the presence of an α-methyl group has little effect, with the lifetimes of the α-methylstyrene and α-methyl-4-methoxystyrene radical cations being similar to those of the styrene and 4-methoxystyrene radical cations, respectively.

Several 1,1-diaryl substituted alkene radical cations have also been generated by either laser flash photolysis or pulse radiolysis in solution (Table 1).[53,56-58] Long-wavelength absorptions (760–800 nm) have been reported for both 1,1-diphenyl-2-methylpropene and 1,1-di(4-methoxyphenyl)-2-methylpropene radical cations generated by PET in acetonitrile.[53] In agreement with these results, the 1,1-diphenylethene radical cation has been reported to absorb at long wavelengths (>900 nm).[13] The 1,1-di(4-methoxyphenyl)-2-propene and 1,1-di-(4-methoxyphenyl)ethene radical cations have been generated by pulse radiolysis in chlorinated hydrocarbons and are reported to have λ_{max} at 400 and 390 nm, respectively.[56,57] The limited amount of data for these systems suggests that the 1,1-diarylalkenes have two UV–visible absorption bands, with the lower energy absorption at considerably longer wavelength than in the case of the styrene radical cations. The lifetimes of these radical cations are limited by either dimerization or back electron transfer with the sensitizer radical anion and have not been studied in detail.

Stilbene radical cations are well known from matrix studies and have been generated by laser flash photolysis techniques.[11,26,27,59,60] The parent *trans* and *cis* radical cations have strong absorption maxima at 482 and 508 nm in acetonitrile solution with weaker bands between 700–800 nm.[27] A number of substituted stilbene radical cations have also been studied and both electron withdrawing and donating substituents result in bathochromic shifts (Table 1). The *cis*-stilbene radical cations typically have λ_{max} values that are 30–40 nm to the red of their *trans* isomers, in agreement with calculations that indicate that the *trans* radical cation is essentially planar, whereas the *cis* radical cation is nonplanar, as is the neutral molecule.[27] Most kinetic studies of stilbene radical cations have focused on their *cis–trans* isomerization and there have been relatively few investigations of their bimolecular reactivity.

Simple alkyl- or alkoxy-substituted alkene radical cations are of particular interest from the point of view of synthetic applications[61] and biological processes. Several of these have been studied by ESR spectroscopy and have been characterized by UV–visible spectroscopy in matrices at low temperature.[11,62–64] However, they have not been the subject of detailed kinetic studies using optical detection methods at room temperature. The radical cation of tetramethylethylene has been generated by pulse radiolysis (λ_{max} 290 nm) in aqueous solution and has a decay rate constant of ~4 × 10^5 s^{-1} that is limited by deprotonation to give an allyl radical.[65] Pulse radiolysis of several other substituted ethenes also generates radical cations that have absorption maxima at 280 nm and react at diffusion controlled rates with their neutral precursors.[66] To our knowledge only a single flash photolysis study of alkoxy-substituted alkene radical cations has been reported.[14] In this work several 1,3-dioxole radical cations were generated by photoionization of the parent alkene in aqueous solution (Eq. 14).[14] The radical cations have λ_{max} between 280 and 290 nm, are relatively long-lived (lifetime of ~20 μs for the parent dioxole, R = H), and, unlike most alkene radical cations, do not react rapidly with the precursor alkene. These results demonstrate that alkyl- and alkoxy-substituted alkene radical cations are sufficiently long-lived in solution for kinetic measurements of their intermolecular reactivity. The lack of kinetic data appears to be largely due to the fact that these radical cations have absorption maxima below 300 nm that preclude their generation and detection using most of the commonly used photosensitizers. Furthermore, they cannot generally be produced by photoionization at short wavelengths, either due to low radical cation yields or complications arising from competing UV absorptions of both substrate and quencher.

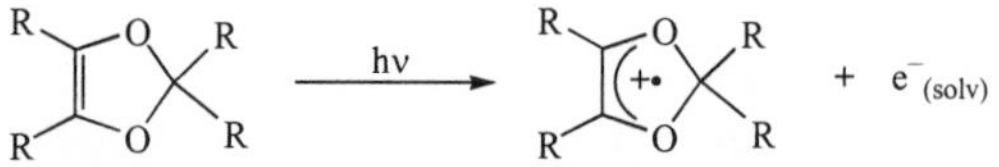

$$\text{(14)}$$

4. REACTIONS WITH NUCLEOPHILES

The photoinduced anti-Markovnikov addition of methanol to 1,1-diphenylethene reported by Arnold and co-workers in 1973 provides the first example of the addition of a nucleophile to an arylalkene radical cation.[67] There are now a number of studies that demonstrate the generality of nucleophilic addition of alcohols, amines, and anions such as cyanide to aryl- and diaryl-alkene radical cations.[67–75] Product studies and mechanistic work have established that addition occurs at the β-position of 1-aryl or 1,1-diarylalkene radical cations to give arylmethyl or diaryl-methyl radical-derived products as shown in Scheme 1 for the addition of methanol to 1,1-diphenylethene. For neutral nucleophiles, such as alcohols and amines, radical formation requires prior deprotonation of the 1,3-distonic radical cation formed in the initial addition reaction. The final product usually results from reduction of the radical by the sensitizer radical anion to give an anion that is then protonated, although other radical

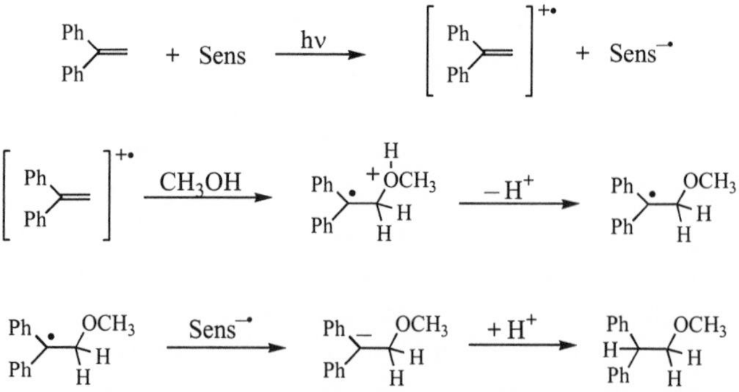

Scheme 1.

reactions such as hydrogen abstraction or coupling can occur if reduction is endergonic.

4.1. Anions

The reaction of a series of substituted styrene radical cations with anions has recently been studied in detail by laser flash photolysis.[15,18] Representative kinetic data are summarized in Tables 3 and 4 and demonstrate that most of the anions studied react with styrene radical cations with diffusion controlled rate constants. These reactions can involve either addition to the β-carbon to give a benzyl radical (Eq. 15) as discussed above or electron transfer to regenerate the precursor alkene plus the oxidized nucleophile (Nu·, Eq. 16). Transient absorption spectra have been used to distinguish between these two possibilities. For example, reaction of the radical cation with either bromide or chloride leads to the formation of a transient that is identified

Table 3. Second-Order Rate Constants, k_{Nu}, for the Reaction of Nucleophiles with Various Substituted Radical Cations in Solution[a,b]

	$k_{Nu} / M^{-1} s^{-1}$			
Radical Cation	N_3^-	Br^-	Cl^-	*MeOH*
styrene	1.4×10^{10}	1.1×10^{10}	9.4×10^9	1.8×10^8
α-methylstyrene	1.2×10^{10}	1.0×10^{10}	9.5×10^9	1.9×10^8
β-methylstyrene	1.1×10^{10}	1.0×10^{10}	6.0×10^9	1.1×10^7
β,β-dimethylstyrene	7.9×10^9		8.0×10^7	2.0×10^5
4-fluorostyrene	1.3×10^{10}	1.0×10^{10}	9.8×10^9	5.1×10^7
4-methylstyrene	1.0×10^{10}	1.3×10^{10}	8.9×10^9	5.9×10^6
4-methoxystyrene	1.2×10^{10c}	2.2×10^{6c}	6.4×10^{6c}	3.0×10^{4c}
	4.2×10^{10d}	4.0×10^{10d}	3.0×10^{10d}	
β-methyl-4-	9.7×10^{9c}			
methoxystyrene	2.9×10^{10d}	3.0×10^{10d}		

Notes: [a]All rate constants are for reaction in TFE unless otherwise noted.
   [b]Data from Ref. 15.
   [c]In 4:1 water:acetonitrile.
   [d]In neat acetonitrile.

Table 4. Second-Order Rate Contants, k_{Nu}, for the Reaction of 4-Methoxystyrene Radical Cation with Various Nucleophiles in 4:1 Water/Acetonitrile or Neat Acetonitrile[a]

| Nucleophile | $k_{Nu}/M^{-1} s^{-1}$ | |
	Aq. Acetonitrile	Acetonitrile
N_3^-	1.2×10^{10}	4.2×10^{10}
CN^-	1.0×10^{8}	2.9×10^{10}
HO^-	5.3×10^{7}	c
Cl^-	6.4×10^{6}	3.0×10^{10}
$CH_3CO_2^-$	2.6×10^{6}	4.0×10^{10}
Br^-	2.2×10^{6}	4.0×10^{10}
$CF_3CO_2^-$	1.6×10^{6}	c
MeOH	3.0×10^{4}	c
NO_3^-	b	2.4×10^{9}

Notes: [a]Data from Ref. 15.

[b]No rate acceleration was observed up to 1.0 M nucleophile.

[c]Not measured.

as a benzyl radical on the basis of its characteristic absorption in the 300–340-nm region and its reactivity towards oxygen.

$$\left[\text{\raisebox{0pt}{structure}} \right]^{+\bullet} + \ Nu^- \longrightarrow \text{\raisebox{0pt}{structure}} \qquad (15)$$

$$\left[\text{\raisebox{0pt}{structure}} \right]^{+\bullet} + \ Nu^- \longrightarrow \text{\raisebox{0pt}{structure}} \ + \ Nu^\bullet \qquad (16)$$

The results for reaction of azide with several 4-methoxystyrene radical cations provide an interesting example of the effect of solvent on the competition between electron transfer and addition.[18] In TFE the 4-methoxystyrene, β-methyl-4-methoxystyrene, and β,β-dimethyl-4-methoxystyrene radical cations react with azide with rate constants of 7.0, 3.5, and 1.0×10^9 $M^{-1}s^{-1}$, respectively. In all three cases the transient spectra in the presence of azide provide evidence for the formation of the benzyl radical generated by addition of azide to the β-carbon. Further, the change in kinetics for the three radical cations with increasing steric bulk at the β-carbon is consistent with an addition reaction. By contrast, reaction of azide with the same three radical cations in acetonitrile occurs with rate constants that are the same ($\sim 3 \times 10^9 \ M^{-1}s^{-1}$) within experimental error and does not generate a transient consistent with adduct radical formation. The observed transient has a broad absorption at 700 nm that is assigned to the dimer radical anion formed by electron transfer from the radical cation to generate an azidyl radical that reacts with excess azide ion to give $N_6^{-\bullet}$ (Eq. 17). The change in mechanism from electron transfer in acetonitrile to addition in TFE is determined by the relative oxidation potentials of the styrenes and azide in the two solvents. For example, in acetonitrile the oxidation potential of azide ion is approximately 0.6 eV lower than that of the styrenes, indicating that electron transfer should occur at the diffusion-controlled rate, as observed. The oxidation potentials for the styrenes in TFE do not change substantially from those in acetonitrile. However, the peak potential for azide increases dramatically in TFE, presumably due to stabilization of the anion by hydrogen bonding. The shift in oxidation potential means that electron transfer is not sufficiently exergonic to occur at a diffusion-controlled rate and allows addition to compete effectively. These results demonstrate the importance of redox properties (which reflect relative solvation energies) in determining the chemoselectivity of reactions of radical cations.

$$\left[\underset{R}{\bigotimes}\!\!= \right]^{+\bullet} + \ N_3^- \ \longrightarrow \ \underset{R}{\bigotimes}\!\!= \ + \ N_3^{\bullet} \ \underset{}{\overset{N_3^-}{\rightleftharpoons}} \ N_6^{-\bullet} \quad (17)$$

With the exception of azide ion there is no evidence that any of the other styrenes react with the anions listed in Tables 3 and 4 by electron transfer. The reactions of most of the styrene radical cations with azide, bromide, and chloride in acetonitrile or TFE approach the diffusion-controlled limit and show little selectivity, with the exception of modest decreases as a result of β-methyl substitution. The same is true for reaction of a wider range of nucleophiles with the 4-methoxystyrene radical cation in acetonitrile (Table 4) with only the nitrite ion reacting at significantly less than 10^{10} $M^{-1}s^{-1}$. However, rate constants for reaction of the same series of nucleophiles vary by 4 orders of magnitude in aqueous acetonitrile. For example, rate constants for addition of the 4-methoxystyrene radical cation to bromide and chloride of 2.6×10^6 $M^{-1}s^{-1}$ have been measured in 80% aqueous acetonitrile[15] and are too slow to measure in water.[20] The decreases in rate constant in aqueous solution are clearly attributable to hydrogen bonding between water and the nucleophile. Similar results have been reported for additions of anions to the retinyl cation and for the addition of amines to styrene and anthracene radical cations and di- and triarylmethyl cations.[76–78] These solvent effects provide a useful method for modulating the reactivity of a particular radical cation/nucleophile combination. They may be of particular utility in controlling the chemoselectivity of a radical cation reaction in cases where nucleophilic addition competes with a reaction that is less strongly influenced by the solvent (e.g., bond cleavage or cycloaddition).

In some cases the addition of bromide to alkene radical cations is reversible. For example, the addition of bromide to the β-methyl-4-methoxystyrene radical cation occurs reversibly, as demonstrated by the formation of the radical cation when the β-bromo radical is generated independently by photolysis of 1-(4-methoxyphenyl)-1,2-dibromopropane (Eq. 18).[15] An equilibrium constant of 2×10^{-4} M has been measured for the loss of bromide from this radical in acetonitrile. The apparent lack of reactivity of 1,3-dioxole radical cations with bromide ion in water has also been explained on the basis of reversible addition with rapid loss of bromide from the product radical.[14] However, on the basis of the solvent effects noted above, it is also possible that the lack of reactivity in water is a solvent effect since decreases in reactivity of 4 to 5 orders of magnitude have been observed for reactions of bromide ion with styrene radical cations in largely aqueous solvent mixtures.[15,20]

$$\text{(structure)} \xrightleftharpoons[k_{Br^-}]{k_{-Br^-}} \text{(structure)} + Br^- \qquad (18)$$

Relatively little kinetic data for the reactions of diarylalkene radical cations with nucleophiles are available. The 4,4'-dimethoxystilbene radical cation reacts with acetate with a rate constant of 8.9×10^9 $M^{-1}s^{-1}$ in acetonitrile.[79] Similarly, the radical cation of a rigid stilbene (5-dibenzosuberenol) reacts with hydroxide and bromide with rate constants of 1.1×10^{10} and 1.7×10^9 $M^{-1}s^{-1}$, respectively, in 3:2 acetonitrile/water.[39] Although the mechanisms for these reactions have not been examined in detail, the oxidation potentials suggest that electron transfer is endergonic for these radical cation/nucleophile pairs. Therefore, it seems likely that additions of stilbene radical cations to nucleophiles occur with rate constants that approach the diffusion-controlled limit, as is the case for most styrene radical cations. These results for nucleophilic addition to alkene radical cations are in contrast to theoretical predictions based on the curve-crossing model.[80] This work suggested that nucleophilic additions to radical cations are formally forbidden and will, in general, occur more slowly than the allowed addition of a nucleophile to a cation of similar electron affinity. However, it is likely that a more detailed theoretical model such as that recently provided for σ-radical cations will be required for predicting reactivity patterns for nucleophilic additions to alkene radical cations.[81]

4.2. Alcohols

As noted above the anti-Markovnikov addition of alcohols to alkenes has attracted considerable mechanistic and synthetic interest. Absolute rate constants for the reaction of alcohols with styrene radical cations have been measured and representative data are summarized in Tables 3 and 5.[15] In this case the high oxidation potentials of simple alcohols effectively rule out the possibility of electron transfer as a competing reaction. Furthermore, transients assigned to the benzyl radical produced by

Table 5. Rate Constants for Reaction
of the β-Methylstyrene Radical Cation
with Alcohols in TFE[a]

Alcohol	$k_{ROH}/M^{-1}s^{-1}$
methanol	1.1×10^7
ethanol	4.3×10^6
2-propanol	2.1×10^6
tert-butanol	1.0×10^6

Note: [a]Data from Ref. 15.

addition of water and alcohols have been observed for a number of styrene radical cations.[15,20] Figure 3 shows an example of the 2-methoxy-1-phenylpropyl radical produced by addition of methanol to the β-methylstyrene radical cation. None of the time-resolved studies of alcohol addition have provided any direct evidence for the distonic 1,3-radical cation (Scheme 1) that is the initial addition product.

The observed rate constants for alcohol addition cover several orders of magnitude in time scale with measured rate constants on the order of 10^8 M^{-1}s^{-1} for the most reactive radical cations. Since the reactions all occur at substantially less than the dif-

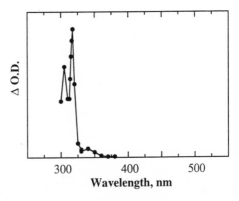

Figure 3. Absorption spectrum of the 2-methoxy-1-phenylpropyl radical generated by reaction of the β-methylstyrene radical cation with methanol in TFE.

fusion-controlled limit, they provide a clear illustration of the effects of varying the substituents on either the alcohol or the aromatic ring or double bond of the radical cation. For example, the rate constants for methanol addition to *para*-substituted styrene radical cations decrease in the order H > F > CH_3 > OCH_3 and span 4 orders of magnitude. Substantial changes in reactivity are observed for alkyl substitution of the double bond, with one and two methyl groups on the β-carbon leading to 19- and 900-fold decreases, respectively, in the rate constant for methanol addition as compared to the parent styrene radical cations. By contrast, α-methyl substitution has a negligible effect on the reactivity. These reactivity trends provide further support for the addition of methanol to the β-carbon. It is also interesting to note that the measured rate constant for methanol addition to the β-methylstyrene radical cation (9.7×10^6 $M^{-1}s^{-1}$) is in excellent agreement with a literature estimate based on steady state photolysis experiments for the same reaction of the 1,1-dimethylindene radical cation (9.6×10^6 $M^{-1}s^{-1}$), thus demonstrating the validity of Stern–Volmer quenching studies for obtaining kinetic data.[73] The addition of methanol, ethanol, 2-propanol and *tert*-butanol to the 4-methylstyrene radical cation (Table 5) shows the expected trend of decreasing reactivity with increasing steric bulk and decreasing nucleophilicity of the alcohol and parallels the trends observed for addition of alcohols to a variety of carbocations.[15,82]

4.3. Amines and Pyridines

Product studies have demonstrated that 1-phenyl and 1,1-diarylalkene radical cations react with nitrogen-centered nucleophiles such as amines and pyridines by both addition and deprotonation.[83–85] The addition reactions occur by a mechanism analogous to that shown in Scheme 1 for methanol addition. Deprotonation by an amine or pyridine base is an alternate possibility for radical cations derived from 2-alkyl-substituted alkenes and leads to an allylic radical (Eq. 19). Reduction of this radical by the sensitizer radical anion generates an anion that is protonated at either the original position to regenerate starting material or at the benzylic position to give the less thermodynamically stable nonconjugated 2-alkene. Although mixtures of addition and deprotonation products have been observed for some primary amines,[83] the nonconjugated 2-alkene has been obtained cleanly for 1-phenylalkenes in the presence of hindered pyridine bases.[85] As for the reactions with anionic nucleophiles discussed above, the energy-wasting electron transfer reaction is also expected to be a competing process for easily oxidized amines. Thus, the reactions with nitrogen-centered nucleophiles provide a particularly interesting example for studies of the factors that control the competition between three different reaction pathways.

$$\left[\underset{R}{\text{Ph}} = CH_3 \right]^{+\bullet} \xrightarrow{\text{Base}} \underset{R}{\text{Ph}} = CH_2 \xrightarrow{\text{Sens}^{-\bullet}} \underset{R}{\text{Ph}} = CH_2 \tag{19}$$

$$\underset{R}{\text{Ph}} = CH_2 \ + H^+ \longrightarrow \underset{R}{\text{Ph}} = CH_3 \ + \ \underset{R}{\text{Ph}} - CH_2$$

A detailed laser flash photolysis study of the reactions of the 4-methoxystyrene radical cation and its β-methyl and β,β-dimethyl analogs with amines and pyridines in acetonitrile and aqueous acetonitrile has been carried out.[19,86] Representative kinetic data are summarized in Table 6 and cover approximately 4 orders of magnitude in time scale. A combination of transient spectra, product studies, and redox potentials has been used to establish which of the three possible reactions contributes to the measured rate constant for any given radical cation/amine pair. For example, transient spectra obtained after quenching of the radical cations with either DABCO or aniline clearly show the formation of the amine radical cation, consistent with the fact that both of these amines have substantially lower oxidation potentials than any of the three styrenes. Reaction with primary amines occurs by addition, as evidenced by the formation of a transient in the 300-nm region that is assigned to the substituted benzyl radical. These results are consistent with the high oxi-

Table 6. Rate Constants, k_{amine}, for Reaction of Three β-Substituted 4-Methoxystyrene Radical Cations with Amines and Pyridines in Acetonitrile[a]

	$k_{amine}/M^{-1}s^{-1}$		
Amine or Pyridine	*β–H*	*β–CH₃*	*β–(CH₃)₂*
aniline	1.3×10^{10}	1.2×10^{10}	8.9×10^{9}
DABCO	1.5×10^{10}	1.4×10^{10}	1.9×10^{10}
triethylamine	6.6×10^{9}	4.7×10^{9}	2.3×10^{9}
n-butylamine	2.5×10^{9}	2.2×10^{9}	8.7×10^{8}
tert-butylamine	2.1×10^{9}	4.6×10^{8}	1.6×10^{8}
2,6-di(*tert*-butyl)pyridine	$<1 \times 10^{6}$	2.6×10^{6}	1.1×10^{6}
2,6-dimethylpyridine	2.4×10^{7}	1.9×10^{6}	8.6×10^{5}
3,5-dimethylpyridine	9.9×10^{8}	5.5×10^{8}	8.8×10^{7}

Note: [a]Data taken from Refs. 19 and 86.

dation potentials of primary amines, relative to the styrenes, and with product studies in related systems.[83,86] Although low yields (5–10%) of products resulting from deprotonation have been observed for the 1,1-diphenylpropene radical cation in the presence of several primary amines, deprotonation has not been observed for the reaction of the β-methyl-4-methoxystyrene radical cation with *n*-butylamine. Rate constants for reactions with primary amines show a substantial decrease upon addition of one or two β-methyl groups, in marked distinction to electron transfer reactions which are relatively insensitive to the steric bulk at the β-carbon. Similarly, the bulky *tert*-butylamine reacts much more slowly than *n*-butylamine with the β,β-dimethyl-substituted radical cation. In fact, this sensitivity to substitution at the β-carbon of the radical cation or to steric bulk of the nucleophile is diagnostic of an addition reaction. Thus the reaction of these styrene radical cations with triethylamine has been suggested to occur by electron transfer, based on the insensitivity of the quenching rate constants to β-methyl substitution and on the relevant redox potentials.

The reactions of the same three styrene radical cations with a number of primary amines of varying basicities but constant steric requirements have also been examined.[86] The results obtained for reaction of five primary amines with the 4-methoxystyrene radical cation in acetonitrile and aqueous acetonitrile are shown as a Bronsted-type plot in Figure 4. In acetonitrile the rate constants increase substantially with increasing basicity of the amine and the plot of log (k_{amine}) versus pK_a of the conjugate acids of the amines is curved and reaches a plateau at ~2.5×10^9 $M^{-1}s^{-1}$. Nonlinear Bronsted plots have also been observed for the additions of amines to both anthracene radical cations and diphenylmethyl carbocations.[77,78] The results have been rationalized in terms of a reaction scheme in which the reactants form an intermediate complex which can either separate or collapse to give addition products, with the curvature indicating a change from rate-limiting product formation to rate-limiting complex formation.

Somewhat different results are obtained for the additions of the same series of amines to the 4-methoxystyrene radical cation

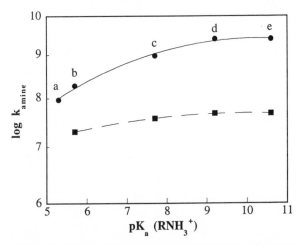

Figure 4. Bronsted-type plot showing the dependence of log k_{amine} on pK_a (RNH$_3^+$) for the reaction of the 4-methoxystyrene radical cation with a series of primary amines in acetonitrile (●) and 4:1 aqueous acetonitrile (■): **a**, cyanomethylamine; **b**, trifluoroethylamine; **c**, cyanoethylamine; **d**, methoxyethylamine; **e**, n-butylamine.

in aqueous acetonitrile. The rate constant for each amine is lower in the aqueous solvent, with the effects being largest for the more basic amines. For example, the rate constant for addition of *n*-butylamine decreases by a factor of approximately 50 in the aqueous solvent, whereas that for aminoacetonitrile decreases by a factor of 10. The net effect of this is a Bronsted-type plot which shows a much less pronounced increase in rate constant with increasing amine basicity, and which reaches a plateau at a rate constant of 5×10^7 $M^{-1}s^{-1}$. The effect of water on the rate constants is consistent with the hydrogen-bonding interactions between the lone pair on nitrogen and the solvent; the more basic amines are more strongly hydrogen bonded and, as a consequence, the effect of water on the rate constant for addition is larger. The results are similar to the solvent effects discussed above for the addition of anionic nucleophiles, further reinforcing the importance of the solvent in determining the overall reactivity for addition reactions.

Rate constants for the reaction of substituted pyridines with the 4-methoxystyrene radical cations have also been measured (Table 6). The bulky 2,6-di-*tert*-butyl pyridine reacts with the two methyl-substituted radical cations with rate constants of approximately 10^6 $M^{-1}s^{-1}$, but is substantially less reactive towards 4-methoxystyrene. This reaction has been attributed to deprotonation since electron transfer would be endergonic by ~0.7 V and since the effects of methyl substitution at the β-carbon are opposite to those observed for other nucleophilic additions. 2,6-Dimethylpyridine also reacts with the two methyl-substituted radical cations with rate constants of 10^6 $M^{-1}s^{-1}$, but is approximately 1 order of magnitude more reactive towards the 4-methoxystyrene radical cation. The latter reaction must be nucleophilic addition since this radical cation cannot undergo deprotonation. Product studies have confirmed that the reaction of 2,6-dimethylpyridine with the β-methyl-4-methoxystyrene radical cation is deprotonation.[86] The major product of irradiation of a mixture of 1,4-dicyanobenzene, 4-methoxystyrene, and 2,6-dimethylpyridine is the rearranged tautomer, 3-(4-methoxyphenyl)propene, formed by a deprotonation, reduction, protonation sequence as shown in Eq. 19. By contrast to these

results, a less sterically hindered pyridine such as 3,5-di-
methylpyridine reacts substantially more rapidly with all three
radical cations, presumably via nucleophilic addition.

5. RADICAL CATION MEDIATED CYCLOADDITIONS

Cycloaddition reactions of alkene radical cations have been the
subject of a number of mechanistic studies and are potentially
useful synthetic reactions.[3,4,7,8] Most of the initial work on radical cation mediated cycloadditions focused on the dimerization
of arylalkenes, with one of the first examples being Ledwith's
report of the chloranil-sensitized dimerization of N-vinylcarba-
zole to generate a diarylcyclobutane.[87] This work led to the
development of the mechanism outlined in Scheme 2, in which
addition of the radical cation to neutral alkene generates an
acyclic 1,4-radical cation as the primary intermediate. This intermediate cyclizes to a cyclobutane radical cation that is then
reduced by the neutral alkene and regenerates a second radical
cation to carry the chain.

Although the mechanism shown in Scheme 2 was satisfactory
to explain the radical cation mediated dimerization of a variety
of arylalkenes and vinyl ethers,[3,88] other studies provided mechanistic evidence for additional reaction pathways. For example,
early studies reported the formation of a [2 + 4] dimer, 1,1,4-
triphenyl-1,2,3,4-tetrahydronaphthalene, in the ET-sensitized dimerization of 1,1-diphenylethylene and postulated a mechanism
involving 1,6-cyclization of an initial 1,4-acyclic radical cation.[67,69] Later work demonstrated that dimerization of this alkene

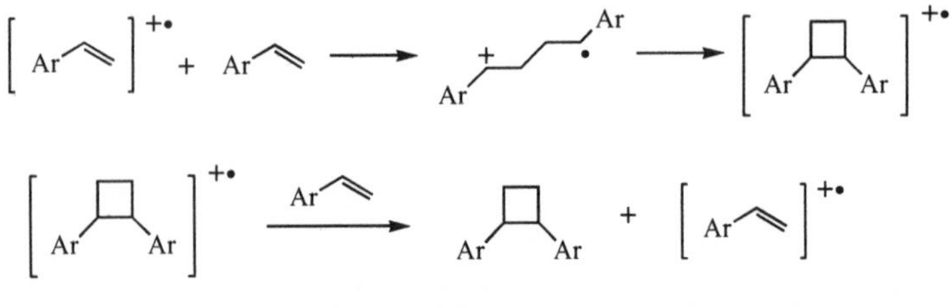

Scheme 2.

also led to both cyclobutane and dihydronaphthalene products, with the ratio of the three products depending on the sensitizer used and on the initial concentration of 1,1-diphenylethylene.[71,89] Mixtures of cyclobutane and di- or tetra-hydronaphthalene products are commonly observed in the dimerization of a variety of styrenes (Eq. 20) and diarylethylenes.[16,71,90–92] It has recently

$$(20)$$

been suggested that these reactions may have important applications in the synthesis of natural products such as lignans and neolignans. In particular, magnoshinin and magnosalin, two neolignans with anti-inflammatory activity, have been prepared by the radical cation mediated dimerization of *trans*-β-methyl-2,4,5-trimethoxystyrene, Eq. 21.[91] Dimerization reactions of appropriately substituted styrenes initiated by electron transfer using triarylaminium salts have also been used in an attempt

$$(21)$$

Ar = 2,4,5-trimethoxyphenyl

LINDA J. JOHNSTON and NORMAN P. SCHEPP

to prepare natural products belonging to the gabulin and isogabu-
lin families.[93]

Farid and co-workers have suggested a further modification
of the initial mechanism shown in Scheme 2 to explain their
results on the photoinduced electron transfer dimerization of
diarylethylenes.[71] This study showed that the relative yield of
cyclobutane and naphthalene products obtained in the radical
cation initiated dimerization of diphenylethylene is strongly dependent on the initial concentration of diphenylethylene, with
cyclobutane being the major product at high concentrations and
the di- and tetrahydro-naphthalenes predominating at lower concentrations. The postulated mechanism involves a competition
between diffusional separation of the initial geminate radical
ion pair to give a free diphenylethylene radical cation and in-
cage trapping of the monomer radical cation to give a dimer
radical cation (Scheme 3). Addition of the free diphenylethylene
radical cation to the neutral alkene leads to an acyclic radical
cation that undergoes both 1,4-cyclization and 1,6-cyclization,
with the latter predominating. Alternatively, in-cage trapping of
the monomer radical cation gives a 1,4-acyclic radical cat-
ion/radical anion geminate pair. Back electron transfer within
the cage generates a 1,4-biradical that collapses to give the neutral cyclobutane. The competition between diffusional separa-

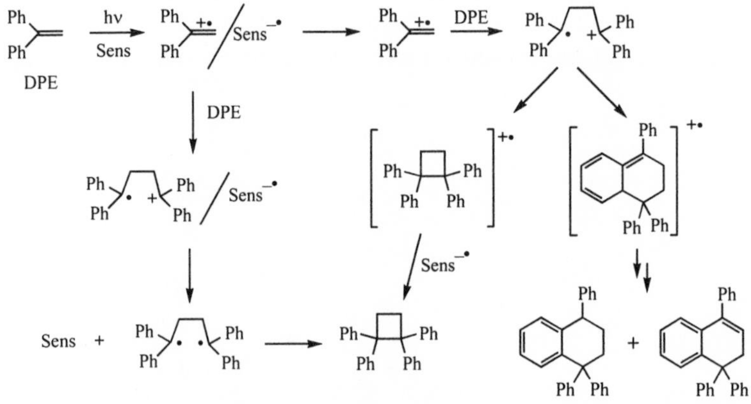

Scheme 3.

tion and in-cage trapping of the initial radical ion pair thus determines the product distribution.

The results summarized above have all been rationalized in terms of the formation of a distonic 1,4-acyclic radical cation as the primary intermediate in the dimerization of alkenes. However, there is equally convincing stereochemical evidence from the work of Lewis and Bauld for a concerted (although non-synchronous) cycloaddition to give a long-bond cyclobutane radical cation.[7,8,52] In particular, Lewis and co-workers have shown that the PET dimerization of *trans*-β-methyl-4-methoxy-styrene generates a mixture of two cyclobutane products, both of which retain the *trans*-configuration of the styrene precursor (Eq. 22).[52] This is inconsistent with the intermediacy of a freely rotating 1,4-acyclic radical cation and has been rationalized on the basis of a concerted cycloaddition to give directly a cyclobutane radical cation that is then reduced to the neutral cyclobutane. Similar stereochemical arguments support a mechanism involving a concerted (or pseudo-concerted) addition for the radical cation cyclobutanation and Diels–Alder cycloaddition of simple alkenes and dienes.[7,8] It has also been pointed out that the 1,3-sigmatropic shift that has been observed for a number of cyclobutane radical cations can account for the formation of the di- and tetra-hydronaphthalene products *without* invoking an acyclic 1,4-radical cation.[7]

The question of a concerted versus stepwise addition of alkene radical cations has been examined in a number of theoretical studies of the ion/molecule reaction between ethene radical cations and ethene.[94–97] An ab initio study by Bauld indicated that both a long-bond complex and a long-bond cyclobutane radical cation were involved in the cycloaddition reaction.[95] The most recent theoretical study of this reaction does not provide any evidence for a stable tetramethylene radical cation, but does conclude that electron-donating substituents stabilize the long-bond cyclobutane radical cation to the extent that it is preferred over the more symmetric delocalized structures.[97] It is clear from both the mechanistic and theoretical studies that there is unlikely to be a single unifying mechanism that will accommodate all the results of radical cation mediated dimerizations. Depending on the reactants and conditions, the reaction may occur via a concerted mechanism to generate an intact cyclobutane radical cation or may involve long-bond cyclobutane or 1,4-acyclic radical cations.

Although much of the early work on radical cation cycloadditions focused on dimerizations, cross-addition reactions of alkene radical cations with other alkenes or dienes are attracting increasing attention for synthetic applications.[6–8,32,98,99] The reaction of a substituted ethene radical cation with a diene can lead to either cyclobutanation or Diels–Alder reactions as illustrated in Eqs. 23 and 24. These reactions are particularly attractive since they have much lower activation energies and can be carried out under considerably milder conditions than the analogous thermal [2 + 2] and [4 + 2] cycloadditions of neutral alkenes. The reactions also occur with predictable stereochemistry and with regiospecificity that equals or surpasses that of the corresponding reaction of the two neutral alkenes. Radical cation cycloadditions are particularly attractive in overcoming the limited success of Diels–Alder reactions involving neutral or electron-rich dienophiles. For example, the Diels–Alder ad-

(23)

(24)

dition of phenyl vinyl sulfide has been used in the synthesis of the natural product (–)-β-selinene.[100]

Bauld has carried out a large number of mechanistic studies of radical cation mediated Diels–Alder and cyclobutanation reactions, as discussed in detail in two recent reviews.[7,8] Much of the above discussion concerning the concerted vs. stepwise nature of the dimerization reactions also applies to the addition of an alkene radical cation to a different alkene. Although the addition of alkene radical cations to dienes can lead to both cyclobutane and Diels–Alder products, the latter usually predominate for dienes with at least modest *s-cis* conformer populations.[8] It is clear that in some cases the Diels–Alder adducts arise via rearrangement of initial divinylcyclobutane products. However, cyclobutanation and Diels–Alder adduct formation have been demonstrated to occur by independent pathways in other systems. There is also considerable experimental and theoretical data in support of a concerted but nonsynchronous mechanism for these reactions.

The following three sections discuss recent time-resolved experiments on inter- and intramolecular cycloadditions of arylalkene radical cations. These studies address some of the mechanistic issues raised by the earlier studies and also provide kinetic data for the cycloadditions of a number of aryl and diarylalkene radical cations. Such kinetic data are essential for the development of this chemistry as a useful synthetic strategy and as a mechanistic probe for radical cation chemistry.

5.1. Dimerizations

As noted in Section 3, the lifetimes of arylalkene radical cations in the absence of added nucleophiles or alkenes are frequently determined by their reaction with excess neutral alkene in solution to generate an adduct radical cation that ultimately gives the 1,2-diarylcyclobutane or substituted naphthalene products described above. Rate constants for the addition of the radical cation to its neutral precursor have been measured recently for both styrene and diarylethylene radical cations using either flash photolysis or pulse radiolysis methods.[13,15,20,101,102]

Table 7. Rate Constants, $k_{dimerization}$, for the Reaction of Substituted Styrene and Diarylethene Radical Cations with Their Neutral Precursors in Solution

Alkene	$k_{dimerization}/M^{-1} s^{-1}$	Solvent
4-chlorostyrene	6.0×10^9	cyclohexane[a]
styrene	8.0×10^9	cyclohexane[a,b]
4-methylstyrene	1.0×10^{10}	cyclohexane[a]
	2.9×10^9	TFE[c]
4-methoxystyrene	1.0×10^{10}	cyclohexane[a]
	1.1×10^9	TFE[c]
	1.7×10^9	aq. acetonitrile[a,c]
β-methylstyrene	$< 6 \times 10^7$	cyclohexane[a]
	1.4×10^9	TFE[c]
β,β-dimethylstyrene	$<1 \times 10^8$	TFE[c]
α-methylstyrene	1.0×10^{10}	cyclohexane[a,b]
β-methyl-4-	$<6 \times 10^7$	cyclohexane[a]
methoxystyrene	$<1 \times 10^8$	acetonitrile[c]
	$<1 \times 10^8$	aq. acetonitrile[c]
1,1-diphenylethene	1.2×10^{10}	cyclohexane[b]
trans-stilbene	3.4×10^8	dichloromethane[d]
cis-stilbene	3.5×10^8	dichloromethane[d]

Notes: [a]Ref. 20.
[b]Ref. 13.
[c]Ref. 15.
[d]Ref. 102.

The data are summarized in Table 7 and demonstrate that the addition is often a remarkably rapid reaction. For example, styrene radical cations without substituents in the β-position react with their neutral precursors with rate constants in the range of 10^9 to 10^{10} M^{-1} s^{-1}, with the rate constant depending to some degree on the nature of the solvent and the aryl substituent. In general, the rate constants are somewhat higher in cyclohexane than in more polar solvents such as alcohols or acetonitrile.

The addition reaction is considerably slower for styrenes with a β-methyl group. For example, 4-methoxystyrene radical cation reacts with neutral 4-methoxystyrene with a second-order rate constant of 1×10^9 M^{-1} s^{-1} in acetonitrile and 1×10^{10} M^{-1} s^{-1}

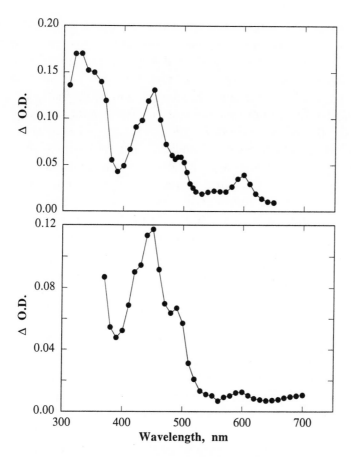

Figure 5. Transient absorption spectra showing the 500-nm transient generated by 355-nm laser irradiation of a solution of chloranil (0.003 M) and 4-methoxystyrene (0.01 M) in acetonitrile (*top*) and chloranil (0.003 M) and *trans*-1,2-bis(4-methoxyphenyl)cyclobutane (0.01 M) in acetonitrile (*bottom*).

in cyclohexane, while the decay of the β-methyl-4-methoxy-styrene radical cation is completely unaffected by the presence of neutral β-methyl-4-methoxystyrene (up to 0.5 M). In fact, an estimate of 2×10^6 M^{-1} s^{-1} for this addition reaction is available from Stern–Volmer quenching studies.[52] A similar ef-fect is seen upon addition of methyl groups to the β-position of the parent styrene; rate constants of 8.0 and 1.4×10^9 $M^{-1}s^{-1}$ have been measured for styrene and β-methylstyrene, respectively, whereas there was no detectable reaction for β,β-dimethylstyrene. The strong rate-retarding effect of the β-methyl group has been attributed to stabilization of the radical cation, and to unfavorable steric interactions between the methyl groups at the β-position of both the radical cation and neutral styrene.

In several time-resolved studies, a new transient with visible absorption has been observed following the addition of styrene radical cations to neutral styrenes.[12,13,16,20,101] The absorption maximum of the transient is sensitive to the structure of the styrene, and varies from 450 nm for the transient produced upon addition of the styrene radical cation to styrene to about 500 nm for the transient generated by the reaction of 4-methoxystyrene radical cation with 4-methoxystyrene (Figure 5). In pulse radiolysis experiments in chloroalkanes or cyclohexane, the rate constant for the formation of this new transient is identical to the rate constant for the decay of the radical cation. This provides good evidence that the transient is produced by addition of the radical cation to the neutral styrene. These transients are quenched by the addition of nucleophiles, and are generally insensitive to oxygen concentration. In addition, they are also observed as intermediates in the reactions of 1,2-diarylcyclobutane radical cations generated by pulse radiolysis.[101] It was initially suggested that these transients be assigned to the distonic 1,4-acyclic radical cations produced by the formation of a bond between the β-position of the radical cation and the β-position of the neutral styrene (Eq. 25).[13,20,101] While this has been the generally accepted interpretation of the results, the absorption maxima of the observed transients are far removed from those expected for either a benzylic cation ($\lambda_{max} \approx 340$ nm) or a benzylic radical ($\lambda_{max} \approx 310$ nm).[103,104] It has been suggested that there is substantial interaction between the two aromatic rings

$$\tag{25}$$

450 - 500 nm

in the acyclic radical cation and that this is responsible for their unexpected visible absorption.[20]

An alternative explanation was recently suggested for the results obtained by addition of the 4-methoxystyrene radical cation to neutral 4-methoxystyrene.[16] In this case the 500-nm transient was assigned to a substituted hexatriene radical cation generated by the rapid rearrangement of an initially formed 1,2-diarylcyclobutane radical cation (Eq. 26). Consistent with this hypothesis, the transient assigned to the substituted hexatriene radical cation has the properties expected for a cationic species and is also generated by ring-opening of the 1,2-dianisylcyclobutane radical cation (Figure 5). The assignment of the transient is therefore completely consistent with the results obtained from both pulse radiolysis and laser flash photolysis studies. In addition, the reaction sequence shown in Eq. 26 agrees with results from Bauld and Lewis that suggest that the addition of β-methyl-4-methoxystyrene radical cation to the neutral alkene is a concerted (or pseudo-concerted) process giving the 1,2-diarylcyclobutane radical cation directly and does not involve a freely equilibrating 1,4-acyclic radical cation.[52,105] Furthermore, the absorption maxima of the transients observed for a number of styrenes are all between 450 and 500 nm and agree well with the absorption spectra of structurally similar hexatriene radical cations.[106,107] Finally, it should also be noted that dihydronaphthalene derivatives have been isolated as the main products upon radical-cation mediated dimerization of a number of styrenes, and therefore, the hexatriene radical cation is likely to be an intermediate in each of these dimerization reactions.[16,90,91]

(26)

450 - 500 nm

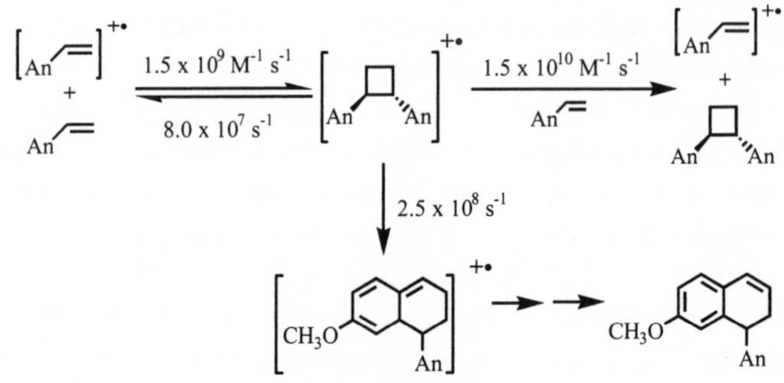

Scheme 4.

A detailed analysis of the radical cation mediated dimerization of 4-methoxystyrene using results from product studies and nanosecond laser photolysis was recently carried out in order to determine the complete dynamics of the dimerization reaction. The results are summarized in Scheme 4, and are based on the assumption that the initial intermediate produced in the cycloaddition reaction is the cyclobutane radical cation, and not the acyclic radical cation. In this study, it was found that the rate constant for the decay of the 4-methoxystyrene radical cation increased in a linear manner with respect to neutral 4-methoxystyrene concentration at low concentrations, but remained unchanged at 1.8×10^7 s^{-1} at concentrations greater than 0.15 M. The products showed a similar concentration dependence, with the dihydronaphthalene being the exclusive product when the addition reaction was carried out at low concentrations of 4-methoxystyrene, and the cyclobutane predominating at concentrations greater than 0.15 M. These results are consistent with the mechanism shown in Scheme 4 in which the initially formed 1,2-dianisylcyclobutane radical cation rearranges to give a substituted hexatriene radical cation at low concentrations of 4-methoxystyrene. At high concentrations, the cyclobutane radical cation is reduced to the neutral cyclobutane by excess 4-methoxystyrene, thus regenerating the 4-methoxystyrene radical cation. Since the redox properties of the distonic radical cation are not likely to be compatible with such an electron transfer, the possibility that the initial intermediate is the distonic radical cation was discounted in favor of the 1,2-dianisylcyclobutane radical cation. Furthermore, it is clear that the 500-nm transient, irrespective of its assignment, is not the primary intermediate in the dimerization or cycloreversion reaction.

Interpretation of the results from the product studies and nanosecond laser photolysis experiments led to the rate constants for each step in the overall dimerization reaction summarized in Scheme 4. The addition step is quite rapid, taking place with a rate constant of 1.5×10^9 M^{-1} s^{-1}, but formation of the cyclobutane radical cation is reversible, with a calculated rate constant of 8×10^7 s^{-1} for cycloreversion to regenerate the 4-methoxystyrene radical cation and neutral 4-methoxystyrene. The two other processes available to the intermediate cyclobutane radical cation are rearrangement to the hexatriene radical cation with a first-order rate constant of 2.5×10^8 s^{-1}, and electron transfer with neutral 4-methoxy- styrene with a rate constant of 1.5×10^{10} M^{-1} s^{-1} to generate the neutral cyclobutane and to regenerate the 4-methoxystyrene radical cation.

The calculated rate constants of 8×10^7 s^{-1} and 2.5×10^8 s^{-1} for cycloreversion and rearrangement indicate that the the 1,2-dianisylcyclobutane radical cation has a lifetime of approximately 3 ns in acetonitrile. Broad, weak absorptions in the 400–650-nm region have been observed upon γ-irradiation of both the *cis*- and *trans*-1,2-dianisylcyclobutanes at 77 K in a matrix and have been assigned to the cyclobutane dimers.[101] While attempts to detect this radical cation by picosecond photoionization of neutral 1,2-dianisylcyclobutane were unsuccessful, the 500-nm transient assigned to the hexatriene radical cation was observed upon 266-nm picosecond irradiation of 1,2-dianisylcyclobutane in acetonitrile.[16] This transient was not produced promptly within the 35-ps pulse, but instead grew in with a rate constant of ~3×10^8 s^{-1}. According to the mechanism shown in Scheme 4, this rate constant corresponds to the lifetime of the 1,2-dianisylcyclobutane radical cation, and agrees well with the 3-ns lifetime calculated from the nanosecond experiments.

Although the most detailed mechanistic studies have focused on the radical cation mediated dimerization of 4-methoxystyrene, a number of other styrenes have also been examined. As noted above, the addition of the *trans*-β-methyl-4-methoxystyrene radical cation to the neutral monomer occurs with retention of stereochemistry of the intial styrene, indicating that a freely rotating 1,4-acyclic radical cation is not involved. A rate constant of ~2 × 10^6 $M^{-1}s^{-1}$ has been estimated for the addition reaction based on Stern–Volmer quenching studies.[52] This estimate is consistent with time-resolved experiments that demonstrate that the decay of the radical cation is independent of the concentration of the precursor up to 0.1 M.[55,101] Generation of the cyclobutane dimer of this styrene by either PET or pulse radiolysis leads to the formation of the monomer radical cation.[55,101] Cleavage of the cyclobutane radical cation occurs with a rate constant of ~8 × 10^7 s^{-1} and there is no evidence for formation of a transient that could be assigned to either a hexatriene or 1,4-acyclic radical cation, in agreement with the product studies.[55] The cleavage rate constant for this cyclobutane radical cation had been estimated at <10^7 s^{-1} in an earlier product study.[108]

Several pulse radiolysis studies have provided evidence that the 450–500-nm transients assigned to 1,4-acyclic radical cations react with the parent styrenes in nonpolar solvents.[13,20] The rate constants for these reactions are generally in the 10^6–10^7 $M^{-1}s^{-1}$ range, several orders of magnitude slower than the intial addition of the monomer radical cation. The reactions have been attributed to the "trimerization" reaction that is the first step in the chain growth in cationic polymerizations (Eq. 27).

$$^+M-M^\bullet \quad + \quad M \rightarrow {}^+M-M-M^\bullet \qquad (27)$$

The dimerization of several 1,1-diarylethenes has been studied by pulse radiolysis.[13,56,57] The reaction of the 1,1-diphenylethene radical cation with the monomer occurred with a rate constant of 1.2 × 10^{10} $M^{-1}s^{-1}$ (see Table 7) in cyclohexane and generated a transient with λ_{max} at 435 nm that was assigned to a 1,4-acyclic radical cation.[13] Similarly, the addition of the 1,1-dianisylethene radical cation to the neutral alkene leads to the rapid formation of a species with absorption bands at 350 and 480 nm.[56,57] These absorption bands were assigned to the radical and cation moieties, respectively, of the 1,4-distonic radical cation (Eq. 28) on the basis of their similarity to the absorption bands of the dianisylmethyl radical and the dianisylmethyl cation. In this case both the 350 and 480 nm absorptions were quenched by oxygen to give a new transient absorption at 500 nm that also corresponds closely to that expected for a dianisylmethyl cation-like moiety.[56,57] The shift of the cation band from 480 to 500 nm was suggested to result from differences in the interactions between the radical center and the cation center of the distonic radical cation as compared to those between the peroxyl group and the cation center in the oxygenated intermediate.[56] The decay of the 1,1-dianisyl-1-propene radical cation is also accompanied by the concomitant formation of a new species with absorption at 510 nm that has been assigned to an acyclic 1,4-radical cation.[57] A detailed assessment of the kinetics for reaction of the radical cation with its neutral precursor has not been carried out for either of the dianisylalkenes, although the results are consistent with previous estimates of $\sim 10^{10}$ $M^{-1}s^{-1}$ for the "dimerization" reaction.[71]

The results summarized above for the diarylalkenes all lead to the conclusion that an acyclic radical cation is involved in

$$\left[\begin{array}{c} An \\ An \end{array} \!\!\!\! \rangle\!\!=\!\! \right]^{+\bullet} + \begin{array}{c} An \\ An \end{array} \!\!\!\! \rangle\!\!=\!\! \longrightarrow \underset{An \quad An}{An\!-\!\langle\!\!+ \quad \bullet\!\!-\!\!An} \overset{O_2}{\longrightarrow} \underset{An \quad An}{An\!-\!\langle\!\!+ \quad \overset{O^-O\bullet}{}\!\!-\!\!An} \quad (28)$$

480 nm, 350 nm   500 nm

the dimerization. The transients assigned to the acyclic radical cations are similar to those that would be expected for the individual chromophores, by contrast to the results for the styrene dimerizations. Product studies indicate that electron and proton transfer reactions occur considerably more rapidly than either 1,4 or 1,6-cyclization for the acyclic radical cation derived from 1,1-dianisylethene.[71] Therefore there is no reason to expect additional radical cation intermediates in this particular case. However, the mixture of cyclobutane and dihydronaphthalene products obtained from 1,1-diphenylethene suggests that both cyclobutane and hexatriene radical cations must also be formed, although no direct transient evidence for these has been reported.[71] Thus, it would seem that the identification of the 1,4-acyclic radical cation is quite reasonable for the 1,1-diaryl-ethenes. However, a definitive answer as to the involvement of this species in arylalkene dimerization may require its independent generation from other sources. It is likely that the initial intermediate in these reactions is determined by the substrate and reaction conditions and may not be the same for pulse radiolysis experiments in relatively nonpolar solvents as for flash photolysis studies in acetonitrile. The latter hypothesis may explain the apparent discrepancies in transient assignments from the two types of experiments.

The dimerization of *trans*- and *cis*-stilbene has also been examined in some detail by several groups.[27,35,102,109] The photoinduced electron transfer isomerization of *cis*-stilbene in acetonitrile was suggested by Lewis and co-workers to involve the formation of an acyclic dimer radical cation that reverted to starting materials with loss of stereochemistry.[27] Although efforts to isolate stilbene dimers or their trapping products were not successful, laser flash photolysis experiments using triphenylpyrylium salts as sensitizers demonstrated that the *trans*-stilbene radical cation reacted with the monomer in dichloromethane with a rate constant of 2×10^7 $M^{-1}s^{-1}$ to give a dimeric species with a slightly different absorption spectrum from that of the monomer radical cation.[35] More recent pulse radiolysis experiments for *cis*- and *trans*-stilbene in dichloromethane indicated that both radical cations react with their respective monomers with rate constants of $\sim 3.5 \times 10^8$ $M^{-1}s^{-1}$ (see Table 7). However, a dimeric species was only observed for *trans*-stilbene. It was suggested that the *trans* radical cation interacts with the neutral stilbene to give a π-dimer, whereas the *cis* radical cation generates a bonded σ-dimer (i.e., an acyclic 1,4-radical cation) that rapidly reverts to starting materials with loss of stereochemistry.[102] A series of γ-radiolysis experiments in butyl chloride matrices at 77 K for *trans*-stilbene and two of its cyclobutane dimers has recently provided direct spectro-

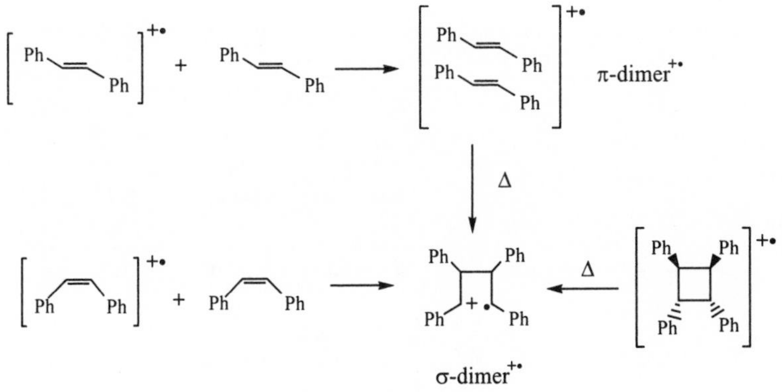

Scheme 5.

scopic evidence for the σ-dimer with absorption maxima at 370, 550, and 770 nm.[109] This bonded dimer is formed either by warming samples of the *trans*-stilbene π-dimer or by warming the initial cyclobutane radical cation which shows broad weak absorption in the 400–800-nm region, depending on the stereochemistry. These results may be summarized as outlined in Scheme 5.

5.2. Alkene Cycloadditions

Despite the demonstrated utility of alkene radical cation cycloadditions, little kinetic data for these reactions are currently available. However, two recent studies have provided rate constants for the initial step in the cyclobutanation or Diels–Alder reactions of a number of styrene radical cations.[17,21] Previous work by Bauld had shown that the *trans*-β-methyl-4-methoxystyrene radical cation reacts with a variety of alkenes to generate either cyclobutane or Diels–Alder adducts (Eqs. 23, 24).[110] The kinetic data for the styrene radical cation cycloadditions, in combination with the dimerization results discussed above, provide a detailed assessment of the effects of radical cation and alkene structure on dimerization and cross addition reactions.

Table 8. Rate Constants, k_{alkene}, for the Reaction of Substituted
Styrene Radical Cations with Alkenes, Dienes, and Vinyl Ethers in
TFE (styrene and 4-methylstyrene) or Acetonitrile[a,b]

$$k_{alkene}/M^{-1}\,s^{-1}$$

Alkene	E_{ox}	Styrene	4-Methyl-styrene	4-Methoxy-styrene	β-Methyl-4-methoxystyrene
⌇	2.85	1.9×10^9	8.3×10^7	$< 5 \times 10^5$	$< 1 \times 10^5$
⌇	2.56	3.9×10^9	1.5×10^9	1.5×10^6	$< 1 \times 10^5$
⌇	2.32	1.2×10^9	9.5×10^6	$< 5 \times 10^5$	$< 1 \times 10^5$
⌇	2.08	4.0×10^9	3.0×10^9	1.4×10^6	$< 1 \times 10^5$
⌇	1.56	6.0×10^9	4.8×10^9	1.6×10^7	$< 1 \times 10^5$
⌇	2.03	4.9×10^9	5.4×10^9	2.5×10^6	1.9×10^5
⌇	1.96	5.9×10^9	4.2×10^9	2.8×10^7	7.4×10^4
⌇	1.82	5.9×10^9	4.2×10^9	2.6×10^7	5.9×10^5
⌇	1.83	5.2×10^9	4.0×10^9	2.7×10^8	$< 1 \times 10^5$
⌇	1.74	4.9×10^9	4.0×10^9	1.8×10^9	3.9×10^6
⌇	1.33	6.0×10^9	5.2×10^9	8.3×10^9	7.2×10^9
⌇	1.99	4.2×10^9	1.3×10^9	7.0×10^7	5.0×10^5
⌇	1.61	5.3×10^9	4.2×10^9	1.3×10^9	9.2×10^6
⌇	1.73	3.0×10^9	2.6×10^9	4.6×10^6	3.6×10^6

Notes: [a]Rate constants in bold-face are for addition (see text).
          [b]Data from Ref. 21.

The data for the reactions of four substituted styrene radical cations with selected dienes are summarized in Table 8.[17,21] As discussed above for the reaction of styrene radical cations with nucleophiles, the interpretation of these data is complicated by the possibility that two competing reactions are responsible for the observed quenching of the radical cation. One of these is electron transfer from the alkene to the styrene radical cation to generate the neutral styrene and the radical cation of the alkene (Eq. 29). In this case, the quenching rate constant is that for electron transfer, k_{ET}, and does not provide any information on the kinetics for the initial addition, although the secondary radical cation/neutral pair may in some cases lead to adduct formation. The other reaction is addition of the alkene to the radical cation to generate an adduct radical cation that is the precursor of the final cyclobutanation and Diels–Alder products (Eq. 30).

$$\left[\; \text{styrene}(R) \;\right]^{+\bullet} + \;/=|=R' \quad \xrightarrow{k_{ET}} \quad \text{styrene}(R) \;=\; + \;\left[\;/=|=R'\;\right]^{+\bullet} \tag{29}$$

$$\left[\; \text{styrene}(R) \;\right]^{+\bullet} + \;/=|=R \quad \xrightarrow{k_{Add}} \quad \text{Adduct}^{+\bullet} \;\longrightarrow\; \begin{array}{l}\text{Cyclobutanation,}\\ \text{Diels-Alder}\\ \text{Products}\end{array} \tag{30}$$

The distinction between addition and electron transfer chemistry is clear in cases for which the product alkene radical cation can be observed directly. For example, the reaction of the styrene radical cations with 2,5-dimethyl-2,4-hexadiene results in the concurrent formation of the diene radical cation (λ_{max} = 360 nm). Observation of an electron transfer reaction in this case is consistent with the low oxidation potential of 2,5-dimethyl-2,4-hexadiene (E_{ox} = 1.3 V) relative to the oxidation potentials of substituted styrenes such as 4-methoxystyrene, 4-methylstyrene, and styrene (E_{ox} = 1.5, 1.9, and 2.05 V, respectively, vs. SCE in acetonitrile).

Reaction of the styrene radical cations with most of the alkenes listed in Table 8 did not yield any evidence for product alkene radical cations, despite the fact that electron transfer is exergonic in a number of cases. This difficulty in distinguishing between addition and electron transfer reactions was addressed by using Marcus theory to calculate the maximum electron transfer rate constant for each styrene radical cation/alkene combination, and then comparing this calculated rate constant to the experimental quenching rate constant. This analysis established that experimental rate constants were considerably greater than those predicted by Marcus theory for all styrene/alkene pairs for which the electron transfer was calculated to be endergonic. On the other hand, the experimental and calculated rate constants were similar for cases for which electron transfer was exergonic. On the basis of these comparisons, it was concluded that experimental rate constants for the reaction of styrene radical cations with alkenes represented addition when the oxidation potential of the alkene was greater than that of the styrene (noted in bold in Table 8).

The data shown in Table 8 demonstrate that the rate constants for addition cover a considerable range from a minimum value of $<1 \times 10^5 \ M^{-1} \ s^{-1}$ to a maximum of $4.0 \times 10^9 \ M^{-1} \ s^{-1}$, indicating that the addition process is strongly influenced by the structure of the radical cation and the alkene. The structure/reactivity trends for these addition reactions can be summarized as follows:

1. The effects of alkyl substitution in substituted ethenes decrease in the order 1,2-dialkyl < 2-alkyl < 2,2-dialkyl ~ trialkyl < tetraalkyl. This indicates that both electronic and steric factors are important in determining the nucleophilicity of the alkene toward radical cations. For example, alkyl substitution increases the nucleophilicity of the alkene, thus rendering 2,2-dialkyl and tetraalkylalkenes more reactive toward styrene radical cations than less-substituted alkenes such as 1-hexene. On the other hand, the kinetic acceleration that results from electronic effects of additional alkyl groups is offset by steric hindrance, as demonstrated by the low reactivity of 1,2-dialkyl-

alkenes and by the decreased reactivity of trialkylalkenes relative to 2,2-dialkylalkenes.

2. The styrene radical cations react more rapidly with both the dienes and vinyl ethers shown in Table 8 than with the corresponding ethene. For example, the β-methyl-4-methoxystyrene radical cation is unreactive toward all the substituted ethenes but reacts with most dienes and vinyl ethers. The substitution of either alkoxy or vinyl for an alkyl group typically leads to increases in rate constants of 1–2 orders of magnitude for the 4-methoxystyrene radical cation.

The rate constants for the reaction of the 4-methoxystyrene radical cation with a number of substituted styrenes also clearly illustrate the importance of electronic and steric effects as the substituents on either the double bond or the aromatic ring are varied (Table 9). For example, rate constants for various ring-substituted styrenes vary by over 4 orders of magnitude; this electronic effect is clearly shown from a plot of the log of the rate constants for the reaction of the 4-methoxystyrene radical

Table 9. Second-Order Rate Constants, $k_{styrene}$, for the Reaction of the 4-Methoxystyrene Radical Cation with Substituted Styrenes in Acetonitrile[a]

Substituted Styrenes	$k_{Styrene}/M^{-1} s^{-1}$
4-trifluoromethylstyrene	9.7×10^6
3-trifluoromethylstyrene	$< 2 \times 10^5$
4-chlorostyrene	$< 2 \times 10^6$
styrene	1.3×10^7
4-fluorostyrene	6.6×10^6
3-methylstyrene	3.2×10^7
4-methylstyrene	7.8×10^7
4-methoxystyrene	1.6×10^9
β-methylstyrene	$< 2 \times 10^5$
β,β-dimethylstyrene	$< 2 \times 10^5$
α-methylstyrene	1.2×10^8
α,β-dimethylstyrene	7.8×10^7

Note: [a]Data from Ref. 21.

cation with aryl substituted styrenes against the σ values of the aryl substituent. The large negative ρ value of -5 (R = 0.96) demonstrates that the addition reaction is strongly influenced by the presence of electron-donating and electron-withdrawing substituents on the alkene. The data in Table 9 also show that β-methylstyrene and β,β-dimethylstyrene are considerably less reactive than the parent styrene toward the 4-methoxystyrene radical cation. Although methyl groups would be expected to increase the rate constant for addition by virtue of their electron-donating ability, the lower rate constants indicate that steric effects are more important in this case.

Electronic and steric effects related to structural changes in the radical cation also play a role in determining the kinetics of the addition reaction and are similar to the results discussed earlier for addition of nucleophiles. For example, the data shown in Table 8 demonstrate that electron-donating groups such as methoxy, and to a lesser extent methyl, cause a significant decrease in the reactivity of the radical cation toward alkenes and dienes. Methyl groups at the β-position also result in a large decrease in the reactivity of the radical cations, although the addition of an α-methyl group has virtually no effect on the observed rate constant for addition. As for the effects of alkyl substitution on the reacting alkene, these substituent effects are attributable to a combination of steric and electronic factors.

The kinetic data discussed above demonstrate the effects of varying the structure of both the styrene radical cation and the alkene on the initial step in the cycloaddition reaction. However, the transient experiments do not provide any evidence that would permit one to distinguish between a concerted or stepwise mechanism. The kinetic data obtained for additions to a range of alkenes do show considerable similarities to those reported for the addition of carbenium ions to the same substrates. For example, rate constants for the addition of the bis(4-methylphenyl)methyl cation to a series of ring-substituted styrenes also correlate with the Hammett σ and σ^+ parameters with ρ and ρ^+ values of -5.2 and -5.0, respectively.[111] The latter reactions are thought to proceed via a partially bridged transition state and might, therefore, be expected to show similarities to concerted addition of a radical cation to an alkene. However, detailed product studies will obviously be required to provide a definitive answer on the concerted vs. stepwise nature of the radical cation additions.

The combined data in Tables 7–9 for the additions of styrene radical cations to their neutral precursors (dimerizations) and to other alkenes lead to a potentially important conclusion with respect to the design of cross-addition reactions. These data indicate that dimerization rate constants are frequently several orders of magnitude greater than the rate constants for cross addition. The absolute rate constants for the two reactions can be used to adjust the concentrations of the neutral styrene that leads to the radical cation and the alkene in order to maximize the yield of the cross-addition product. The kinetic and mechanistic data obtained for these reactions thus provides the basis for the development of synthetic strategies that utilize radical cation chemistry.

5.3. Intramolecular Radical Cation Probes

The pioneering work on the calibration of intramolecular cyclization of the 5-hexenyl radical by Ingold and co-workers provided the basis for the development of a large number of radical clocks.[112] These are now used both for the calibration of rate constants for intermolecular radical reactions and as mechanistic probes to test for the intermediacy of radical intermediates in a variety of processes. Furthermore, the ready availability of bimolecular rate constants from competitive product studies using free radical clocks without the use of time-resolved experiments has greatly enhanced the synthetic utility of free radical chemistry. The same concept has recently been extended to radical ion chemistry. For example, rate constants for carbon–carbon bond cleavage reactions of a variety of radical cations and anions derived from substituted diarylethanes have been measured by direct time-resolved techniques.[45,113,114]

Intramolecular radical cation cycloadditions of three β-alkyl-4-methoxystyrene-containing substrates have been used recently as mechanistic probes to test for the intermediacy of radical cations in the metalloporphyrin-catalyzed oxidation of alkenes and the thermal cycloaddition of tetracyanoethylene.[115–117] Independent generation of the radical cations using triarylaminium salts produced the cyclized products expected from the intramolecular dimerization (Eqs. 31, 32) or Diels–Alder (Eq. 33) cycloaddition of the β-alkyl-4-methoxystyrene radical cation. The basic approach in using these substrates as radical cation probes involves carrying out the alkene oxidation for the probe molecule and measuring the relative amounts of the normal oxidation product and the intramolecular cyclization product. The observation of the intramolecular cyclization product provides confirmation of the involvement of a radical cation and the relative yields of this material and the oxidized alkene can be used to obtain an estimate of the lifetime of the alkene radical cation. The latter requires prior knowledge of the rate constant for the intramolecular cyclization. These rate constants were originally estimated by a combination of Stern-Volmer quenching and competitive product studies, with reported rate constants of $>3 \times 10^9$ s^{-1} for the two dimerization reactions (Eqs. 31, 32) and 3×10^7 s^{-1} for the Diels–Alder reaction (Eq. 33).[115,116] The rate constants for these intramolecular cyclizations were measured recently by using nanosecond and picosecond laser flash photolysis.[55] In addition to providing more accurate rate constants, the time-resolved measurements provide mechanistic information that is not available from product studies and that illustrates some of the potential problems of using radical cation probes.

(31)

(32)

$$\text{(33)}$$

3

Direct laser excitation of probes **1–3** leads to the formation of the β-alkyl-4-methoxystyrene radical cations, presumably via biphotonic photoionization as observed for other styrenes. The lifetimes of the radical cations vary considerably. For example, the radical cation of **1** can only be observed in a picosecond experiment (Figure 6) since it decays with a rate constant of $1.2 \times 10^9 \text{ s}^{-1}$. No other transients are detected in the 400–700-nm region up to ~5 ns after the laser pulse. The initial monomer radical cation is not observed in a nanosecond experiment but a transient at 500 nm does grow in with a rate constant of ~1.1 $\times 10^7 \text{ s}^{-1}$ and then decays on a slightly slower timescale. The results are interpreted in terms of intramolecular cyclization of the initial β-alkyl-4-methoxystyrene radical cation to give a bicylic cyclobutane radical cation. This intermediate rearranges to generate a 500-nm transient that is similar to that observed for 4-methoxystyrene; this species was tentatively assigned to a hexatriene radical cation on the basis of its observed reactivity towards nucleophiles and by analogy with the previous results. Although the cyclobutane radical cation is not directly observed in these experiments, its lifetime can be estimated as ~100 ns based on the growth of the 500-nm transient derived from it. Similar results were obtained using 9,10-dicyanoanthracene/biphenyl as an electron transfer sensitizer.

The original product studies carried out using a triarylaminium salt as the electron transfer agent to generate **1**[+•] provided no evidence for the formation of rearranged products derived from a hexatriene radical cation. However, under conditions of chloranil photosensitization, both cyclobutane and rearranged di- and tetrahydronaphthalenes were observed, with the latter being a secondary photoproduct.[55] Thus, the electron transfer chemistry of probe **1** can be summarized as shown in Scheme 6. Both the transient experiments and the product studies are in good agree-

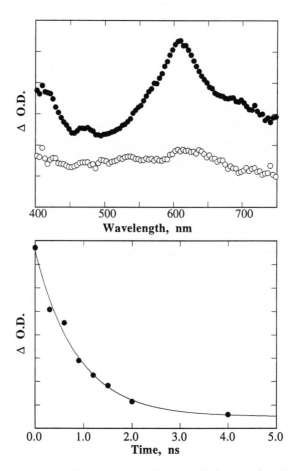

Figure 6. Transient absorption spectra recorded immediately (●) and 5 ns after (○) 266-nm picosecond laser irradiation of probe **1** in acetonitrile (*top*). The decay of the transient absorption for the same sample at 600 nm (*bottom*).

ment as to the fate of the initial cyclobutane radical cation, with rearrangement to give a hexatriene radical cation and reduction by starting material or sensitizer radical anion being competitive processes.

Excitation of probe **2** generates a transient with λ_{max} at 640 nm that is slightly shifted from the 620- and 600-nm maxima

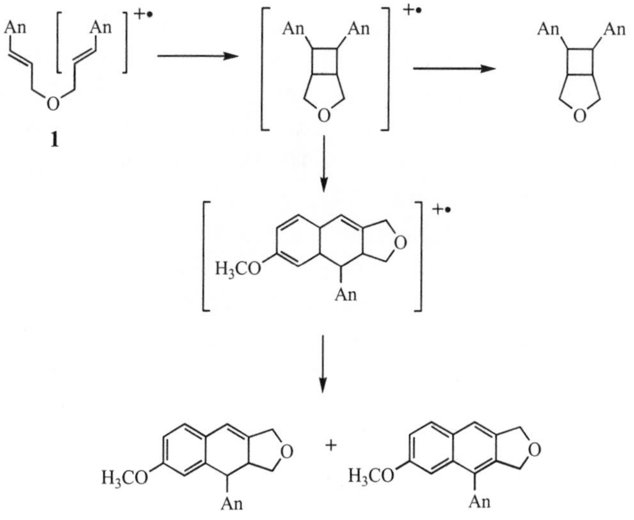

Scheme 6.

observed for the *cis-* and *trans*-β-methyl-4-methoxystyrene radical cations, respectively. The transient is assigned to the β-alkyl-4-methoxystyrene radical cation on the basis of its kinetic behavior. The radical cation decays with a rate constant of 3×10^6 s^{-1}. An additional transient is observed at 500 nm but it grows and decays on a similar timescale to the signal for the monomer radical cation, making it difficult to obtain detailed kinetic data. The results suggest that a similar rearrangement to that shown in Scheme 6 may also occur for probe **2**.

The measured rate constant for decay of the initial monomer radical cation from probe **1** of 1.2×10^9 s^{-1} agrees reasonably well with Bauld's earlier estimate, although the agreement appears to be fortuitous.[55] By contrast, the rate constant for the cyclization of the monomer radical cation of probe **2** is almost 3 orders of magnitude faster than both the earlier estimate from product studies for this system ($>3 \times 10^9$ s^{-1}) and the measured rate constant for **1**. It is possible that some of the discrepancy may be due to cleavage of the initial adduct radical cation to regenerate the monomer radical cation, which would mean that the rate constant measured in the laser experiments does not reflect only the initial cyclization rate. The apparently slower cyclization for **2** may also reflect the more rigid structure of the probe. It is also interesting to note that the apparent rate constants for the intramolecular cyclization of both of the "dimerization" probes are faster than the intermolecular equivalent for which a rate constant of 2×10^6 $M^{-1}s^{-1}$ has been estimated.[52]

Photoionization of probe **3** in acetonitrile generates a styrene radical cation that decays with a rate constant of 3×10^8 s^{-1}. This decay is not accompanied by the formation of a 500-nm signal, as is observed for the other two probes. Additional cationic signals in the 300–400-nm region are observed but have not been conclusively identified. The rate constant for cyclization of this probe is 2–3 orders of magnitude faster than the intermolecular additions of the β-alkyl-4-methoxystyrene radical cation to 2,4-hexadiene and 1,3-cyclohexadiene (6×10^5 and $\sim 6 \times 10^6$ $M^{-1}s^{-1}$, respectively). Interestingly, the cyclization rate constant for **3** agrees well with the earlier estimate from product studies, after correction of an error in one of the rate constants used for calibration purposes.[55,116]

These results provide the first detailed calibration for a series of intramolecular radical cation probes based on cycloaddition chemistry. The cyclization rate constants cover several orders of magnitude in timescale, an ideal case for using **1–3** as probes for radical cations of different lifetimes. However, the time-resolved experiments demonstrate that the application of radical cation probes, at least those based on aryl alkene cycloaddition chemistry, may be considerably less straightforward than similar experiments with free radical probes or clocks. Some of the problems that need to be addressed include the variation of products with the reaction conditions and method of radical cation generation, and the possibility of reversibility of the initial adduct formation. Furthermore, at least some radical cation reactions are quite sensitive to solvent and this may mean that calibrations for radical cation cycloadditions will have to be done in a variety of solvents.

Several intramolecular dimerizations of diarylalkenes have also been reported.[57,58,118,119] For example, pulse radiolysis of 1,1,7,7-tetrakis(4-methoxyphenyl)-1,6-heptadiene in 1,2-dichloroethane gives a transient that is identified as the diarylalkene radical cation. This species decays with a rate constant of 1×10^8 s^{-1} to give a transient absorbing at 485 nm that is assigned to the 1,4 radical cation (Eq. 34, $n = 3$).[57] This intermediate is trapped by oxygen in a manner analogous to that shown in Eq. 28 for the intermolecular dimerization. The same reaction has also been studied in acetonitrile using photosensitization with 9,10-dicyanoanthracene to generate the radical cation.[58] In this case only the dimer radical cation is observed. Pulse radiolysis experiments on the 1,ω-bis(diarylethenyl)alkane with $n = 4$ (Eq. 34) gave a similar cyclization rate to that measured for the $n = 3$ substrate. However, the apparent rate constant for cyclization of 3.6×10^6 s^{-1} measured for the $n = 2$ derivative was much slower. Although these diarylalkene cyclizations have not been used as intramolecular probes they also cover a reasonable range in timescale. Their use as such would, of course, be limited by the same considerations noted above for the β-methyl-4-methoxystyrene probes.

$$\text{(34)}$$

An = 4-CH$_3$OPh; n = 2, 3, 4

6. CONCLUDING COMMENTS

A variety of aryl and diarylalkene radical cations have been generated in solution and characterized using transient absorption spectroscopy. Many of these are sufficiently long-lived for detailed kinetic studies of their intermolecular reactivity under conditions that are comparable to those used in mechanistic and synthetic studies. Reactions with nucleophiles typically occur by either addition or electron transfer, with the latter dominating in cases where the oxidation potential of the nucleophile is lower than that of the alkene. The data summarized herein indicate that most arylalkene radical cations are unselective in their additions to anionic nucleophiles in nonprotic solvents. By contrast, the additions to neutral nucleophiles such as alcohols and amines cover a range of timescales and clearly demonstrate the steric and electronic effects of varying both the radical cation and nucleophile structure. Reactions with nucleophiles are also sensitive to the solvent, with changes in chemoselectivity (i.e., addition vs. electron transfer reactions) and decreases in reactivity of several orders of magnitude being observed in protic solvents such as aqueous acetonitrile or alcohols.

The data on cycloadditions of alkene radical cations indicate that dimerization will usually compete efficiently with cross additions and demonstrate the necessity for obtaining detailed kinetic data in order to design appropriate synthetic methods based on radical cation chemistry. The mechanistic data obtained from both time-resolved and steady-state experiments demonstrate the complexity of cycloaddition chemistry. This may be a particular limitation in the use of cycloaddition reactions in the design of mechanistic probes for assessing whether a particular reaction involves radical cation intermediates. The results also highlight the importance of using both product studies and the kinetic and mechanistic data obtained from time-resolved methods to develop a detailed understanding of the reactions of radical cations.

The reactivity trends observed for both the nucleophilic addition and cycloaddition of alkene radical cations parallel trends observed for the reactions of carbocations with nucleophiles and alkenes. However, the observed variations in reactivity towards oxygen[51,53] and substituent effects on the competition between addition of methanol and the neutral monomer for diphenylethene radical cations[74] indicate that variations in *both* spin and charge density are important in determining the overall reactivity patterns. It is clear that further experimental and theoretical studies are required to provide a detailed model for understanding and ultimately predicting the reactivity of radical cations.

REFERENCES

1. Issued as NRCC-39112.
2. Fox, M. A.; Chanon, M., Eds. *Photoinduced Electron Transfer*; Elsevier: Amsterdam, 1988, Parts A–D.
3. Mattes, S. L.; Farid, S. *Org. Photochem.* **1983**, *6*, 233–326.

4. Lewis, F. D. In *Photoinduced Electron Transfer*; Fox, M. A.; Chanon, M., Eds.; Elsevier: Amsterdam, 1988, Part C, Ch. 4.1.

5. Mariano, P. S. In *Photoinduced Electron Transfer*; Fox, M. A.; Chanon, M., Eds.; Elsevier: Amsterdam, 1988, Part C, Ch. 4.6.

6. Mattay, J. *Synthesis* **1989**, 233–252.

7. Bauld, N. L. *Tetrahedron* **1989**, *45*, 5307–5363.

8. Bauld, N. L. *Adv. Electron Transfer Chem.* **1992**, *2*, 1–66.

9. Yoon, U. C.; Mariano, P. S. *Acc. Chem. Res.* **1992**, *25*, 233–240.

10. Roth, H. D. *Topics Curr. Chem.* **1992**, *163*, 133–245.

11. Shida, T. *Electronic Absorption Spectra of Radical Ions*; Elsevier: Amsterdam, 1988.

12. Egusa, S.; Tabata, Y.; Kira, A.; Imamura, M. *J. Polym. Sci.* **1978**, *16*, 729–741.

13. Brede, O.; Bos, J.; Helmstreit, W.; Mehnert, R. *Radiat. Phys. Chem.* **1982**, *19*, 1–15.

14. Trampe, G.; Mattay, J.; Steenken, S. *J. Phys. Chem.* **1989**, *93*, 7157–7160.

15. Johnston, L. J.; Schepp, N. P. *J. Am. Chem. Soc.* **1993**, *115*, 6564–6571.

16. Schepp, N. P.; Johnston, L. J. *J. Am. Chem. Soc.* **1994**, *116*, 6895–6903.

17. Schepp, N. P.; Johnston, L. J. *J. Am. Chem. Soc.* **1994**, *116*, 10330–10331.

18. Workentin, M. S.; Schepp, N. P.; Johnston, L. J.; Wayner, D. D. M. *J. Am. Chem. Soc.* **1994**, *116*, 1141–1142.

19. Johnston, L. J.; Schepp, N. P. *Pure Appl. Chem.* **1995**, *67*, 71–78.

20. Brede, O.; David, F.; Steenken, S. *J. Chem. Soc., Perkin Trans. 2* **1995**, 23–32.

21. Schepp, N. P.; Johnston, L. J. *J. Am. Chem. Soc.* **1996**, *118*, 2872–2881.

22. Rehm, D.; Weller, A. *Isr. J. Chem.* **1970**, *8*, 259–271.

23. Wayner, D. D. M. In *Handbook of Photochemistry*; Scaiano, J. C., Ed.; CRC Press: Boca Raton, 1989, Vol. II, Ch. 18.

24. Gould, I. R.; Ege, D.; Mattes, S. L.; Farid, S. *J. Am. Chem. Soc.* **1987**, *109*, 3794–3796.

25. Gould, I. R.; Ege, D.; Moser, J. E.; Farid, S. *J. Am. Chem. Soc.* **1990**, *112*, 4290–4301.

26. Lewis, F. D.; Dykstra, R. E.; Gould, I. R.; Farid, S. *J. Phys. Chem.* **1988**, *92*, 7042–7043.

27. Lewis, F. D.; Bedell, A. M.; Dykstra, R. E.; Elbert, J. E.; Gould, I. R.; Farid, S. *J. Am. Chem. Soc.* **1990**, *112*, 8055–8064.

28. Arnold, D. R.; McManus, K. A.; Du, X. *Can. J. Chem.* **1994**, *72*, 415–429.

29. Andre, J. J.; Weill, G. *Mol. Phys.* **1968**, *15*, 97–99.

30. Creed, D. In *Organic Photochemistry and Photobiology*; Horspool, W. M.; Song, P.-S., Eds.; CRC Press: Boca Raton, FL, 1995, Ch. 59.

31. Todd, W.; Dinnocenzo, J.; Farid, S.; Goodman, J.; Gould, I. *J. Am. Chem. Soc.* **1991**, *113*, 3601–3602.

32. Mattay, J.; Trampe, G.; Runsink, J. *Chem. Ber.* **1988**, *121*, 1991–2005.

33. Kuriyama, Y.; Arai, T.; Sakuragi, H.; Tokumaru, K. *Chem. Lett.* **1988**, 1193–1196.

34. Mattay, J.; Vondenhof, M.; Denig, R. *Chem. Ber.* **1989**, *122*, 951–958.

35. Akaba, R.; Sakuragi, H.; Tokumaru, K. *Chem. Phys. Lett.* **1990**, *174*, 80–84.

36. Steenken, S.; Warren, C. J.; Gilbert, B. C. *J. Chem. Soc., Perkin Trans. 2* **1990**, 335–342.
37. Del Giacco, T.; Baciocchi, E.; Steenken, S. *J. Phys. Chem.* **1993**, *97*, 5451–5456.
38. Delcourt, M. O.; Rossi, M. J. *J. Phys. Chem.* **1982**, *86*, 3233–3239. Schulte-Frohlinde, D.; Simic, M. G.; Gorner, H. *Photochem. Photobiol.* **1990**, *52*, 1137–1151. Hirata, Y.; Mataga, N. *J. Phys. Chem.* **1991**, *95*, 1640–1644.
39. Johnston, L. J.; Lobaugh, J.; Wintgens, V. *J. Phys. Chem.* **1989**, *93*, 7370–7374.
40. Bell, I. P.; Rodgers, M. A. J.; Burrows, H. D. *J. Chem. Soc., Faraday Trans. 1* **1977**, *73*, 315–326.
41. Habersbergerova, A.; Janovsky, I.; Teply, J. *Radiat. Res. Rev.* **1968**, *1*, 109–181.
42. Gould, I. R.; Young, R. H.; Moody, R. E.; Farid, S. *J. Phys. Chem.* **1991**, *95*, 2068–2080.
43. Masnovi, J. M.; Kochi, J. K.; Hilinski, E. F.; Rentzepis, P. M. *J. Am. Chem. Soc.* **1986**, *108*, 1126–1135.
44. Sankararaman, S.; Haney, W. A.; Kochi, J. K. *J. Am. Chem. Soc.* **1987**, *109*, 7824–7838.
45. Perrier, S.; Sankararaman, S.; Kochi, J. K. *J. Chem. Soc., Perkin Trans. 2* **1993**, 825–837.
46. Sankararaman, S.; Yoon, K. B.; Kochi, J. K. *J. Am. Chem. Soc.* **1991**, *113*, 1419–1421.
47. Lednev, I. K.; Mathivanan, N.; Johnston, L. J. *J. Phys. Chem.* **1994**, 11,444–11,451.
48. Brede, V. O.; Helmstreit, W.; Mehnert, R. *J. Prakt. Chem.* **1974**, *316*, 402–414.
49. Mehnert, R.; Brede, O.; Cserep, G. *Ber. Bunsenges Phys. Chem.* **1982**, *86*, 1123–1127.
50. Tabata, Y., Ed. *Pulse Radiolysis*; CRC Press: Boston, 1991.
51. Tsuchiya, M.; Ebbesen, T. W.; Nishimura, Y.; Sakuragi, H.; Tokumaru, K. *Chem. Lett.* **1987**, 2121–2124.
52. Lewis, F. D.; Kojima, M. *J. Am. Chem. Soc.* **1988**, *110*, 8664–8670.
53. Konuma, S.; Aihara, S.; Kuriyama, Y.; Misawa, H.; Akaba, R.; Sakuragi, H.; Tokumaru, K. *Chem. Lett.* **1991**, 1897–1900.
54. Andrews, L.; Harvey, J. A.; Kelsall, B. J.; Duffey, D. C. *J. Am. Chem. Soc.* **1981**, *103*, 6415–6422.
55. Schepp, N. P.; Shukla, D.; Johnston, L. J.; Bauld, N. L., manuscript in preparation.
56. Kojima, M.; Ishida, A.; Takamuku, S. *Chem. Lett.* **1993**, 979–982.
57. Tamai, T.; Mizuno, K.; Hashida, I.; Otsujo, Y.; Ishida, A.; Takamuku, S. *Chem. Lett.* **1994**, 149–152.
58. Mizuno, K.; Tamai, T.; Hashida, I.; Otsuji, Y.; Kuriyama, Y.; Tokumaru, K. *J. Org. Chem.* **1994**, *59*, 7329–7334.
59. Ebbesen, T. *J. Phys. Chem.* **1988**, *92*, 4581–4583.
60. Kuriyama, Y.; Arai, T.; Sakuragi, H.; Tokumaru, K. *Chem. Phys. Lett.* **1990**, *173*, 253–256.
61. Arnold, D. R.; Du, X. *Can. J. Chem.* **1994**, *72*, 403–414.

62. Behrens, G.; Bothe, E.; Koltzenburg, G.; Schulte-Frohlinde, D. *J. Chem. Soc., Perkin Trans. 2* **1980**, 883–889.
63. Behrens, G.; Bothe, E.; Koltzenburg, G.; Schulte-Frohlinde, D. *J. Chem. Soc., Perkin Trans. 2* **1981**, 143–154.
64. Koltzenburg, G.; Behrens, G.; Schulte-Frohlinde, D. *Angew. Chem. Int. Ed. Engl.* **1983**, *22*, 500–501.
65. Asmus, K.-D.; Williams, P. S.; Gilbert, B. C.; Winter, J. N. *J. Chem. Soc., Chem. Commun.* **1987**, 208–210.
66. Mehnert, R.; Brede, O. *Radiat. Phys. Chem.* **1985**, *26*, 353–363.
67. Neunteufel, R. A.; Arnold, D. R. *J. Am. Chem. Soc.* **1973**, *95*, 4080–4081.
68. Maroulis, A. J.; Shigemitsu, Y.; Arnold, D. R. *J. Am. Chem. Soc.* **1978**, *100*, 535–541.
69. Majima, T.; Pac, C.; Nakasone, A.; Sakurai, H. *J. Am. Chem. Soc.* **1981**, *103*, 4499–4508.
70. Jiang, Z. Q.; Foote, C. S. *Tetr. Lett.* **1983**, *24*, 461–464.
71. Mattes, S. L.; Farid, S. *J. Am. Chem. Soc.* **1986**, *108*, 7356–7361.
72. Mizuno, K.; Nakanishi, I.; Ichinose, N.; Otsuji, Y. *Chem. Lett.* **1989**, 1095–1098.
73. Mattes, S. L.; Farid, S. *J. Am. Chem. Soc.* **1982**, *104*, 1454–1456.
74. Arnold, D. R.; Du, X.; Hensleit, K. M. *Can. J. Chem.* **1991**, *69*, 839–852.
75. Arnold, D. R.; Du, X.; Chen, J. *Can. J. Chem.* **1995**, *73*, 307–318.
76. Pienta, N. J.; Kessler, R. J. *J. Am. Chem. Soc.* **1992**, *114*, 2419–2428.
77. Workentin, M. S.; Johnston, L. J.; Wayner, D. D. M.; Parker, V. D. *J. Am. Chem. Soc.* **1994**, *116*, 8279–8287.
78. McClelland, R. A.; Kanagasabapathy, V. M.; Banait, N. S.; Steenken, S. *J. Am. Chem. Soc.* **1992**, *114*, 1816–1823.
79. Mathivanan, N.; Johnston, L. J.; Wayner, D. D. M. *J. Phys. Chem.* **1995**, *99*, 8190–8195.
80. Shaik, S. S.; Pross, A. *J. Am. Chem. Soc.* **1989**, *111*, 4306–4312.
81. Shaik, S.; Reddy, A. C.; Ioffe, A.; Dinnocenzo, J. P.; Danovich, D.; Cho, J. K. *J. Am. Chem. Soc.* **1995**, *117*, 3205–3222.
82. Bartl, J.; Steenken, S.; Mayr, H. *J. Am. Chem. Soc.* **1991**, *113*, 7710–7716.
83. Yamashita, T.; Shiomori, K.; Yasuda, M.; Shima, K. *Bull. Chem. Soc. Jpn.* **1991**, *64*, 366–374.
84. Arnold, D. R.; Mines, S. A. *Can. J. Chem.* **1987**, *65*, 2312–2314.
85. Arnold, D. R.; Mines, S. A. *Can. J. Chem.* **1989**, *67*, 689–698.
86. Teoli, G.; Schepp, N. P.; Malenfant, P.; Johnston, L. J., manuscript in preparation.
87. Ledwith, A. *Acc. Chem. Res.* **1972**, *5*, 133–139.
88. Mattes, S. L.; Luss, H. R.; Farid, S. *J. Phys. Chem.* **1983**, *87*, 4779–4781.
89. Mattes, S. L.; Farid, S. *J. Am. Chem. Soc.* **1983**, *105*, 1386–1387.
90. Asanuma, T.; Yamamoto, M.; Nishijima, Y. *J. Chem. Soc., Chem. Commun.* **1975**, 608–609.
91. Kadota, S.; Tsubono, K.; Makino, K.; Takeshita, M.; Kikuchi, T. *Tetr. Lett.* **1987**, *28*, 2857–2860.
92. Kojima, M.; Sakuragi, H.; Tokumaru, K. *Bull. Chem. Soc. Jpn.* **1989**, *62*, 3863–3868.

93. Wilson, R. M.; Dietz, J. G.; Shepherd, T. A.; Ho, D. M.; Schnapp, K. A.; Elder, R. C.; Watkins, J. W.; Geraci, L. S.; Campana, C. F. *J. Am. Chem. Soc.* **1989**, *111*, 1749–1753.

94. Bauld, N. L.; Bellville, D. J.; Pabon, R.; Chelsky, R.; Green, G. *J. Am. Chem. Soc.* **1983**, *105*, 2378–2382.

95. Pabon, R. A.; Bauld, N. L. *J. Am. Chem. Soc.* **1984**, *106*, 1145–1146.

96. Bauld, N. L.; Bellville, D. J.; Harirchian, B.; Lorenz, K. T.; Pabon, R. A.; Reynolds, D. W.; Wirth, D. D.; Chiou, H.-S.; Marsh, B. K. *Acc. Chem. Res.* **1987**, *20*, 371–8.

97. Jungwirth, P.; Bally, T. *J. Am. Chem. Soc.* **1993**, *115*, 5783–5789.

98. Schmittel, M.; von Seggern, H. *Angew. Chem. Int. Ed. Engl.* **1991**, *30*, 999–1001.

99. Wiest, O.; Steckhan, E. *Angew. Chem. Int. Ed. Engl.* **1993**, *32*, 901–903.

100. Harirchian, B.; Bauld, N. L. *J. Am. Chem. Soc.* **1989**, *111*, 1826–1828.

101. Tojo, S.; Toki, S.; Takamuku, S. *J. Org. Chem.* **1991**, *56*, 6240–6243.

102. Kuriyama, Y.; Sakuragi, H.; Tokumaru, K.; Yochida, Y.; Tagawa, S. *Bull. Chem. Soc. Jpn.* **1993**, *66*, 1852–1855.

103. McClelland, R. A.; Kanagasabapathy, V. M.; Steenken, S. *J. Am. Chem. Soc.* **1988**, *110*, 6913–6914.

104. Tokumura, K.; Ozaki, T.; Nosaka, H.; Saigusa, Y.; Itoh, M. *J. Am. Chem. Soc.* **1991**, *113*, 4974–4980.

105. Bauld, N. L.; Pabon, R. *J. Am. Chem. Soc.* **1983**, *105*, 633–634.

106. Kelsall, B. J.; Andrews, L. *J. Am. Chem. Soc.* **1983**, *105*, 1413–1419.

107. Bally, T.; Nitsche, S.; Roth, K.; Haselbach, E. *J. Phys. Chem.* **1985**, *89*, 2528–2533.

108. Pac, C.; Fukunaga, T.; Go-An, Y.; Sakae, T.; Yanagida, S. *J. Photochem. Photobiol., A* **1987**, *41*, 37–51.

109. Tojo, S.; Morishama, K.; Ishida, A.; Majima, T.; Takamuku, S. *Bull. Chem. Soc. Jpn.* **1995**, *68*, 958–966.

110. Reynolds, D. W.; Bauld, N. L. *Tetrahedron* **1986**, *42*, 6189–6194.

111. Mayr, H. *Angew. Chem. Intl. Ed. Engl.* **1990**, *29*, 1371–1384.

112. Griller, D.; Ingold, K. U. *Acc. Chem. Res.* **1980**, *13*, 317–323.

113. Sankararaman, S.; Perrier, S.; Kochi, J. K. *J. Am. Chem. Soc.* **1989**, *111*, 6448–6449.

114. Maslak, P.; Vallombroso, T. M.; Chapman, W. H.; Narvaez, J. N. *Angew. Chem. Int. Ed. Engl.* **1994**, *33*, 73–75.

115. Mirafzal, G. A.; Kim, T.; Liu, J.; Bauld, N. L. *J. Am. Chem. Soc.* **1992**, *114*, 10968–10969.

116. Kim, T.; Mirafzal, G. A.; Liu, J.; Bauld, N. L. *J. Am. Chem. Soc.* **1993**, *115*, 7653–7664.

117. Kim, T.; Sarker, H.; Bauld, N. L. *J. Chem. Soc., Perkin Trans. 2* **1995**, 577–580.

118. Gollnick, K.; Schnatterer, S.; Utschick, G. *J. Org. Chem.* **1993**, *58*, 6049–6056.

119. Tamai, T.; Mizuno, K.; Hashida, I.; Otsuji, Y. *Tetr. Lett.* **1993**, *34*, 2641–2644.

THE PHOTOCHEMICAL REACTION BETWEEN ARENENITRILES AND BENZYLIC DONORS

Angelo Albini, Elisa Fasani, and Mauro Freccero

Advances in Electron Transfer Chemistry
Volume 5, pages 103–140.
Copyright © 1996 by JAI Press Inc.
All rights of reproduction in any form reserved.
ISBN: 0-7623-0062-0

1. INTRODUCTION

Side-chain functionalization of aromatics via a radical pathway
is a well-established procedure; the reaction is usually initiated
by hydrogen abstraction by a suitable reagent (Scheme 1, path
a).[1,2] More recently, the same goal has been approached through
a different strategy. Here, single-electron oxidation (SET) followed by fragmentation of the aromatic radical cation yields,
as in the previous case, a benzylic radical (path b).[3,4] In both
mechanisms the initiation can involve an excited state instead
of a ground state oxidant, taking advantage respectively of the
radical properties of the excited state in the first case and of
the large change in the redox properties of organic molecules
introduced by electronic excitation in the latter one.[5–9] In the
SET path, the benzyl radical is generated in the presence (and
usually in the close vicinity, path c) of a radical anion, and its
fate is primarily determined by this situation. As an example,
when the acceptor is itself an aromatic molecule, efficient and
specific arene benzylation can occur.[10,11] This procedure has

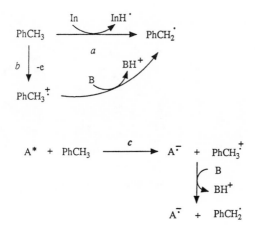

Scheme 1.

been developed particularly for arenenitriles, and in this chapter we will discuss our studies in the field as well as related results from other laboratories.

2. THE ARENENITRILE–BENZYLIC DONORS PHOTOCHEMICAL REACTION: MECHANISM AND SCOPE

2.1. Typical Reactions

We came to this area quite by chance. Our interest in nucleophilic functionalization of aromatics led us to consider photochemical reactions for this purpose. In several cases, such reactions involve ionization of the substrate.[12] Furthermore, we were impressed by the work of Arnold and his co-workers showing that SET often occurs upon photoexcitation yielding an ion radical pair.[13] In view of this fact, one of the experiments we carried out involved irradiation of the photochemical oxidant 1,4-naphthalenedicarbonitrile (DCN) in the presence of toluene and cyanide in deareated acetonitrile. Arnold's work had shown that cation radicals of alkenes add nucleophiles under this condition, and we wanted to test whether a similar reaction with

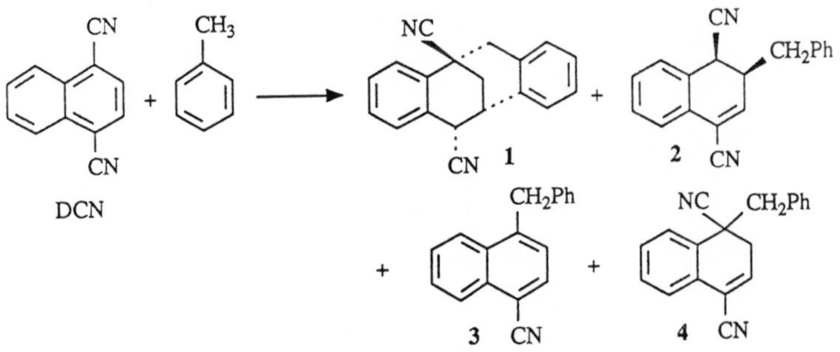

Scheme 2.

aromatics also took place. A reaction did occur, and led to several products which were separated and identified (Scheme 2).[14] None of them arose from cyanide addition (indeed, the irradiation omitting cyanide gave exactly the same results). The main product was the tetracyclic derivative **1**, the structure of which was finally solved by X-ray determination.

Thus, the reaction observed was an alkylation, whether with reduction of the ring or not (products **2** and **4** vs. product **3**), and complicated in the case of the main product **1** by the formation of a second C–C bond. This result suggested several mechanistic questions. In later work we tried to clarify the mechanistic issues, and more generally attempted to define the scope and potential of the alkylation of aromatics via photoinduced electron transfer (PET). It turned out that useful preparative results are obtained in a number of cases and that the observed reactions can be grouped in two main classes, for both of which a satisfactory mechanism can be proposed. The main conclusions from this work are presented below. It is felt that they reveal general information about the chemistry of ion radical *pairs*, a type of intermediate which is exclusively in the realm of photochemistry and potentially unlike ion radicals which are intermediates common to other methods, e.g. electrochemistry (although, even there photochemically generated ion radicals have distinctive features of their own).

2.2. General Mechanistic Scheme: Photoinduced Electron Transfer

Dissection of the reactions shown in Scheme 2 leads to the following elementary steps: electron transfer, cleavage of a C–H bond in the cation radical to yield the benzylic radical species, formation of a C–C bond, and, in the case of product **1** formation, repetition of the sequence to form a new C–C bond. The steps are separately discussed below.

As is well known, SET is a quite common process in photochemistry, since ΔG_{et} (Eq. 1) in the excited state is lowered with respect to the ground state process by an amount corresponding to the excitation energy (Weller equation)[6,7]:

$$\Delta G_{et} = E_{ox}(\text{Donor}) - E_{red}(\text{Acceptor}) - E_{exc} + e^2/\varepsilon\alpha \qquad (1)$$

Aromatic nitriles are strong oxidants in their excited states (see Table 1). Since they fluoresce strongly, the involvement of the singlet states can be easily proved by application of fluorescence quenching techniques. In all of the tested cases, it has been found that the Stern–Volmer constant obtained from fluorescence analysis and that obtained from the double reciprocal plots of reaction quantum yield vs. quencher concentration are nearly equal,[15–18] thus proving that the singlet state is actually involved in the photochemical reaction. Actually it has been observed that a $\Delta G_{et} \leq 0$ and polar solvents are necessary (although not sufficient, see Section 3) conditions for the photochemical proc-

Table 1. Ground State and Singlet Excited State Reduction Potential for Some Arenenitriles[a]

Nitrile	$E_{red}(S_0)$	$E_{red}(S_1)$
1,4-Benzenedicarbonitrile, DCB	−1.6	2.67
1,2,4,5-Benzenetetracarbonitrile, TCB	−0.7	3.45
1-Naphthalenecarbonitrile, 1-CN	−1.98	1.9
1,4-Naphthalenedicarbonitrile, DCN	−1.28	2.17
9,10-Anthracenedicarbonitrile, DCA	−0.89	1.97

Note: [a]V vs. SCE in acetonitrile.

ANGELO ALBINI, ELISA FASANI, and MAURO FRECCERO

esses.[19] In an apolar solvent the electrostatic term $e^2/\varepsilon a$ would give a strong contribution to ΔG_{et}, making SET too slow. Usually, pairs of reagents which give photochemical alkylation in acetonitrile solution display only fluorescence quenching in an apolar solvent such as cyclohexane.[14,20] In most cases the quenching is accompanied by the appearance of an exciplex emission,[14,20] which is shifted towards the red by an amount

Table 2. Photochemical Reaction between Arenenitriles and Benzylic Derivatives[a]

Nitrile	Donor	Ipso-Substitution	Reductive Addition	Cycloaddition	Bibenzyl	Ref.
PhCN	$C_6H_3Me_3$	—	—	—	high	19
DCB	PhMe	high	—	—	—	19
DCB	$[PhCH_2]_2$	34	—	—	low	89a
DCB	$[PhCMe_2]_2$	—	—	—	b	89a
TCB	PhMe	68	—	—	low	21
TCB	$C_6H_2Me_4$	high	—	—	—	19
TCB	$[PhCMe_2]_2$	87	—	—	c	89a
1-CN	$C_6H_2Me_4$	—	—	—	90	20
1-CN	4-MeOC$_6$H$_4$Me	—	30	—	50	20
DCN	PhMe	12	9	23	traces	17
DCN	$C_6H_4Me_4$	10	49[d]	30[e]	present	17
DCN	4-MeOC$_6$H$_4$Me	19	53[d,f]	—	present	34
DCN	4-FC$_6$H$_4$Me	2	55[d]	40	present	34
DCN	PhCHMe$_2$	—	10[g]	45	—	16
DCN	PhEt	10	50[d]	17	—	103
DCN	$[Ph_2CH]_2$	—	57	—	h	16
DCN	PhCH$_2$SiMe$_3$	—	100[d]	—	—	103
DCN	PhCH$_2$SnBu$_3$	39	50[d]	—	—	103
DCA	PhCH$_2$SnBu$_3$	28	—	—	3	66

Notes: [a]Representative results in MeCN, unless otherwise specified; isolated yields by chromatography.
[b]By irradiation in MeOH-MeCN, PhCMe$_2$H (12) and PhCMe$_2$OMe (54) also formed.
[c]By irradiation in MeOH-MeCN, PhCMe$_2$OMe (50) also formed.
[d]Sum of 1-benzyl- and 2-benzyl-1,2-dihydronaphthalenes.
[e]Two diastereoisomers.
[f]The 2-benzyl derivatives are a mixture of the *trans* and the *cis* derivative.

proportional to the charge transfer character of the complex. On the other hand, formation of a ground state complex has been only rarely observed,[21-23] and seems not to have a profound effect on the chemistry occurring. It should be noted that the donor–acceptor character of a pair of aromatic reagents influence the observed photochemistry also in the $\Delta G_{et} \geq 0$ region; e.g. it determines the efficiency and the regiochemistry of photocycloaddition reactions involving the aromatic rings,[24] but this is not related with the benzylic functionalization process with which the discussion here is concerned.

Although electron transfer to singlet excited nitrile is in all cases the first step, this is neither a sufficient condition for the chemical reaction to occur, nor a guarantee that a single mechanism is followed in all cases. Indeed, as will be shown, it appears that products of type **1** and products of type **2–4** are formed through different, although related mechanisms. In order to gain an idea of the scope of the reaction, some representative results are reported in Table 2 in which the yields of the different processes occurring—viz. benzylation with ipso substitution of the cyano group, benzylation with ring reduction, and benzylation with cyclization—are reported.

3. ALKYLATION OF THE NITRILES

3.1. Deprotonation of the Cation Radical

As can be seen by viewing Table 2, several nitriles can be efficiently benzylated by irradiation in the presence of various donors, giving either aromatic or dihydro products (e.g. in the DCN–toluene reaction products **2–4**). The general mechanism proposed for these processes is depicted in Scheme 3. Since, as mentioned above, the reaction is SET-initiated, its efficiency is related to the relative rates of fragmentation of the benzyl radical cations vs. back electron transfer which leads to energy wasting. The likelihood of such a process can be evaluated by inspecting the appropriate thermochemical cycle (Scheme 4),[11,25-32] where the oxidation potential of the starting substrate (PhCHR–X), that of the resulting cation (X$^+$) and the bond dis-

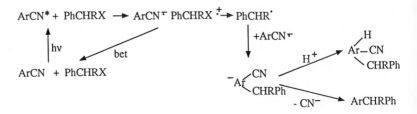

Scheme 3.

sociation energy of the C–X bond in the substrate, can be used to determine the corresponding quantity in the radical cation [BDE(PhCHRX$^{+\bullet}$)] through Eq. 2:

$$BDE(PhCHRX^{+\bullet}) =$$

$$BDE(PhCHRX) - [E_{ox}(PhCHRX) - E_{ox}(X\bullet)] \qquad (2)$$

Since $E_{ox}(H)$ is strongly negative (−1.77 V vs. NHE),[33a,b] BDE(PhCH$_2$R$^{+\bullet}$ → PhCHR• + H$^+$) has usually a small and often a negative value, thus the cation radicals of aromatic hydrocarbons are expected to have a low or negative BDE and to dissociate easily. Of course, fragmentation involves the weakest C–H bond, i.e. the benzylic bond. Indeed, Arnold showed several years ago that the radical cations of such molecules are strong acids. For example, the toluene cation radical is an acid comparable to mineral acids (pK_a ca. −12) having a BDE of −17 kcal mol^{-1}; indeed, the benzene radical cation too is a strong

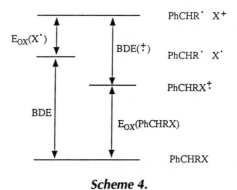

Scheme 4.

acid (pK_a ca. -2), although there is no unambiguous evidence for the exchange of aromatic ring protons.[32] Thus, toluene undergoes a drop of 60 pK_a units on ionization; this has no parallel in ground state chemistry (e.g. complexation with metals bring about a change of only 12–15 pK_a units).[33c]

Experimentally, it is uniformly observed that an aromatic hydrocarbon will suffer deprotonation from the benzylic position when irradiated in the presence of an SET sensitizer provided that: (1) the sensitizer is a strong enough acceptor in the excited state to cause electron transfer from the substrate; (2) the reaction is carried out in a polar solvent which does not interfere which any step of the process (acetonitrile is routinely used, but dimethylsulfoxide, which is competitively oxidized is not suitable[19]; the role of nucleophilic or acidic solvents will be discussed later); and (3) the BDE of the radical cation, evaluated as above, is negative or only slightly positive and there are no competing fragmentations with a sufficiently low BDE(RX$^{+•}$), with X≠H (see Section 3.2).

Point 2 above is understandable (Eq. 1) since in apolar solvents the energy for charge separation is large and makes electron transfer slow. In the case of aromatic nitriles as acceptors, with which we are particularly concerned, there is obviously also a strong π-interaction that can occur between donor and acceptor, and irradiation in aprotic solvents usually causes no reaction but only quenching of the nitrile monomolecular fluorescence and appearance of a new red-shifted emission attributable to the exciplex (see Section 2.2). Independent solvation of the radical ions is also important. For example, the bichromophoric molecules **5** and **6** show strong exciplex emission and

5   R = H
6   R = Me

very little photochemical reaction even in acetonitrile.[20] This is reasonably due to the fact that the short chain connecting the two chromophores allows sufficient superimposition of the two π-systems leading to internal exciplex formation rather than independent solvation of the ions.

With regard to point 3 above, since the departing cation remains the same and the energies of the benzylic C–H bond vary only marginally in a series of related benzylic donors (unless for triarylmethanes), BDE(RH$^{+\bullet}$) is mainly determined by the oxidation potential of the substrate. Hydrocarbons with high oxidation potential will experience a greater weakening of the C–H bond upon oxidation. In practice, cation radicals of phenyl derivatives (and those containing no strong electron-donating substituent) will cleave efficiently from the benzylic position, but in methoxyphenyl or naphthyl derivatives[19,20,34] where the fragmentations are generally near to thermoneutral, cleavage is inefficient. As an example, deprotonation of the toluene cation radical is, as pointed out above, a strongly exothermic process (Eq. 3), but for p-methoxytoluene the process is slightly endothermic (Eq. 4):

$$BDE(PhCH_3^{+\bullet} \rightarrow PhCH_2{}^{\bullet} + H^+) = -17 \text{ kcal mol}^{-1} \qquad (3)$$

$$BDE(p\text{-}MeOC_6H_4CH_3^{+\bullet} \rightarrow p\text{-}MeOC_6H_4CH_2{}^{\bullet} + H^+) = 3 \text{ kcal mol}^{-1}(4)$$

Indeed, comparison of the photochemical reaction of these two donors with the same acceptor, DCN, shows that the first one reacts efficiently while the latter one reacts poorly (quantum yield lower by at least 2 orders of magnitude.[14,34]

3.2. Other Fragmentations of the Cation Radical

The proton is obviously not the only electrofugal group participating in benzylic cation radical fragmentation, and different fragmentations of benzyl ion radicals are amply documented. Thus, fragmentation of a carbon-carbon bond occurs efficiently in many instances. Convenient electrofugal groups are benzyl or diphenylmethyl cations, since the oxidation potential of the

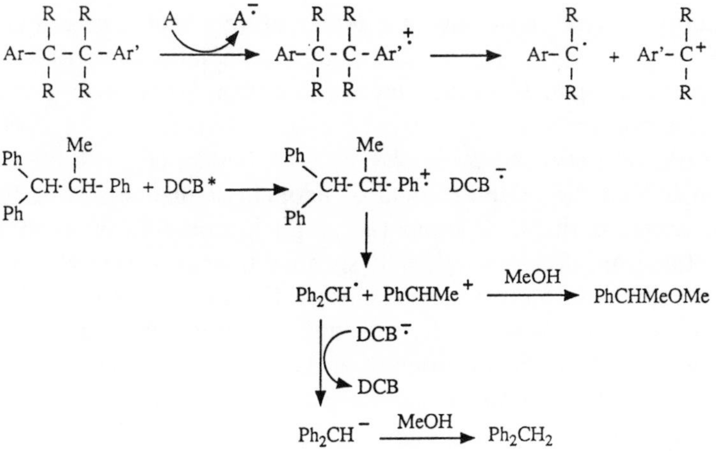

Scheme 5.

corresponding radicals is low (e.g. $E_{ox}(PhCH_2\cdot) = 0.73$ V, and the value is 0.37 V for $Ph_2CH\cdot$ and 0.16 V for $PhCMe_2\cdot$).[26] This is apparent in the "mesolytic" cleavage of bibenzyl derivatives often obtained by irradiation in the presence of acceptors (Scheme 5).[27,29,35–40] In the specific example shown (1,1,2-triphenylpropane), the selectivity of the observed cleavage is well rationalized on the basis of Eq. 2 (the group split off as a cation is the one corresponding to the most easily oxidized radical). Obviously, the success of the reaction depends also on the bond energy. Thus, bibenzyl does not suffer cleavage of the C–C bond since this would be largely endothermic (ca. 30 kcal mol^{-1}), while such a process is observed both with α,α'-alkyl substituted and aryl-substituted bibenzyls where the substituents both lower the BDE of the substrate and make the oxidation potential of the leaving group less positive. Thus, as an example, the radical cation of 2-methyl-1,1,2-triphenylpropane (BDE 5 kcal mol^{-1}) cleaves easily. Differently from the deprotonation case seen above, fragmentation of the benzylic C–C bond also occurs at a useful rate when the process is moderately endothermic (up to 10–15 kcal mol^{-1}).[27] In some cases, the intervention of such a sizeable energy barrier shows up in a temperature effect. For example, the DCB-sensitized cleavage of tetraphenylethane or of 1,1,2-triphenylpropanes is much more efficient at 80 °C than at room temperature.[35]

The *tert*-butyl radical is also easy to oxidize (E_{ox} = 0.09 V),[26] and in fact the cation radical of neopentylbenzene also suffers cleavage of the C–C bond (although in competition with deprotonation, see below)[17] and so does that of 2-phenyl-2,3-dimethylbutane.[17] Other convenient C-centered electrofugal groups are α-alkoxymethyl[41–47] and α-aminomethyl groups[48,49] as well as the carboxy group of arylacetic acids[50,51] (in the latter case the donor is probably the carboxylate anion, rather than the undissociated acid). The fragmentation of cation radicals of arylated three-[52–56] and four-membered[57–61] cyclic compounds as well as those of other strained derivatives such as the anthracene dimer[62] also pertains to this class. On the contrary, the cleavage of diphenylpinacol and related compounds occurs via a different mechanism and is discussed below (see Section 3.8).

A carbon–heteroatom bond can likewise be fragmented under these conditions (see Scheme 6). Convenient substrates are silanes, germanes, and stannanes[17,63–66] as well as isoelectronic boron derivatives (as in the cleavage of benzyltriphenylborates after oxidation to the corresponding radical).[67,68]

Rationalization via a thermochemical cycle is not straightforward here. In the case of the largely used silanes, for example, the required oxidation potential of a trialkylsilyl radical is not known. One can resort to the use of gas phase measured ionization potentials instead of the solution oxidation potentials (Eq. 5 instead of Eq. 2)[27,69]:

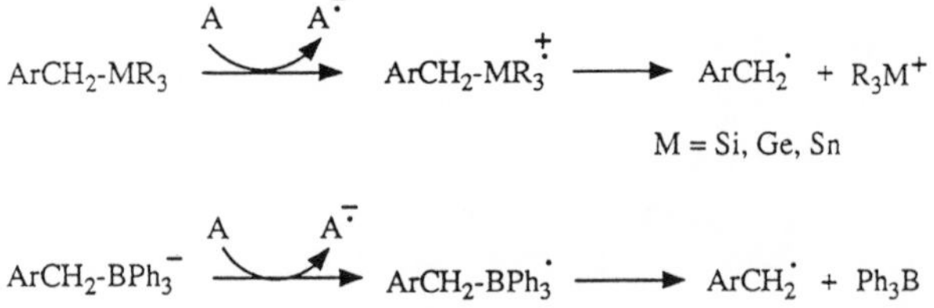

$$ArCH_2\text{-}MR_3 \xrightarrow{\;\;A\quad A^{\overline{\cdot}}\;\;} ArCH_2\text{-}MR_3^{\overset{+}{\cdot}} \longrightarrow ArCH_2^{\cdot} + R_3M^+$$

$$M = Si, Ge, Sn$$

$$ArCH_2\text{-}BPh_3^{-} \xrightarrow{\;\;A\quad A^{\overline{\cdot}}\;\;} ArCH_2\text{-}BPh_3^{\cdot} \longrightarrow ArCH_2^{\cdot} + Ph_3B$$

Scheme 6.

$$BDE(PhCH_2SiMe_3^{+\bullet}) = BDE(PhCH_2SiMe_3)$$

$$- [IP(PhCH_2SiMe_3) - IP\,(SiMe_3{}^{\bullet})] \qquad (5)$$

Such an approximation is based on the assumption that the solvation energy contributes equally to stabilization of both the starting cation radical and the resulting cation (and is not important for uncharged species). This appears reasonable when both starting and final species have similar structures. This is exemplified by the cleavage of bibenzyl derivatives shown below, where a π-delocalized ion radical yields a similar π-cation. Indeed, there are experimental results which support this view,[25] but it is hardly expected to hold when from a π-ion radical the σ-localized $SiMe_3$ cation is split off. Indeed, evaluation according to Eq. 5 predicts that desilylation of the benzyltrimethylsilane cation radical should encounter a severe barrier (30 kcal mol^{-1}), and a fortiori this holds for a more easily oxidized substrate such as the corresponding 4-methoxy derivatives, whereas in both cases fragmentation is a fast process in MeCN. Therefore, the $SiMe_3$ cation is strongly stabilized in acetonitrile and this lowers the barrier for fragmentation. Said in another way, MeCN is a strong enough nucleophile to assist the ion radical cleavage (Eq. 6).

$$[A^{-\bullet}\;PhCH_2SiMe_3^{+\bullet}]_{MeCN} \rightarrow PhCH_2{}^{\bullet} + MeC{=}N{-}SiMe_3^{+} \qquad (6)$$

On the other hand, with substrates which are relatively good donors, and thus have a more positive $BDE(RX^{+\bullet})$, C–Si bond fragmentation may be slow in MeCN. As an example, α-trialkylsilylamines undergo electron transfer induced C–Si cleavage faster in the more nucleophilic MeOH than in MeCN.[70] Steric effects may also operate. Thus with trialkyl(p-methoxybenzyl)silanes where the alkyl group is bulky the relatively slow fragmentation of the cation radical in MeCN is accelerated by better nucleophiles like alcohols.[69]

3.3. Fragmentation of the Cation Radical: Dynamics

Thermochemical considerations are not sufficient, in predicting the quantum efficiencies of these processes since competition with back electron transfer ($k \gg 10^7$ mol^{-1} sec^{-1}) dominates all but the fastest fragmentation processes. Rate constant measurements have been made only in a few cases. Thus, desilylation of the benzyltrimethylsilane cation radical occurs with a rate constant $k_r \geq 10^9$ s^{-1} in MeCN, and the value is $k_r = 2 \times 10^6$ s^{-1} for the corresponding 4-methoxy derivative,[69,71] but rates of deprotonation are not known. The only systematic survey has been carried out for the C–C bond fragmentation of some bicumene cation radicals, and it has been concluded that there is no "kinetic overhead," viz. the reaction occurs at a rate close to that predicted by taking into account only the thermodynamic barrier.[29,36–38,72] This is in accordance with the discussion above, viz. fragmentation of a C–C bond occurs efficiently whenever it is exothermic or even slightly endothermic. Also, in the latter case, it is fast enough to compete with back electron transfer, contrary to the case of deprotonation which is sufficiently fast only when largely exothermic.

Indirect evidence about the rate of cleavage of different electrofugal groups has come from intramolecular competition experiments. Thus in p-xylyl derivatives of type 7 (see Scheme 7), the rate constants for fragmentation according to Eq. 7 are in the order[51] $k_r(SiMe_3^+) > 10 \, k_r(CO_2 + H^+) > 10 \, k_r(H^+)$.

$$ArCH_2X^{+\bullet} \rightarrow ArCH_2{}^\bullet + X^+ \tag{7}$$

Clearly, this is not the order that would be expected from mere consideration of the thermochemistry of these reactions. Thus, there are other factors that determine the actual rate of fragmentation, and solvent reorganization certainly contributes heavily since charged species are formed here.

3.4. Fragmentation of the Cation Radical: Selectivity

In various cation radicals in which benzylic C–H and C–C fragmentations are possible, the latter process usually predominates provided that it is not overly endothermic, despite the fact that deprotonation would in all cases be the thermodynamically preferred reaction. Thus, in the photochemical reaction of

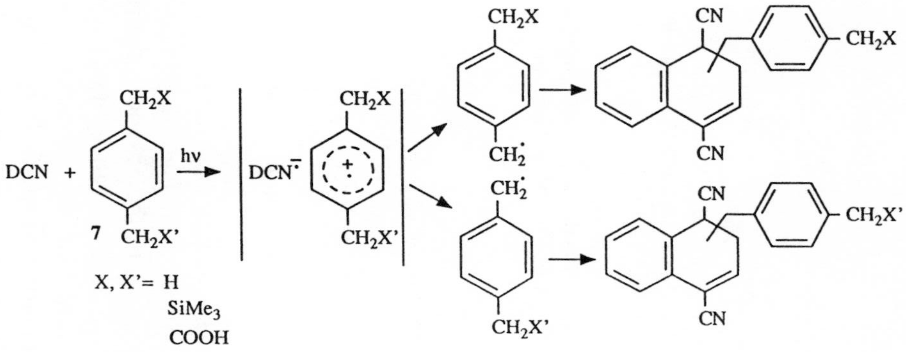
DCN +
CH_2X
hν
7
CH_2X'
X, X'= H
$SiMe_3$
COOH
$DCN^{\bar{\cdot}}$
CH_2X
CH_2X'
CH_2X
$\dot{C}H_2$
$\dot{C}H_2$
CH_2X'
CN
CN
CH_2X
CN
CN
CH_2X'

Scheme 7.

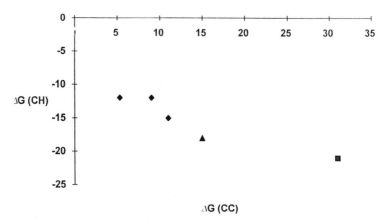

Figure 1. Comparison of the observed fragmentation of some benzylic radical cations with the calculated ΔG. From left: 1, Ph_2CHCMe_2Ph; 2, $Ph_2CHCHPh_2$; 3. Ph_2CHCH_2OMe (for all three only the somewhat endothermic C–C bond cleavage, and none of the largely exothermic C–H cleavage is observed. 4. PCH_2CMe_3, both C–C and C–H cleavages observed. 5. $PhCH_2CH_2Ph$, only C–H and none of the extremely endothermic C–C cleavage observed.

bibenzyl with DCN the cation radical of the hydrocarbon (in which ΔG for C–C cleavage is 30 kcal mol^{-1} and for C–H cleavage is –21 kcal mol^{-1}) undergoes only deprotonation,[34] but with the neopentylbenzene cation radical (where ΔG for C–C fragmentation drops to 2 kcal mol^{-1}) both reactions occur competitively.[17]

Figure 1 shows a comparison the two processes and the relevant thermochemical data. The preference for C–C cleavage is apparent. Thus, even in the absence of direct determination of the deprotonation rate, it can be concluded that this process involves a relevant "kinetic overhead." As a result, when heterolytic fragmentation of the C–H bond is strongly exothermic it can be relatively slow even in polar solvent. The barrier for solvent reorganization required to accommodate the detachment of the proton is arguably larger than that involved for the liberation of a larger (and in most cases delocalized) carbocation. In some cases deuteration has been shown to slow down atom transfer (not, of course, the previous electron transfer step).[15]

As mentioned above, there are only a few reported rate measurements for cation radical fragmentation. Stationary state data like quantum yields offer no direct indication of these rate constants. However, since the chemical yields of the isolated products are usually good and the following steps are well understood, one can assume that the structure of the final products faithfully represents the fact that benzyl radicals are formed as key intermediates, and, when there are different paths available, they are the preferred fragmentations. The quantum yields for product formation in these cases may be taken as a rough indication of the rate of fragmentation, depending on the competition of such a process with back electron transfer. As shown in Table 3, quantum yields for reactions involving deprotonation are quite variable; in some instances they are relatively high, as in the case where a weak C–H bond is involved both when the proton is transferred to the solvent and when in cage proton transfer takes place. Carbon–carbon bond cleavage seems to be slow (in the few cases known), though it overcomes deprotonation in many donors. Also, C–Si and C–Sn fragmentations are very fast, competing efficiently with back electron transfer, and in particular substrates, O-H deprotonation also occurs efficiently (see Section 3.11).

Table 3. Photochemical Reaction between Arenenitriles and Benzylic Donors[a]

Nitrile	Donor	Φ^b	Ref.
DCB	PhMe	0.014	19
TCB	PhMe	0.048	19
DCN	PhMe	0.07	87
DCN	PhMe	0.04[c]	87
DCN	PhCHMe$_2$	0.3	16
DCN	C$_6$H$_2$Me$_4$	0.045	15
DCN	[Ph$_2$CH]$_2$	0.021	16
DCN	PhCH$_2$SiMe$_3$	0.25	87
DCN	[Ph$_2$C(OH)]$_2$	0.14	45

Notes: [a]Representative quantum yield data.
[b]Limiting quantum yield or quantum yield at a concentration of the donor 0.1 to 0.2 M.
[c]In MeOH-MeCN 1:1.

3.5. Fragmentation of the Cation Radical: Medium Effect

The above discussion focused on photo-SET processes in which non-nucleophilic anion radicals such as those of aromatic nitriles served as intermediates. As detailed studies by Mariano[70,73] and Whitten[74,75] have shown, the anion radicals of ketones can be strong bases in which case deprotonation is faster since it involves direct transfer to the anion rather than to the solvent. This also holds true for benzyl derivatives. We have found that intramolecular selectivity is in some cases different with nitriles and ketones. For example, in the photochemical reaction between trifluoroacetophenone and benzytrimethyllsilane, where the first step is electron transfer (ΔG_{et} = –4 kcal mol^{-1}), deprotonation of the cation radical occurs to an extent of 96%. With p-methoxybenzyltrimethylsilane, where single electron transfer is still more exothermic, SET (ΔG_{et} = –15 kcal mol^{-1}), desilylation becomes predominant (74%).[71] As discussed above, desilylation is always the exclusive process when aromatic nitriles serve as the acceptors. Likewise, alteration in the medium characteristics causes changes in the nature of the preferred reaction pathway. Thus, diminishing the nucleophilicity of the ketone anion radical by complexation with a metal cation, by its protonation or alternatively by increasing of the medium nucleophilicity (changing from acetonitrile to methanol), causes a decrease in the proportion of deprotonation with an increase in desilylation.[70,71,73] For example, in the benzylsilane–TFA reaction, desilylation grows from 4 to 61% adding 0.1 M LiClO$_4$ and to 80% in MeCN–MeOH 4:6.[71] It should be noted that in other cases it has been reported that proton transfer is facilitated in apolar solvents, where the CIP predominates (this holds, however, only for *kinetically* favored processes, such as O–H deprotonation, not C–H deprotonation, see Section 3.11).[74,75]

3.6. Fragmentation of the Cation Radical: Stereoelectronic Effect

The selectivity of reactions of polymethylbenzenes cation radicals is interesting. Thus, in the reaction of TCB with isodurene

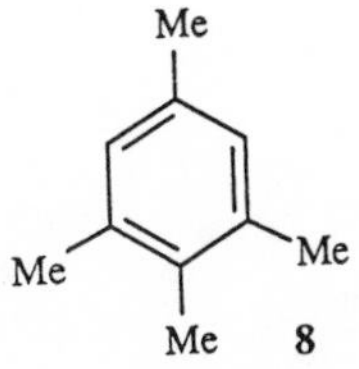

(8) the alkylation selectivity follows the order ^{2}Me>^{5}Me> ^{1,3}Me,[19] viz. the same order observed with thermal one-electron oxidants.[76] The similarity between the regioselectivity seen in the photoinduced SET reactions and with those of other SET oxidation methods is gratifying, particularly since the free radical reactions afford well-differentiated product distributions. Another example is the reaction of DCN with cymenes which leads to preferential reaction at the methyl group (at least as far as products of type **2** and **3** are concerned, Schemes 8 and 9),[77] and not the isopropyl group which in contrast is attacked by radicals[78,79] and radicalic excited states such as $n\pi^*$ ketones.[71,80]

These regioselectivities can be rationalized on the basis of stereoelectronic effects since it is assumed that colinearity between the scissible bond and the donating orbital (the ring π-orbital in the case of benzyl cation radicals, see Scheme 10) is required during fragmentation; the reaction is faster for bonds

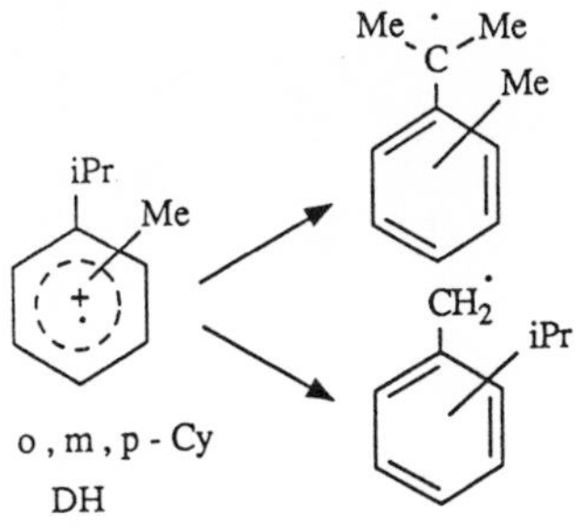

Scheme 8.

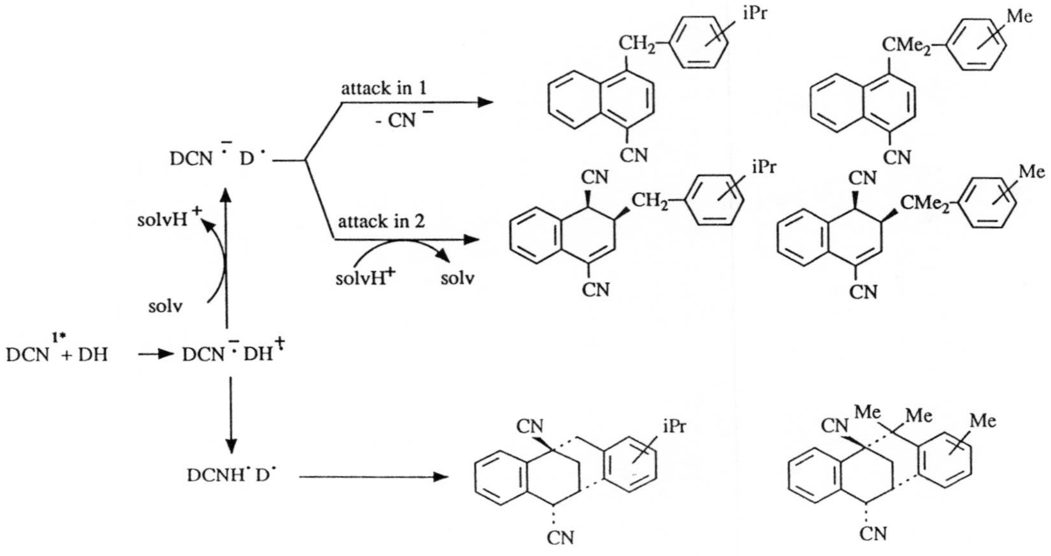

Scheme 9.

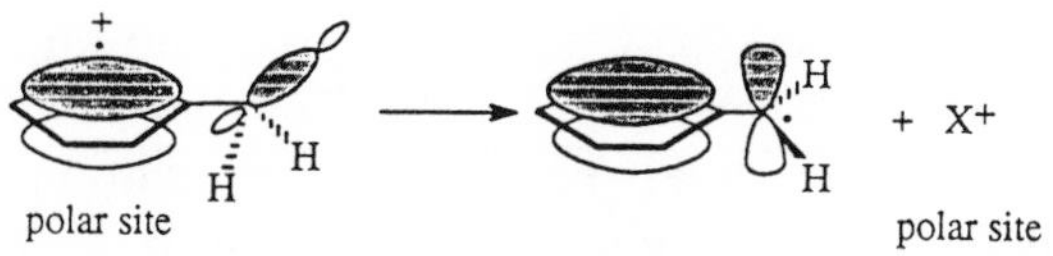

Scheme 10.

perpendicular to the ring in the preferred conformation(s) (see formula **9** in Scheme 11).[29,81]

Indeed, at least in some rigid models (indane derivatives), it has been shown that benzylic deprotonation only occurs when an accessible conformation (determined through molecular mechanics calculations) has a sufficient overlap between the SOMO located on the aromatic ring and the scissible C–H bond.[82] Related stereoelectronic effects have also been observed for fragmentations of C–C bonds.[83] In reactions of a pair of stereoisomeric 2-phenyl-3-methoxyindanes it has been found that one undergoes only C–H fragmentation and the other one only C–C cleavage, depending on which one is correctly oriented in a low-energy conformation.[82] On the other hand, this principle is not without exceptions since it has been observed that 2-silaindane undergoes C–Si bond cleavage upon SET oxidation even if it can not reach the correct orientation.[84]

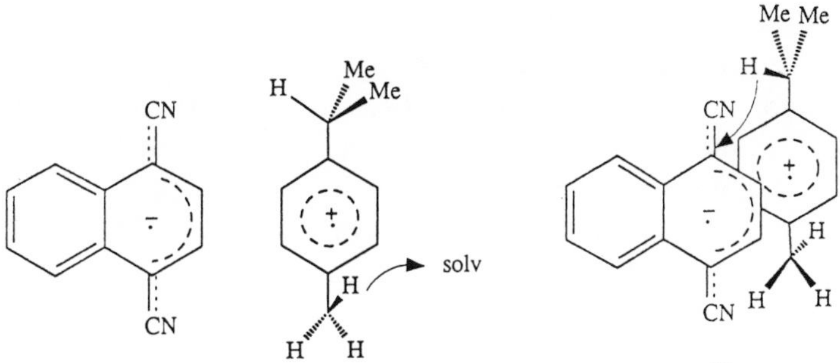

Scheme 11.

3.7. Fate of Benzyl Radicals: Addition to the Anion Radical

In many cases the final results of the irradiation induced reactions of aromatic nitriles in the presence of benzylic donors
are ring benzylation with ipso substitution of a cyano group
(see Table 2, Scheme 3).[10,11] Different mechanisms can be en-
visaged for the formation of these types of products which vary
in the sequence of the bond-forming and bond-breaking steps.
Although many pieces of evidence could be interpreted in favor
of proton transfer between the benzylic radical cation and the
nitrile anion radical (on reencounter of the opposedly charged
species, since, as it will be discussed below, the reaction is
sensitive to quenching by various reagents),[19] this information
is equally in accordance with the hypothesis of proton transfer
from the cation radical to the medium. Furthermore, some observations, including the fact that no deuterium incorporation
occurs even when it would be expected (as in the case of ben-
zenetricarbonitrile),[85] and that similar product distributions are
obtained when the benzyl radical arises both by deprotonation
and by an alternate fragmentation,[16,17] point to a pseudo uni-
molecular cleavage (or the kinetically indistinguishable solvent-
assisted fragmentation) of the cation radical, followed by
radical–anion radical addition and formation of the final products
through cyanide loss (see Scheme 3). It should also be stressed
that independent generation of benzyl radicals in the presence of
aromatic nitriles does not lead to alkylation,[14] showing that neutral
arenenitriles are not sufficiently reactive with radicals.

Although this mechanism well accounts for a large part of
the reactions discussed here, there is a specific group of reactions for which proton transfer between ion radicals does take
place. In these cases, however, the processes occur in geminate
pairs, and not on reencounter of free ion radicals. Such reactions
will be discussed separately in Section 4.

In accord with the mechanism shown in Scheme 3, benzylation
always occurs at the center(s) of highest spin density in the
anion radical, and this holds true for unsubstituted ring carbons
as verified in the case of 1,3,5-benzenetricarbonitrile.[85] Furthermore, under conditions where the anion radical is protonated

(e.g. when a few percent water or methanol or traces of protic acids are present), the alkylation reaction is quenched.[14,19] Thus, addition of 0.01 M trifluoroacetic acid completely quenches alkylation and, in the case of DCN, it has been ascertained that the main product becomes 1,2-dihydro-1,4-naphthalenedicarbonitrile.[14]

Correspondingly, quenchers of benzylic radical also suppress the alkylation. However, the situation is more complicated here. Thus, while benzylic radicals are efficiently trapped by oxygen (see below), their reaction with other known radical traps (e.g. electron-poor alkenes) does not succeed either with benzyl or with allyl radicals, while this is perfectly feasible with simple alkyl radicals.[86] Thus, even if delocalized radicals would be expected to diffuse out of cage more efficiently, and thus become more available for trapping by species different from the acceptor anion radical, this factor is more than overcome by adverse factors such as the lower intrinsic rate of addition to alkenes by these stabilized species and the stabilization offered by the interaction between the two π-delocalized odd electron species, the radical and the anion radical, which are initially formed face-to-face and tend to react that way.

A hint of the importance of this contribution is given by the fact that the quantum yield for benzylation of DCN by toluene is strongly depressed in going from MeCN to MeOH–MeCN 1:3. But when a faster cleaving group is involved, as in the case of benzyltrimethylsilane, the quantum yield is practically unaffected by this solvent change. Apparently, fragmentation is so fast that in the latter case the sequence—electron transfer–cation radical fragmentation–radical–anion radical addition—takes place before diffusion in the medium.[87] Other factors may also have an influence on the nature of the reaction path followed. As an example, in the reaction with DCN, the proportion of attack at position 1 to position 2 tends to increase with more stabilized benzyl radicals—e.g. with α-substituted benzyl radicals,[88] while with more bulky species like acenaphthenyl, radical attack at position 2 seems to be favored (Scheme 12).[89]

The competition between addition to the acceptor radical anion and other reactions of benzyl radicals (see below) depends pri-

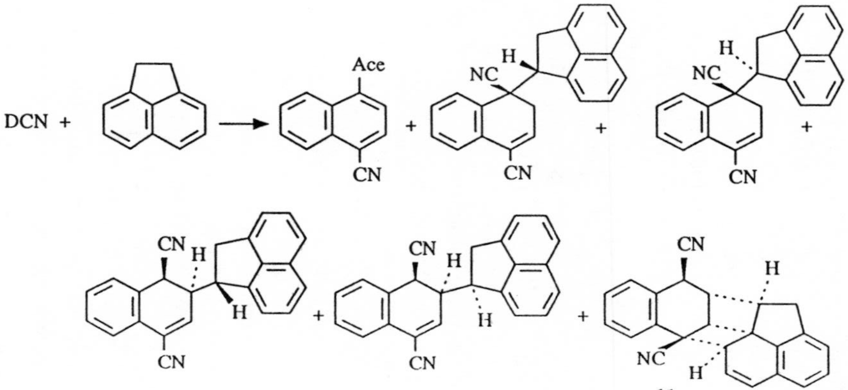

Scheme 12.

marily on the nature of the former. Thus, as shown in Table 2, benzylic adducts are obtained with 1,2- and 1,4-benzenedicarbonitrile, but not with the 1,3-isomer nor benzonitrile itself,[19] and with DCN, but not with either of the naphthalene mononitriles.[20] A rationale for this selectivity can be formulated in terms of the nature of the anion radical's SOMO. This may be either with reference to its energy or to the spin localization at the relevant radical centers. Ohashi has pointed out the fact that coupling occurs for those nitriles having an accessible *second* wave in cathodic voltammetry, e.g. with 1,3,5-benzenetrinitrile but not with the 1,3-dinitrile.[85] This may be due to the fact that only in the former case is the anion radical's SOMO low enough in energy to have a correct matching with the benzyl radical's SOMO. The same holds for the naphthalenemononitriles vs. dinitriles. Raising the benzyl radical's SOMO has the same effect as lowering the anion radical's SOMO. Thus, 1-naphthalenenitrile couples with the *p*-methoxybenzyl but not with the unsubstituted benzyl radical.[20] On the other hand, with anthracenenitriles the anion radical's SOMO is of lower energy and coupling is inefficient.[66,89] Essentially the same conclusions are reached if one considers the spin localization in the radical anions, which is highest in less conjugated and more substituted nitriles.

The structure of the benzyl radical also plays an important role in determining this competition, and here there are two effects. The first one depends again on the SOMO energy. Besides the above mentioned case of *p*-methoxy derivatives with naphthalenemononitriles, one may explain in this way the reduced efficiency of addition to DCN observed for α-alkoxy- and α-thioalkoxybenzyl radicals, which is accompanied by an increased efficiency of homocoupling.[17] The other effect depends on the rate of cleavage of the cation radical. Thus, DCA is not alkylated by acenaphthene,[89] where a bulky radical formed through relatively slow deprotonation of the cation radical is involved, yet DCA is alkylated efficiently by benzyltrimethylstannane, where the radical is formed through the much faster C–Sn fragmentation.[66]

3.8. Formation of the Final Products

In all of the above cases where the intermediate benzyl radical is consumed through different pathways, the arene nitrile anion radical is protonated and dihydroaromatics are obtained (prolonged irradiation leads also to the formation of tetrahydro derivatives, as it has been shown in the case of 1-CN).[20] Obviously if the reaction is carried out under basic conditions, rearomatization via dehydrocyanation takes place (e.g. 1-CN from DCN by irradiation with toluene in basic MeOH–MeCN),[87] and in the presence of oxygen, rearomatization regenerates the cyanoarene which, therefore, only serves the role of sensitizer (see Section 3.10). Otherwise, the anion adduct formed undergoes rearomatization as the final step, either through direct cyanide loss, or through protonation and dehydrocyanation of the resulting dihydro derivative.

It is not simple to distinguish between these two alternatives, and from what is known from reviewing most reports on preparative reactions, rearomatization may occur either in the photoreaction medium or during the workup. As far as the product distributions are concerned, it can be observed that starting from benzenenitriles, alkylated benzenes are always obtained even when attack at an unsubstituted position is involved, as in the case of the 1,3,5-trinitrile[85] (in this case an unspecified dehydrogenation mechanism is operating). In contrast, with naphthalenes usually 1,2 dihydroderivatives are isolated unless of course the reaction is carried out under basic conditions which promote rearomatization. With anthracenes, dihydro derivatives or rearomatized products[66,69] may be obtained, although the usual chromatographic work may also lead to hydrolysis products (anthrones).[90]

In view of the selectivity and predictability of both the cleavage reaction of the cation radical and the addition of benzyl radicals to the anion radical, this process can be considered a useful method for aromatic alkylation, although, as it appears from the foregoing discussion, it is limited to arene polynitriles. Provided that the thermodynamic requirements for the various steps are met, chemical yields are often satisfactory since, as

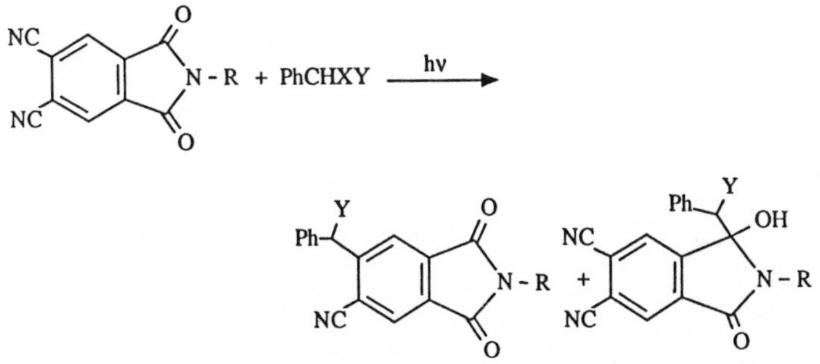

Scheme 13.

discussed above, homocoupling of the benzylic radicals is minimal. In this sense the reaction contrasts with other methods involving generation of benzylic radicals with other photosensitizers, e.g. ketones. In those cases, even when the reaction involves a SET pathway, the ketone radical anion is rapidly protonated and the two stable radicals (ketyl and benzyl) undergo coupling to yield a statistical 1:2:1 mixture of bibenzyl, alcohol, and pinacol and, therefore, it is not of preparative interest.[71]

Some exploratory studies have been devoted to the competition between radical attack to different functionalities. Thus, with dicyanophthalimides, benzylation occurs both on the aromatic ring with cyano group substitution and with reductive addition to the C–O moiety (Scheme 13).[18] The competition seems to be determined by bulk of the donor with ipso substitution of the cyano group being favored by less hindered donors (presumably the corresponding cation radical cleaving when at a close distance from the acceptor anion radical).

3.9. Other Reactions of the Benzyl Radical

Competing reactions of the benzyl radical which might be expected are coupling, hydrogen abstraction, and addition to oxygen, as well as electron transfer with the aromatic nitrile or its anion (see Scheme 14). One should note that benzylic radicals are not very easily oxidized (see below). Thus, while

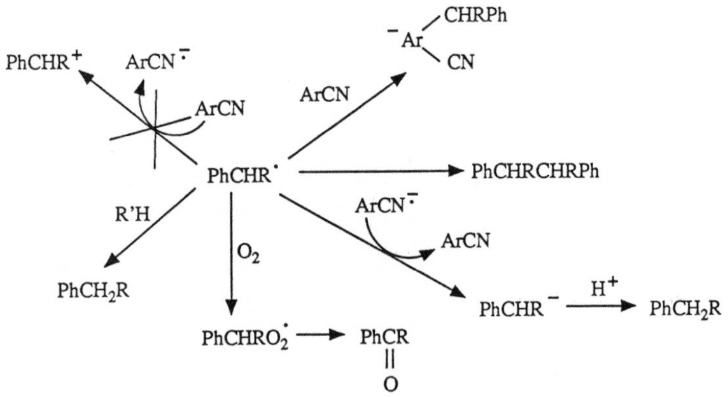

Scheme 14.

with better donors such as α-aminoalkyl radical (E_{ox} = ca. -1 V) oxidation by the *ground state* nitrile is an expected, and verified, possibility.[91] This is not the case with benzylic radicals (E_{ox} = +0.2–0.7 V).[26] On the other hand, oxidation by the excited state of the nitrile present at a negligibly small steady-state concentration is kinetically prohibitive. Reduction by the persistent anion radical, on the contrary, is a common occurrence in view of the accessible E_{red} of such compounds [e.g. $E_{red}(PhCH_2\cdot) = -1.45$ V, $E_{red}(Ph_2CH\cdot) = -1.14$ V][26] at least when sensitizers such as dicyanobenzenes are used [$E_{red}(DCB) = 1.6$ V]. The anion formed in this way is then protonated. Thus, if the fragmentation of the cation radical involves a C–C bond, the final result is hydrolytic cleavage of the substrate (see Scheme 5).[27,41] If deprotonation is the fragmentation pathway followed, the starting substrate is regenerated, a sequence which may explain why some of the reactions observed are inefficient though the initial SET event is efficient.[88] This does not hold, obviously, with nitriles having a highly negative *ground state* reduction potential (e.g. when TCB is used instead of DCB) since then SET according to Scheme 13 cannot take place with radical–anion radical addition taking place instead (see below).[89a,92]

The competition between the different *chemical* reactions of the benzylic radicals depends on various factors. Thus, irradiation of DCN in MeCN–MeOH containing toluene leads both to benzylated and to hydroxymethylated naphthalene derivatives.[87] Apparently, the benzylic radical diffuses out of cage and hydrogen exchange with MeOH competes with trapping by the DCN anion radical on reencounter. This is accompanied by partial quenching of the DCN anion radical by the protic medium; a strong drop of the alkylation quantum yield is observed under this condition. On the contrary, no change in either product distribution or quantum yield is observed with the more efficient cleaving benzyltrimethylsilane.[87] Bibenzyl formation takes place in all cases, but it is always a minor process. This is in accord with the fact that more thermodynamically favored processes are generally available for the benzylic radicals, except when they are heavily hindered, as in the case of the acenaphthenyl radical.[89b]

3.10. Photoinduced Benzylic Oxygenation

Interestingly from a preparative point of view, benzylic oxygenation can be obtained under these conditions as a selective process which affords aldehydes and minor amounts of acids (see representative examples in Table 4). In these instances, the nitrile is not consumed and thus serves as a SET photosensitizer.[19,93–98] The initial efficiency of anion radical formation is the same in the presence and in the absence of oxygen, but this species is oxidized by oxygen while the cation radical fragments.[19] Apparently oxygen is a more powerful radical trap for the benzyl radical than either electron-withdrawing substituted alkenes or aromatic anion radicals. Carbonyl derivatives are formed with satisfactory quantum yields independent of whether the radical is formed via C–H, C–C,[94] or C–Si[97] benzylic bond cleavage in the cation radical. Noteworthy, even benzylic derivatives, which are quite unreactive in the photoalkylation of arenenitriles, are labile to photooxygenation, as shown by the case of methylnaphthalene.[93] This may indicate that reaction with the superoxide anion (formed through reduction of oxygen

Table 4. Electron Transfer Photosensitized Oxygenation of Benzylic
Derivatives[a]

Substrate	Product (Quantum Yield)
PhMe	ArCHO (0.014)
$C_6H_2Me_4$	ArCHO (0.1)
$[PhCH_2]_2$	ArCHO (0.012)
$[Ph_2C(OH)]_2$	Ar_2CO (0.125)
$[PhCMe(OMe)]_2$	ArCOR(0.025), $ArCO_2Me$ (0.02)

Note: [a]In MeCN. Sensitizer DCN. See Ref. 94.

with the sensitizer radical anion) has a role, since it may itself induce deprotonation. Methods related to these processes, and using polymer-immobilized[99] or heterogeneous sensitizers,[100] may have a preparative significance.

3.11. Reactions Not Involving α-Fragmentation of the Benzylic Cation Radical

In only a few cases, formation of the benzyl radical by α-fragmentation of the cation radical is not the preferred process. Thus reactions occurring with pinacols involve O–H, not C–H deprotonation (Scheme 15). This is followed by fragmentation of the resulting radical so that the overall process is C–C fragmentation.[101] That this is not a primary process from the cation radical is shown by the fact that C–C fragmentation of the corresponding dimethyl ether cation radicals is quite inefficient. Thus, the faster O–H heterolytic deprotonation overcomes other thermodynamically more favored processes. Notice that this is due to the relative stability of benzylic cation radicals. Indeed, the more energized cation radicals of aliphatic alcohols suffer C–H and not O–H deprotonation (Eq. 8).[102]

$$CH_2OH\bullet + H^+ \leftarrow CH_3OH^{+\bullet} \rightarrow CH_3O\bullet + H^+ \qquad (8)$$

Several fragmentations of α,α'-hydroxyaminobibenzyls and related compounds have also been reported.[74,75]

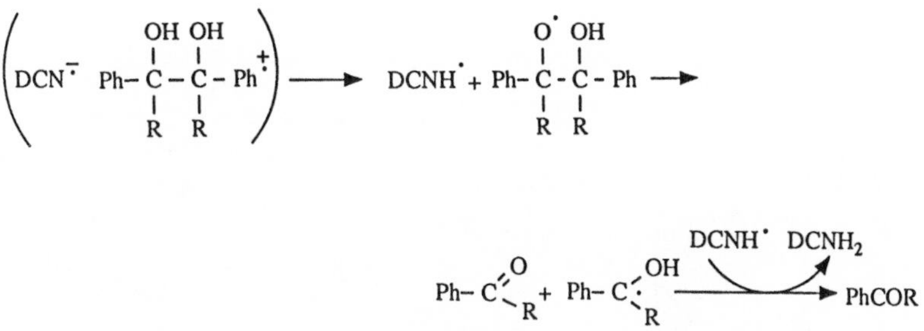

$$\left(\text{DCN}^{\overline{\cdot}} \quad \begin{array}{c} \text{OH} \;\; \text{OH} \\ | \quad\;\; | \\ \text{Ph-} \text{C} - \text{C} - \text{Ph}^{\overset{+}{\cdot}} \\ | \quad\;\; | \\ \text{R} \quad\; \text{R} \end{array} \right) \longrightarrow \quad \text{DCNH}^{\overset{\cdot}{}} + \begin{array}{c} \text{O}^{\overset{\cdot}{}}\; \text{OH} \\ | \quad\;\; | \\ \text{Ph-} \text{C} - \text{C} - \text{Ph} \\ | \quad\;\; | \\ \text{R} \quad\; \text{R} \end{array} \longrightarrow$$

$$\text{Ph-} \text{C}\underset{\text{R}}{\overset{\text{O}}{\diagdown}} + \text{Ph-} \text{C}\underset{\text{R}}{\overset{\text{OH}}{\diagdown}} \quad \xrightarrow{\;\; \text{DCNH}^{\cdot} \;\; \text{DCNH}_2 \;\;} \text{PhCOR}$$

Scheme 15.

4. REACTIONS VIA THE *GEMINATE* ION PAIR

4.1. Formation of a Tetracyclic Derivative in the DCN–Alkylbenzenes Reaction: Scope and Mechanism

The reaction of DCN with toluene is not well explained by the mechanism presented in Section 3, therefore it requires a specific discussion (see Scheme 16). In particular, the tetracyclic derivative **1** is not formed through a secondary photochemical reaction from a dihydro benzyl derivative (although such a cyclization does occur under proper conditions, although very slowly).[102] This reaction is limited to toluene and a few alkylbenzenes containing more than one α-hydrogen and carrying no substituent with an important electronic effect either at the α-position or on the ring; a bulky α-substituent is also detrimental. In all these cases the free energy for electron transfer is close to zero, thus we are on the borderline between exciplex and radical ion pair chemistry, a factor which is probably determining the reaction course. Deuteration experiments show that the first step is proton transfer to the DCN anion radical, not to the solvent as in the previous cases.[15] Proton transfer can occur either directly, as shown with α-deuterocumene, or via a proton transfer agent such as water in the case of deuterotoluene. In the first case, direct transfer is facilitated by the enhanced acidity of the cation radical (due to the weakness of the bond, pK = ca. −15). Apparently, the formed radical pair undergoes 3+3 coupling with formation of two new C–C bonds

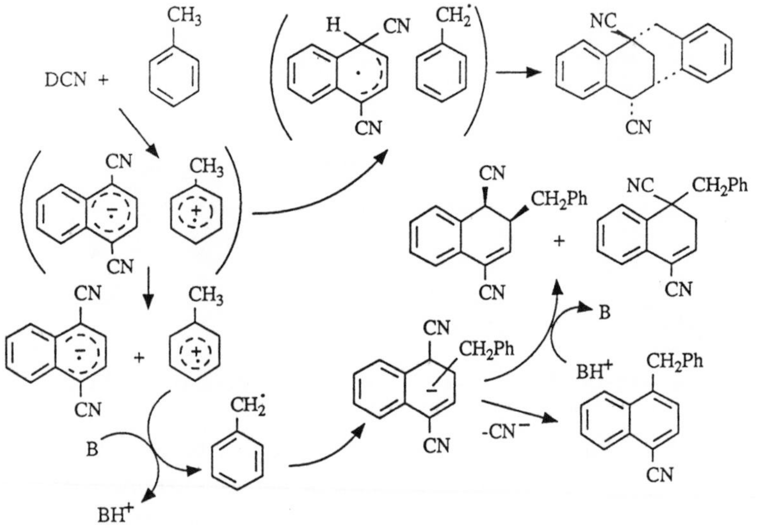

DCN +

Scheme 16.

and a second hydrogen transfer. Except in the cases with bulky substrates, the reaction is completely diastereoselective and the final hydrogen transfer step also occurs stereoselectively.[14,15]

Neither this type of radical–radical addition nor the selectivity have precedent. We believe that it is most reasonable to attribute this selectivity to a process occurring directly from the initial complex where interaction between the two π-systems is very strong. Thus, the reaction incorporates some of the features of typical exciplex chemistry (importance of π-interaction and conservation of the initial geometry of the complex in the final product) and some features of the ion radicals chemistry (the single steps through which the reaction is, perhaps arbitrarily, depicted, are typicals of ion radicals). There are many indications of the importance of the structure of the initial complex in controlling this reaction profile. Thus, sterically demanding groups severely diminish the stereoselectivity, and often the efficiency, of this type of cycloaddition.[103] Likewise, in the reaction with cymenes it is found that the isopropyl vs. methyl selectivity is the same as in all reactions involving deprotonation

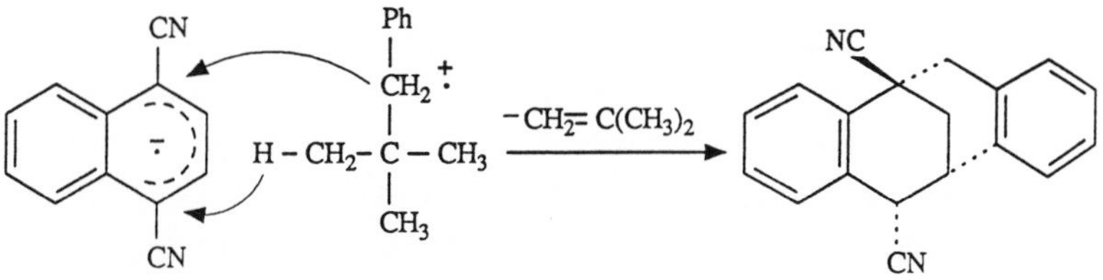

Scheme 17.

of cation radical (i.e. shows a strong preference for the methyl group) in the benzylation leading to products **2** and **4**. Exactly the opposite selectivity is found for products of type **1**.[77] Apparently, the key intermediate leading to **1** is a "tight complex," as one would expect for a reaction involving proton transfer within the *geminate* pair. In that case the isopropyl group is forced close to coplanarity, whereas proton transfer to the solvent takes place from a more loose complex (compare formulae **9** and **10** in Scheme 11). The same hypothesis also explains why reaction of DCN with cumene is more efficient ($\Phi_{lim} = 0.3$) than with toluene, whereas in other reactions via the radical cation generally the opposite is true. Obviously this type of product is not formed when the donor electrofugal group is different from a proton, with one interesting exception: the formation of the tetracyclic derivative from neopentylbenzene,[17] a fact explained by proton transfer from the *t*-butyl cation occurring concertedly with C–C bonds formation (Scheme 17).

4.2. Limitation and Competition with Exciplex Reactions

Apparently, the conditions for the occurrence of a complex cycloaddition process are quite stringent as emphasized by the fact that it is limited to small family of benzylic donors. Nevertheless, it has some interest because in several cases the process is quite efficient and it occurs with high selectivity leading to a single diastereoisomer starting from planar reagents (this selectivity is strongly diminished with bulky side chains, however).[103] Also, the cycloaddition reaction is a manifestation of the peculiar properties of *geminate* ion radical pairs.

We also note that when ion radical reactivity is slowed, exciplex chemistry (which is completely different) becomes competitive. Thus, in the reaction with acenaphthene several
products corresponding to the expected pattern for benzylation
(see Scheme 12) are formed. However, here product **11** (which
does not arise from secondary photocycloaddition from one of
the previously mentioned products) is also produced. This can
be explained by an initial [2+2] photocycloaddition between
the two naphthalene rings which precedes alkylation (Scheme
3). Thus, when the donor is a naphthalene rather than a benzene
derivative, the twofold effect of the diminished acidity of the
benzylic position and of the increased π-donor–acceptor interaction makes the exciplex path sufficiently important to compete
with the ion pair chemistry. Going further this way, i.e. toward
more positive ΔG_{et}, cycloaddition via exciplex completely dominates, as indicated in Section 2.

5. CONCLUSIONS

Photoinduced electron transfer is an area currently experiencing
very lively development. While several mechanistic generaliza-
tions are still to be proved or further substantiated, new prepa-
ratively appealing processes are beginning to arise. The future
will show whether this area will indeed contribute new per-
spectives of general interest to the area of organic chemistry
based on the still little explored chemistry of ion radicals.

The reaction between excited arenenitriles and benzylic donors
may appear now to be a curiosity and a rather exotic one in
view of the complex mechanistic hypothesis that one has to
consider. This is particularly true since the characteristics of
the process (several steps, involving different intermediates,
most of which too short-lived for detection) generally impedes
supplementing product studies with time-resolved measurements. However, we feel that the preparative appeal of these SET
processes is high and that the proposal of specific *geminate* ion
radical pair vs. free ion radical chemistry is relevant to a comprehensive understanding of electron transfer photochemistry.

ACKNOWLEDGMENTS

The work reported here has been supported by the National Research Council of Italy, the Italian Department of Education, and the European Community. The enthusiastic contribution of young co-workers whose names appear in the references is also gratefully acknowledged.

REFERENCES

1. Husyser, E. S. *Free-Radical Chain Reactions*; Interscience, New York, 1970.
2. Giese, B. *Radicals in Organic Synthesis: Formation of Carbon-Carbon Bonds*; Pergamon Press: Oxford, 1986.
3. Minisci, F. *Top. Curr. Chem.* **1976**, *62*, 1.
4. Baciocchi, E.; Crescenzi, M.; Fasella, E.; Mattioli, M. *J. Org. Chem.* **1992**, *57*, 4684; Baciocchi, E. *Acta Chem. Scand.* **1990**, *44*, 645; Baciocchi, E.; Bietti, M.; Mattioli, M. *J. Org. Chem.* **1993**, *58*, 7106.
5. Eberson, L. *Electron Transfer Reactions in Organic Chemistry*; Springer Verlag: Berlin, 1987.
6. Fox, M. A.; Chanon, M., Eds. *Photoinduced Electron Transfer*; Elsevier: Amsterdam, 1988.
7. Kavarnos, G. J.; Turro, N. J. *Chem. Rev.* **1986**, *86*, 401; Kavarnos, G. J. *Top. Curr. Chem.* **1991**, *156*, 21.
8. Mattay, J.; Vondenhof, M. *Top. Curr. Chem.* **1991**, *159*, 219.
9. Mariano, P. S.; Stavinoha, J. L. In *Synthetic Organic Photochemistry*; Plenum Press: New York, 1984, p. 145.
10. Albini, A.; Sulpizio, A. In Ref. 6, Vol. C, p. 88.
11. Albini, A.; Fasani, E.; Mella, M. *Top. Curr. Chem.* **1993**, *168*, 143.
12. Havinga, E.; Cornelisse, J. *Pure Appl. Chem.* **1976**, *47*, 1. Albini, A.; Bettinetti, G.; Fasani, E.; Minoli, G. *J. Chem. Soc., Perkin Trans. 1* **1978**, 299.
13. Maroulis, A. J.; Shigemitsu, J. C.; Arnold, D. R. *J. Am. Chem. Soc.* **1978**, *100*, 535; Neunteufel, R. A.; Arnold, D. R. *J. Am. Chem. Soc.* **1973**, *95*, 4080.
14. Albini, A.; Fasani, E.; Oberti, R. *J. Chem. Soc., Chem. Commun.* **1981**, 50. Albini, A.; Fasani, E.; Oberti, R. *Tetrahedron* **1982**, *38*, 1034.
15. Albini, A.; Fasani, E.; Sulpizio, A. *J. Am. Chem. Soc.* **1984**, *106*, 3562.
16. Albini, A.; Fasani, E.; Mella, M. *J. Am. Chem. Soc.* **1986**, *108*, 4119.
17. Sulpizio, A.; Albini, A.; d'Alessandro, A.; Fasani, E.; Pietra, S. *J. Am. Chem. Soc.* **1989**, *111*, 5773.
18. Freccero, M.; Fasani, E.; Albini, A. *J. Org. Chem.* **1993**, *58*, 1740.
19. Lewis, F. D.; Petisce, J. R. *Tetrahedron* **1986**, *42*, 6207.
20. Albini, A.; Spreti, S. *Tetrahedron* **1984**, *40*, 2975.
21. Yoshino, A.; Ohashi, M.; Yonezawa, T. *Chem. Commun.* **1971**, 97.
22. Yoshino, A.; Yamazaki, K.; Yonezawa, T.; Ohashi, M. *J. Chem. Soc., Perkin Trans. 1* **1975**, 735.
23. Ohashi, M.; Nakayama, N. *Chem. Lett.* **1976**, 1143.

24. Albini, A.; Fasani, E.; Faiardi, E. *J. Org. Chem.* **1987**, *52*, 155 and therein quoted references.
25. Wayner, D. D. M.; Dannenberg, J. J.; Griller, D. *Chem. Phys. Lett.* **1986**, *131*, 189.
26. Wayner, D. D. M.; McPhee, D. J.; Griller, D. *J. Am. Chem. Soc.* **1988**, *110*, 132.
27. Popielartz, R.; Arnold, D. R. *J. Am. Chem. Soc.* **1990**, *112*, 3068.
28. Saeva, F. D. *Top. Curr. Chem.* **1991**, *156*, 59.
29. Maslak, P. *Top. Curr. Chem.* **1993**, *168*, 1.
30. Albini, A.; Fasani, E.; d'Alessandro, N. *Coord. Chem. Rev.* **1993**, *125*, 269.
31. Wayner, D. D. M.; Parker, V. D. *Acc. Chem. Res.* **1993**, *26*, 287.
32. Nicholas, A. M. P.; Arnold, D. R. *Can. J. Chem.* **1982**, *60*, 2165.
33. (a) Parker, V. D. *J. Am. Chem. Soc.* **1992**, *114*, 7458; (b) Parker, V. D. *J. Am. Chem. Soc.* **1993**, *115*, 1201; (c) Trujillo, H. A.; Casado, M. C.; Astruc, D. *J. Chem. Soc., Chem. Commun.* **1995**, 7.
34. Albini, A.; Fasani, E.; Montessoro, E. *Z. Naturforsch* **1984**, *39b*, 1409.
35. Okamoto, A.; Snow, M. J.; Arnold, D. R. *Tetrahedron* **1986**, *42*, 6175.
36. Maslak, P.; Chapman, W. H. *Tetrahedron* **1990**, *46*, 2715.
37. Maslak, P.; Kula, J. *Tetrahedron Lett.* **1990**, *31*, 4969.
38. Maslak, P., Chapman, W. H. *J. Org. Chem.* **1990**, *55*, 6334.
39. Kochi, J. K.; Sankararaman, S.; Perrier, S. *J. Am. Chem. Soc.* **1989**, *111*, 6448.
40. Sankararaman, S.; Kochi, J. K. *J. Chem. Soc., Chem. Commun.* **1989**, 1800.
41. Arnold, D. R.; Maroulis, A. J. *J. Am. Chem. Soc.* **1976**, *98*, 5931.
42. Lamont, L. J.; Arnold, D. R. *Can. J. Chem.* **1990**, *68*, 391.
43. Arnold, D. R.; Lamont, L. J. *Can. J. Chem.* **1989**, *67*, 2119.
44. Arnold, D. R.; Lamont, L. J.; Perrot, A. L. *Can. J. Chem.* **1991**, *69*, 225.
45. Albini, A.; Mella, M. *Tetrahedron* **1986**, *42*, 6129.
46. Reichel, W. L.; Griffin, G. W.; Muller, A. J.; Das, P. K.; Ege, S. *Can. J. Chem.* **1984**, *62*, 424.
47. Davis, H. F.; Das, P. K.; Reichel, L. W.; Griffin, G. W. *J. Am. Chem. Soc.* **1984**, *106*, 6968.
48. Kellet, M. A.; Whitten, D. G. *J. Am. Chem. Soc.* **1986**, *108*, 175.
49. Lee, L. Y. C.; Ci, X.; Giannotti, C.; Whitten, D. G. *J. Am. Chem. Soc.* **1991**, *113*, 3893.
50. Libman, J. *J. Am. Chem. Soc.* **1975**, *97*, 4139.
51. d'Alessandro, N.; Albini, A.; Mariano, P. S. *J. Org. Chem.* **1993**, *58*, 937.
52. Mizuno, K.; Kamiyama, N.; Ichinose, N.; Otsuji, Y. *Tetrahedron* **1985**, *41*, 2207.
53. Ichinose, N.; Mizuno, K.; Yoshida, K.; Otsuji, Y. *Chem. Lett.* **1988**, 723.
54. Albini, A.; Arnold, D. R. *Can. J. Chem.* **1978**, *56*, 2985.
55. Clawson, P.; Lunn, P. M.; Whiting, D. A. *J. Chem. Soc., Perkin Trans. 1* **1990**, 153 and 159.
56. Mueller, F.; Mattay, J.; Steenken, S. *J. Org. Chem.* **1993**, *58*, 4462.
57. Ikeda, H.; Yamashita, Y.; Kabuto, C.; Miyashi, T. *Tetrahedron Lett.* **1988**, *29*, 5779.
58. Hasegawa, E.; Okada, K.; Ikeda, H.; Yamashita, Y.; Mukai, T. *J. Org. Chem.* **1991**, *56*, 2170.

59. Takayashi, Y.; Kochi, J. R. *Chem. Ber.* **1988**, *121*, 253.
60. Kadota, S.; Tsubono, K.; Makino, K.; Takeshita, M.; Kikuchi, T. *Tetrahedron Lett.* **1987**, *28*, 2857.
61. Nakabayashi, K.; Fujimura, S.; Yasua, M.; Shima, K. *Bull. Chem. Soc. Jpn.* **1989**, *62*, 2733.
62. Masnovi, J. M.; Kochi, J. K. *J. Am. Chem. Soc.* **1985**, *107*, 6781.
63. Mizuno, K.; Ikeda, M.; Otsuji, Y. *Tetrahedron Lett.* **1985**, *26*, 461.
64. Mizuno, K.; Nakanishi, K.; Otsuji, Y. *Chem. Lett.* **1988**, 1833.
65. Mizuno, K.; Terasaka, K.; Yasueda, M.; Otsuji, Y. *Chem. Lett.* **1988**, 145.
66. Eaton, D. F. *J. Am. Chem. Soc.* **1980**, *102*, 3280.
67. Lan, J. Y.; Schuster, G. B. *J. Am. Chem. Soc.* **1985**, *107*, 6710.
68. Lan, J. Y.; Schuster, G. B. *Tetrahedron Lett.* **1986**, *27*, 4261.
69. Dinnocenzo, J. P.; Farid, S.; Goodman, J. L.; Gould, I. R.; Todd, W. P.; Mattes, S. L. *J. Am. Chem. Soc.* **1989**, *111*, 8973.
70. Hasegawa, E.; Brumfield, M.; Mariano, P. S.; Yoon, U. C.; Kim, J. U. *J. Am. Chem. Soc.* **1988**, *110*, 8099.
71. Cermenati, L.; Freccero, M.; Venturello, P.; Albini, A. *J. Am. Chem. Soc.* **1995**, *117*, 7869.
72. Maslak, P.; Kula, J.; Chateauneuf, J. E. *J. Am. Chem. Soc.* **1991**, *113*, 2304.
73. Yoon, U. C.; Mariano, P. S. *Acc. Chem. Res.* **1992**, *25*, 233.
74. Ci, X.; Whitten, D. G. *J. Am. Chem. Soc.* **1987**, *109*, 7215.
75. Ci, X.; Kellet, M. A.; Whitten, D. G. *J. Am. Chem. Soc.* **1991**, *113*, 3893.
76. Baciocchi, E.; Mandolini, L.; Rol, C. *J. Org. Chem.* **1980**, *45*, 3906.
77. Albini, A.; Sulpizio, A. *J. Org. Chem.* **1989**, *54*, 2147.
78. Sulpizio, A.; Mella, M.; Albini, A. *Tetrahedron* **1989**, *45*, 7545.
79. Baciocchi, E.; Del Giacco, T.; Rol, C.; Sebastiani, G. V. *Tetrahedron Lett.* **1985**, 541.
80. Wagner, P. J.; Truman, R. J.; Puchalski, A. E.; Wake, R. *J. Am. Chem. Soc.* **1986**, *108*, 7277.
81. Onopchenko, A.; Schulz, G. D.; Seekircher, R. *J. Org. Chem.* **1972**, *37*, 1414.
82. Arnold, D. R.; Du, X.; Chen, J. *Can. J. Chem.* **1995**, *73*, 307.
83. Perrott, A. L.; Arnold, D. R. *Can. J. Chem.* **1992**, *70*, 272.
84. Baciocchi, E.; Bernini, R.; Lanzalunga, O. *J. Chem. Soc., Chem. Commun.* **1993**, 1691.
85. Ohashi, M.; Aoyagi, N.; Yamada, S. *J. Chem. Soc., Perkin Trans. 1* **1990**, 1335.
86. Mella, M.; Fagnoni, M.; Albini, A. *J. Org. Chem.* **1994**, *59*, 5614.
87. Fasani, E.; d'Alessandro, N.; Albini, A.; Mariano, P. S. *J. Org. Chem.* **1994**, *59*, 829.
88. d'Alessandro, N.; Mella, M.; Fasani, E.; Toma, L.; Albini, A. *Tetrahedron* **1991**, *47*, 5043.
89. (a) Bardi, L.; Fasani, E.; Albini, A. *J. Chem. Soc., Perkin Trans. 1* **1994**, 545; (b) Boggeri, E.; Fasani, E.; Mella, M.; Albini, A. *J. Chem. Soc., Perkin Trans. 2* **1991**, 2097.
90. Hasegawa, E.; Brumfield, M. A.; Mariano, P. S.; Yoon, U. C. *J. Org. Chem.* **1988**, *53*, 5435.

91. Jeon, Y. T.; Lee, C. P.; Mariano, P. S. *J. Am. Chem. Soc.* **1991**, *113*, 8847.
92. Fasani, E.; Mella, M.; Albini, A. *J. Chem. Soc., Perkin Trans. 2* **1995**, 449.
93. Albini, A.; Spreti, S. *Z. Naturforsch.* **1986**, *41b*, 1286.
94. Albini, A.; Spreti, S. *J. Chem. Soc., Perkin Trans. 2* **1987**, 1175.
95. Santamaria, J.; Ouchabane, R. *Tetrahedron* **1986**, *42*, 5559.
96. Juillard, M.; Chanon, M. *Bull. Soc. Chim. Fr.* **1992**, *129*, 242.
97. Santamaria, J.; Jroundi, R. *Tetrahedron Lett.* **1991**, *34*, 4291.
98. Tamai, T.; Mizuno, K.; Hashida, I.; Otsuiji, Y. *Chem. Lett.* **1982**, 781.
99. Juillard, M.; Legris, C.; Chanon, M. *J. Photochem. Photobiol., A: Chem.* **1991**, *61*, 137.
100. Baciocchi E.; Rol, C.; Rosato, G. C.; Sebastiani, G. V. *J. Chem. Soc., Chem. Commun.* **1992**, 59.
101. Albini, A.; Mella, M. *Tetrahedron* **1986**, *42*, 6219.
102. Fagnoni M.; Vanossi, M.; Mella, M.; Albini, A. *Tetrahedron* **1996**, *52*, 1785.
103. d'Alessandro, N.; Fasani, E.; Mella, M.; Albini, A. *J. Chem. Soc., Perkin Trans. 2* **1991**, 1977.

APPLICATIONS OF PHOTOINDUCED ELECTRON TRANSFER PROCESSES TO KETONE, ALDEHYDE, AND ESTER DERIVATIVES IN ORGANIC SYNTHESIS

Janine Cossy and Jean-Pierre Pete

Advances in Electron Transfer Chemistry
Volume 5, pages 141–195.
Copyright © 1996 by JAI Press Inc.
All rights of reproduction in any form reserved.
ISBN: 0-7623-0062-0

1. INTRODUCTION

Electron transfer reactions have been extensively studied in chemistry[1] and the photochemical approach to reactions of this type has become familiar to most organic chemists as the result of a better understanding of the primary processes involved. Recognition of charge transfer in photochemical reactions and direct characterization and determination of kinetic and thermodynamic properties of radical ion intermediates have induced a renewed interest in applications of photochemical reactions to organic synthesis.[2]

Photoinduced electron transfer (PET) processes involve a donor (D), an acceptor (A) and an electronic excitation step (Eq. 1).

$$D + A \xrightarrow{h\nu} D^{\bullet+} + A^{\bullet-} \rightarrow Products \tag{1}$$

Production of radical ions ($D^{\bullet+}$) and ($A^{\bullet-}$) depends on the oxidation potential $E_{ox;1/2}(D)$, and the reduction potential $E_{red;1/2}(A)$ of the starting molecules and on the electronic excitation energy E_{oo}, according to the simple relationship shown in Eq. 2, where the coulombic interaction term, in polar solvents such as acetonitrile, can be neglected in a first approximation.[3]

$$\Delta G_{set} = E_{ox;1/2}(D) - E_{red;1/2}(A) - \Delta E_{oo} + \Delta E_c \tag{2}$$

When PET is thermodynamically favorable ($\Delta G < 0$), electron transfer proceeds close to a diffusion-controlled rate. However, the fate of the formed radical ion pair depends strongly on the nature of the solvent and on the rate of the reverse electron transfer to molecules (A) and (B) in their ground state. Use of polar solvents favors formation of solvent-separated ion pairs and limits this reverse electron transfer process. Furthermore the selective transformation of one of the radical ion often promotes efficient chemical transformations.

PET processes between carbonyl derivatives (A) and amines (D) have received considerable attention since the pioneering studies on photoreduction of aromatic ketones with tertiary amines. Numerous developments have appeared during the last 20 years. The purpose of this review is to consider recent applications of PET processes of carbonyl and ester groups and to discuss the influence of the chemical environment on the scope of the reactions and their synthetic development. Furthermore, several reactions such as the photolysis of sulfonyl derivatives, which have been reexamined in connection with electron transfer processes, will also be described. Finally, where possible, a comparison of the photochemical process with similar reactions carried out in the ground state will be made.

2. PHOTOREDUCTION OF SULFONATES AND SULFONAMIDES

Arenesulfonyl derivatives are frequently employed in organic synthesis to activate hydroxyl groups in nucleophilic substitution reactions or to protect primary and secondary amines. The interest in arenesulfonyl substituents as protective groups for unactivated aliphatic alcohols and amines has been recognized[5] and their removal by photolysis has been described.[6]

The photolysis of *N*-alkyl arenesulfonamides or alkyltosylates, when carried out in the presence of sodium borohydride,[7] hydrazine, or in a basic medium affords amines or alcohols in high chemical and quantum yields. In the presence of bases, quenching of the fluorescence of arenesulfonates can be observed.[8] These observations indicate that a PET process might be involved during the photolysis. Indeed when electron-donating aromatics are present in the reaction mixture either in the starting sulfonamide or as an additive, PET promoted processes lead to high-yielding detosylation.[9,10]

With triethylamine as the electron-donating reagent in acetonitrile, the photoinduced desulfonation reaction is still observed (Scheme 1). Direct evidence for electron transfer

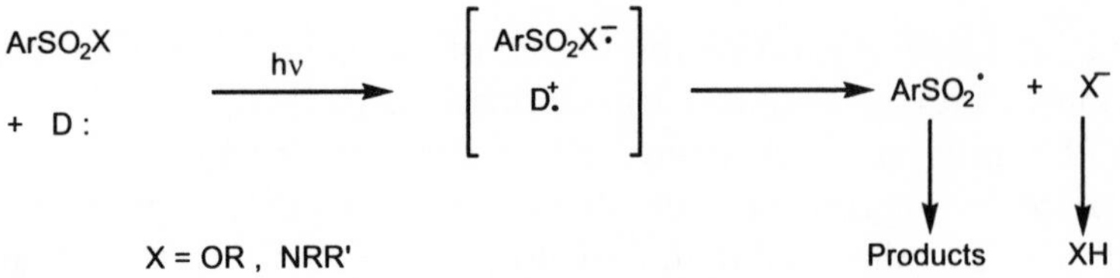

Scheme 1.

processes was obtained by examining the flash photolysis of tosylates[11] and *p*-toluenesulfonamides[12] in the presence of an amine donor and detecting the $ArSO_2$ radical immediately after the laser pulse.

The PET expulsion of tosyl groups is closely related to the process induced by reduction by metals in ammonia or hex-

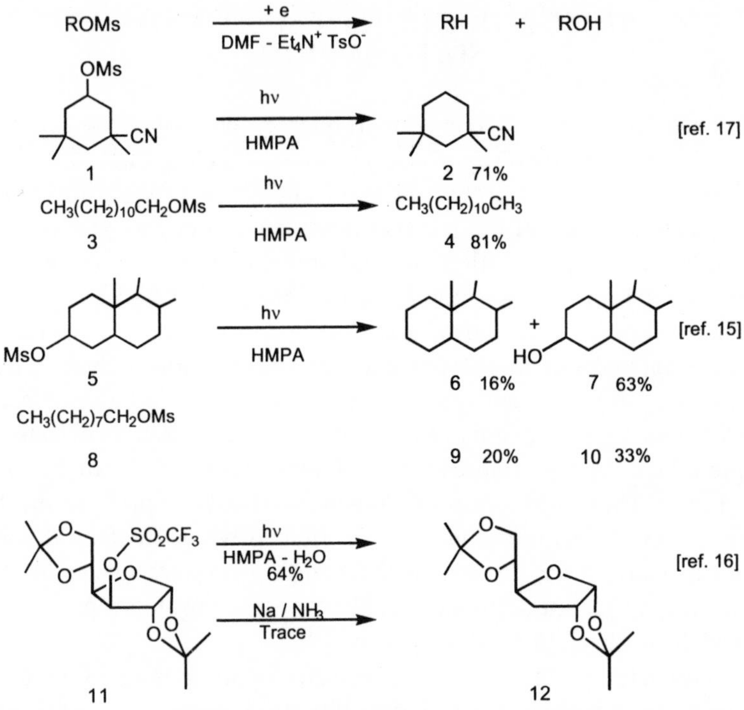

Scheme 2.

amethylphosphotriamide (HMPA)[13] and electroreduction.[14] Observation of a reduction of alkyl mesylates with formation of a mixture of alcohols and alkanes led to the examination of the photoreduction of alkyl mesylates[15] and triflates[16] in a HMPA–H_2O mixture (Scheme 2). As in the electrochemical process,[17] mixtures of alcohols and alkanes are isolated.

An increase in the electron deficiency of the sulfonates, by replacement of a mesyl by a trifluoromethanesulfonyl group, induces an increase in the proportion of alkanes versus alcohols in the product mixture. Thus deoxysugars can be obtained in good yield, either by photolysis of the triflate derivatives in aqueous HMPA or reduction by sodium in liquid ammonia.[16]

The detosylation reactions of arenesulfonates and arenesulfonamides do not always require PET processes. When the photolysis is carried out in solvents such as Et_2O or MeOH, the alcohol can be recovered in high yields from arenesulfonates while a mixture of amine and ammonium tosylate is usually obtained from tosylamides.[18] A mechanistic study of the reaction indicated that the bond initially cleaved is different in sulfonates and sulfonamides (Scheme 3).[8,19]

From a preparative point of view, photolysis of tosylates in the presence of a small amount of base provides an efficient way to regenerate cleanly and with high yield the corresponding alcohols. As compared with a direct photohydrolysis, regenera-

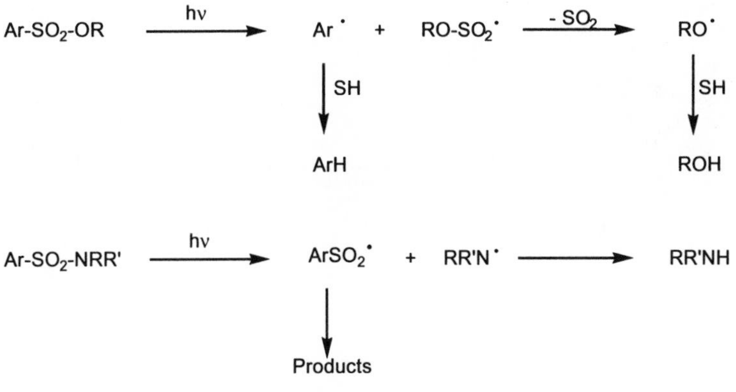

$$Ar\text{-}SO_2\text{-}OR \xrightarrow{h\nu} Ar^{\bullet} + RO\text{-}SO_2^{\bullet} \xrightarrow{-SO_2} RO^{\bullet}$$

$$\downarrow SH \qquad\qquad\qquad\qquad \downarrow SH$$

$$ArH \qquad\qquad\qquad\qquad\qquad ROH$$

$$Ar\text{-}SO_2\text{-}NRR' \xrightarrow{h\nu} ArSO_2^{\bullet} + RR'N^{\bullet} \longrightarrow RR'NH$$

$$\downarrow$$

$$\text{Products}$$

Scheme 3.

tion of alcohols and amines by means of a PET process present the advantage of irradiation at longer wavelengths, provided that the electron donor strongly absorbs UV light. This deprotection method, which was applied efficiently to the regeneration

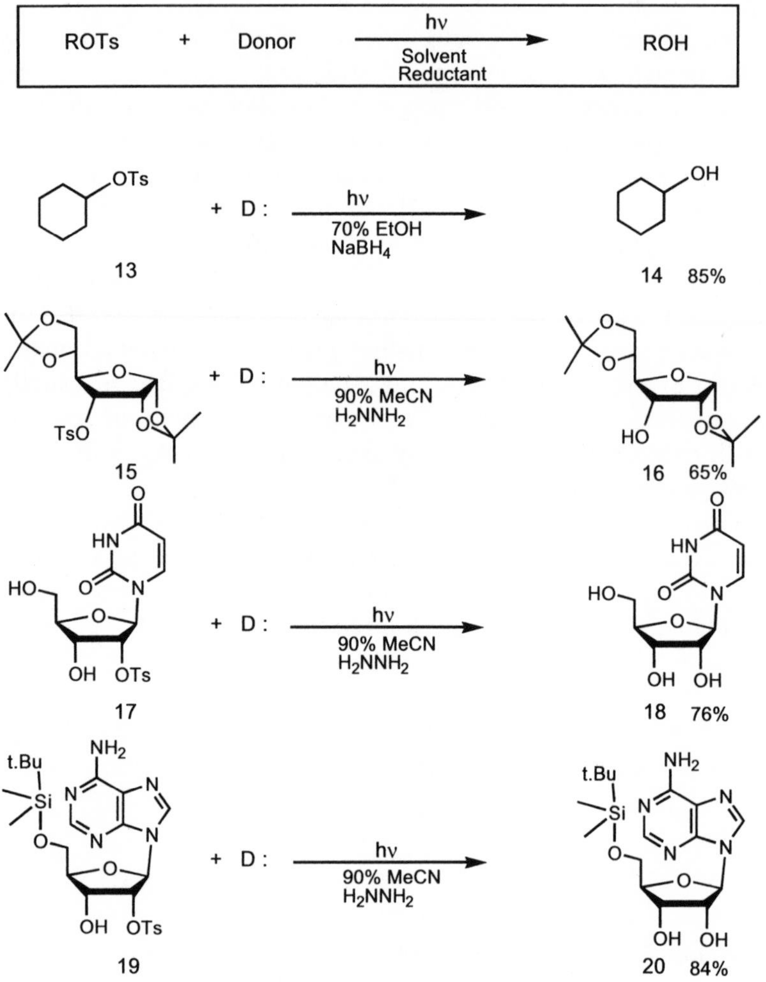

D : = Donor = (4,8-dimethoxynaphthyl)propionic acid = DMNP

Scheme 4.

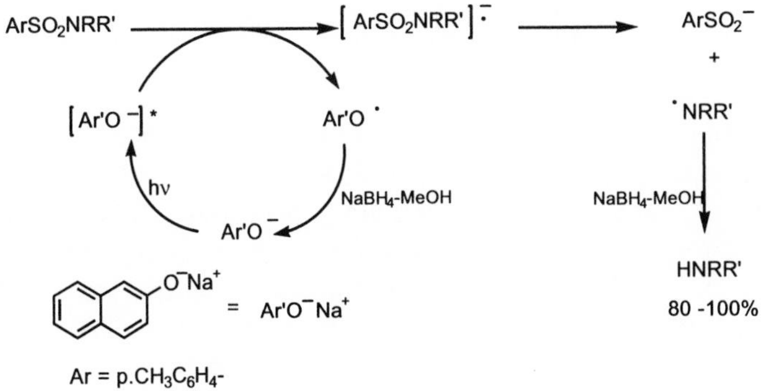

Scheme 5.

of hydroxyl groups in sugar **16** or nucleosides **18** and **20** from the corresponding sulfonates **15**, **17**, and **19**, respectively,[20] can be very useful for the selective deprotection of alcohols from their tosylates in multiprotected polyhydroxyl groups (Scheme 4). It has also been applied successfully to a selective deprotection of lysine peptides.[9,10]

Furthermore, the PET process can be made catalytic in electron donors when small quantities of sodium β-naphtholate and a large excess of sodium borohydride are used. Dialkylamines can thus be regenerated almost quantitatively from their tosylamides (Scheme 5).[21]

Finally, the 4-(4,8-dimethoxynaphthylmethyl)benzenesulfonyl group, which has the capability of undergoing an efficient intramolecular PET process and almost quantitative photohydrolysis has been proposed as a protecting group for the amine function (Scheme 6).[22]

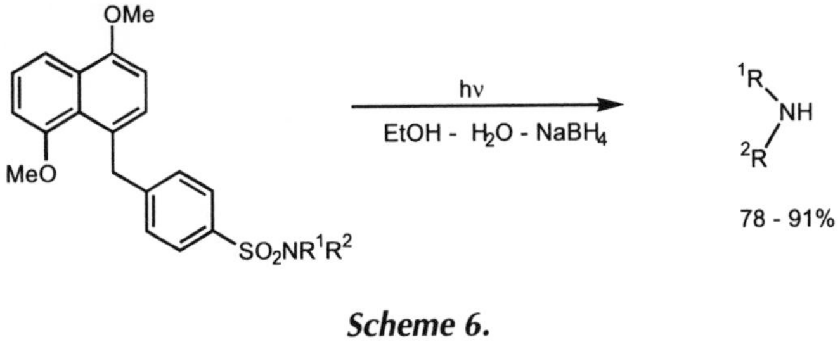

Scheme 6.

3. PHOTOREDUCTION OF ESTERS

In the absence of activating groups, reduction of carboxylic esters requires strong reducing conditions. Until recently, and although the photoreactivity of esters as a functional group has
been well documented,[23] satisfactory conditions for preparative
photodeoxygenation of carboxylic esters were still unknown because of their highly negative reduction potential. However, in
connection with a general interest in the use of HMPA,[24] it was
reported that cholestane could be produced in small amounts
during the photolysis of the corresponding 3β-acetoxy derivative
in pure HMPA (Scheme 7).[25]

It was later recognized that the reaction could be made very
efficient and of preparative value, provided that small amounts
of water or of a protonic species are introduced into the reaction
mixture.[26] Under these conditions, alkanes R'H could be isolated
in high chemical and convenient quantum yields from simple
aliphatic esters.

The mechanism for the process shown in Scheme 7 indicates
an electron transfer between excited HMPA* and the carboxylic
ester in its ground state with formation of a radical ion pair.[27]
It was proposed that, at least for acetates, the presence of water
is essential to allow protonation of the radical anion and to
prevent the reverse electron transfer to regenerate HMPA and
ester in their ground state. Subsequently, fragmentation of the
protonated radical leads to a radical R'. Finally, abstraction of
a hydrogen from HMPA leads to the deoxygenated compound
R'–H.

By laser flash photolysis, it was later determined that excitation of HMPA at 248 nm produces solvated electrons as the
reducing species.[28,29] The fate of HMPA in the reaction is not

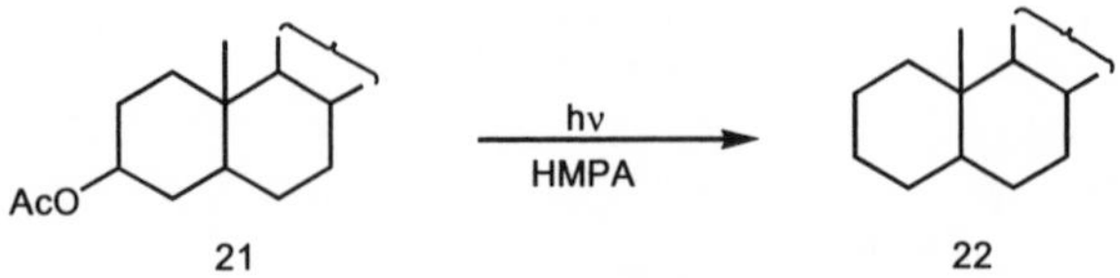

Scheme 7.

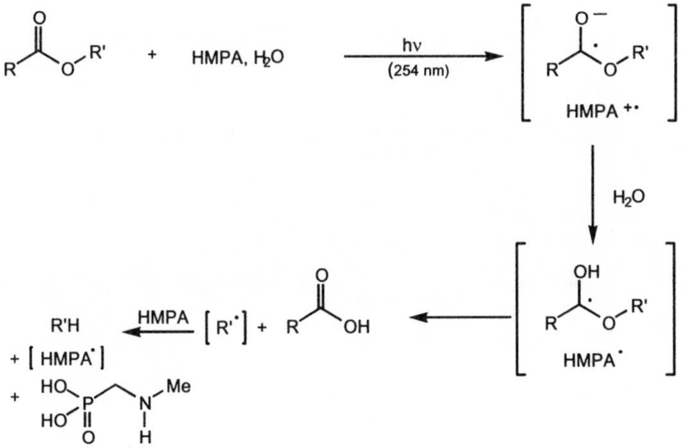

Scheme 8.

yet well-defined, but it has been shown by use of labeling techniques that HMPA is the hydrogen source for the ultimate conversion of the radical to the alkane.

Characterization of the by-products derived from HMPA has proved to be very difficult due to their high dilution in the reaction mixture, their high solubility in water, and to simultaneous photodecomposition of HMPA. Photolysis of HMPA produces hydrogen or a mixture of H_2, HD, and D_2 if small amounts of D_2O are introduced in the reaction mixture. The only product derived from HMPA which could be completely characterized indicated that a hydrolytic process was involved.[27,30] The lowering of chemical yields observed when double bonds are present in the starting material and for reactions occurring in the presence of cyclohexene indicate that coupling products between the HMPA radical and the substrate or cyclohexene have been formed (Scheme 8).[31]

Deoxygenation of alcohols through photolysis of their carboxylic esters and especially their acetates is a general process as illustrated by the examples given in Table 1. For acetates, the photolysis in HMPA gives the corresponding alkanes in high yields independent of the nature (primary, secondary, or tertiary) of the starting alcohol. However the nature of the carboxylic

Table 1. Photoreduction of Esters in HMPA

R^1	R	Conditions	$R'{-}H(\%)^b$	$R'{-}OH(\%)$
CH_3	α-H	HMPA	traces	—
CH_3	α-H	HMPA H_2O^b	84	traces
CH_3	β-methyl	HMPA H_2O	67	—
CH_3	α-methyl	HMPA H_2O	70	—
H	α-H	HMPA	52	42^c
H	α-H	HMPA H_2O	79	19^c
C_6H_5	α-H	HMPA	26	30^c
	α-H	HMPA H_2O	52	36^c

Notes: [a] A quantum yield φ = 0,03 was measured.
[b] The chemical yield is based on unrecovered ester.
[c] α-H

ester residue does have some influence on the reaction and the best yields are usually obtained from acetates. Interestingly, photohydrolysis products are formed competitively when less hindered formates, benzoates, or phenylacetates are used. Although a few examples of photohydrolysis processes have already been described,[32] more complex mechanisms involving hydrogen abstraction by the ketyl radical intermediate can also be proposed.[33] If HMPA cannot be replaced easily by other donors in the photoreduction of aliphatic esters, use of more reducible esters such as aromatic esters might allow a photoinduced electron transfer even in the absence of HMPA. In principle, replacement of the acetyl group in aliphatic acetates by acyl substituents bearing strong electron-withdrawing groups should

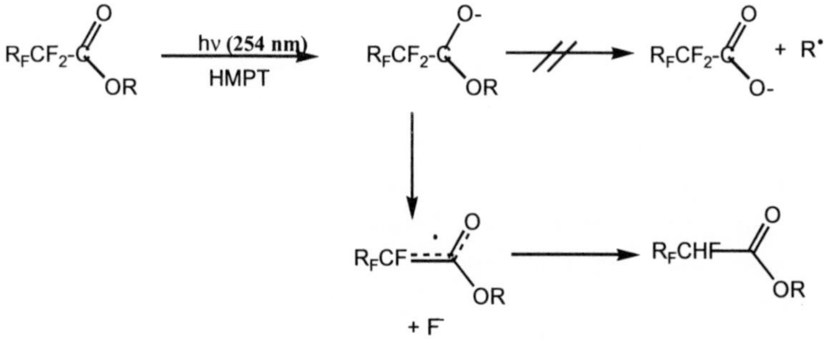

Scheme 9.

have the same effect on their reduction potential as that of aromatic groups. For this reason, trifluoroacetyl derivatives have received some attention. Replacement of aliphatic esters by perfluoroesters indeed has a dramatic effect on the reduction process. The efficiency of the photoinduced electron transfer was found to be far higher than for the corresponding acetates and the reverse electron transfer is no longer competitive, in the ion pair intermediate, with the fragmentation processes. However, expulsion of a fluoride anion is now preferred to the previous C–O bond cleavage, as shown in Scheme 9 and in Table 2, and a mixture of partially defluorinated esters is obtained.[34]

Table 2. Photoreduction of Fluoroesters in HMPA

R_F–CF_2–CO_2R		Conv.	$R_F CHFCO_2R$	$R_F CH_2 CO_2 R$	
RF	R	%	%	%	RH
F	(5α) Cholestanyl	55	53	4	1
	(5α) Cholestanyl	91	26	12	20
CF_3	(5α) Cholestanyl	55	75	12	1
CF_3	(5α) Cholestanyl	100	13	59	9
C_2F_5	Menthyl	67	63	—	—
n-C_5H_{11}	n-Heptyl	71	46	1[a]	—
n-C_7F_{15}	n-Heptyl	69	48	3.5[a]	—

Note: [a]Alkane RH is not formed in significant amounts. However the product $R'_F CF{=}CH{-}CO_2R$ of elimination of HF is isolated (~ 7%).

Although efforts to replace HMPA by other reducing agents have not been that successful, a general and convenient method for selective deoxygenation of secondary alcohols via their benzoates, by using an intermolecular PET from N-methylcarbazole (NMC) as the donor, has recently been described. High yields were claimed for irradiations of alkylbenzoates, or better m-trifluorobenzoates, in a THF–water mixture or isopropanol–water mixture (10:1) solution. From the free energy a near diffusion-controlled rate was deduced for quenching of NMC* fluorescence by the starting ester.[35] During the reaction, NMC was not consumed as can be seen in the following sequence (Scheme 10):

An illustration of an intramolecular PET from an electron-rich aromatic ring to a benzoate by irradiation at 254 nm in methanol as the solvent is given in Scheme 11. The radical ion pair is then transformed to the observed fragmentation and reduction products.[36] Interestingly, no reaction was detected at 300 nm in methanol, even though ethylbenzoate was found to quench the fluorescence of p-N,N-dimethyltoluidine.

The proposed mechanism involving PET for the photolysis of esters indicates that similar fragmentation processes of radical anions or of the corresponding protonated intermediates should

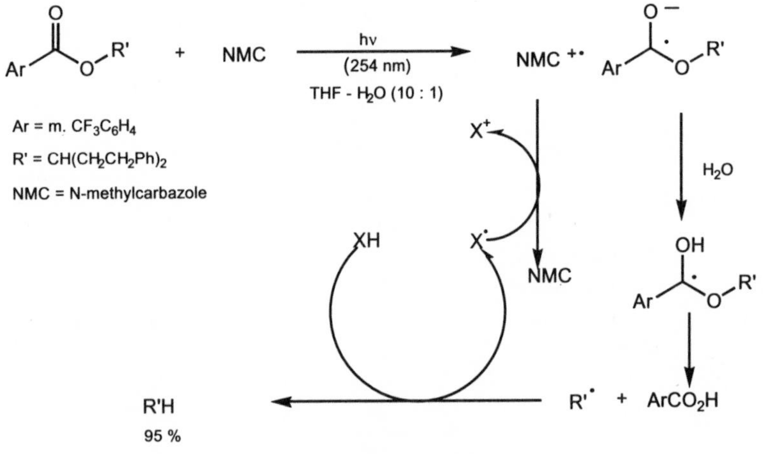

Scheme 10.

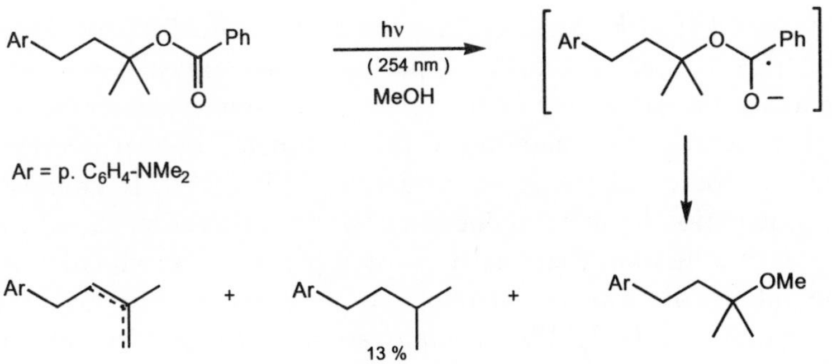

Ar = p. C6H4-NMe2

13 %

Scheme 11.

occur in other reactions, independent of the manner in which they are produced. However, although reduction of esters by metals was known to give alcohols (in the Bouveault et Blanc reaction)[37] or acyloins,[38] there were at that time no specific reports of an efficient cleavage of such radical anions. It has since appeared that reduction of esters by metals in amines[39,40] or esters and lactones in HMPA[41] in more dilute solutions and in the presence of a proton source indeed gives the same fragmentation process according to Scheme 12.

As compared with their photochemical reactions, reduction of carboxylic esters by metals differs in several ways. In the

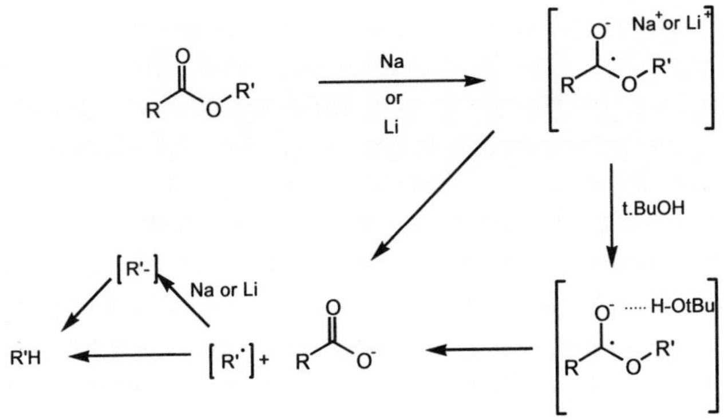

Scheme 12.

ion pair (RCO$_2$R'$^{\bullet-}$–HMPA$^{\bullet+}$) produced in the PET reaction, water is needed to transfer a proton to the radical anion and decrease the efficiency of the reverse electron transfer process. Subsequently, fragmentation of the protonated radical intermediate is possible because of the acidity of HMPA$^{\bullet+}$. In contrast, fragmentation by metal reduction seems to proceed via a radical anion in a thermodynamically favored process.[42] Protonation of the intermediate by an alcohol has been reported to be very unfavorable.[43] In HMPA, complexation of cations by solvent molecules might favor hydrogen bonding between the intermediate and the hydroxyl groups of the solvent. Such associations have been observed during a study of picosecond dynamics of the ion pair produced during the photoreduction of benzophenone by tertiary amines,[44] and with the radical anion derived from p-cyanonitrobenzene in a mixture of HMPA and methanol.[45] Furthermore, from kinetic studies of the fragmentation of the radical anion, it indeed appears that this intermediate is stabilized in protic solvents.[46] Although the rates of cleavage seem to be proportional to the bond dissociation energy of the O–R' bond, it has been proposed that an increase in the steric hindrance of the hydrogen-bonded radical anion intermediates might also favor the fragmentation process by steric relaxation.[41b]

Formation of alcohols, which is often an important side reaction during the photolysis of esters and especially benzoates in HMPA, might be the result of photohydrolysis. For the reduction of esters by metals, alcohol formation is due to the presence in the reaction mixture of metal amides.[40] Thus, in the presence of t-butanol as a hindered alcohol, these metal amides are neutralized and the proportion of alcohol formed decreases. Reaction of t-butylate anions is slow enough to be neglected under these reaction conditions. However, the strong basic conditions in the reduction by metals make this reaction less attractive than the photoreduction process for applications in the multistep syntheses of polyfunctional molecules.

Derivatives of carbonic acid, which are commonly used in organic synthesis as protective groups[47] or reaction intermediates, might be good candidates for photoinduced reduction of

alkoxy groups. In the ground state, decomposition of these derivatives by stannyl hydrides has been developed as an important
process for deoxygenation of alcohols through their *N,N*-di-
methylthiocarbamates.[39,48,49] However, photoreduction of car-
bonates, thiocarbonates, dithiocarbonates, and thiocarbamates in
HMPA led to no better yields than with acetates in the deoxygenation sequence of alcohol derivatives by PET (Scheme 13
and Table 3).[50]

Usually, PET processes are preferred to other fragmentation
processes in HMPA, but only dialkylthiocarbamates give satisfactory yields of R'–H. Again a very good parallel can be drawn
between the PET reaction of carbonic acid derivatives and their
reduction by dissolving metals in primary amines or HMPA.[39]

Deoxygenation of alcohols is a very important reaction in the
synthesis of natural products and there is a need for improved
performance methods.[39] Among the available methods, photochemical deoxygenation of aliphatic esters presents several interesting features: its simplicity, use of a neutral reaction
mixture, control of the concentration of reducing agent by the
flux of photons of the light source, and, above all, the radical
nature of the intermediate. Intermediacy of a radical can be
useful in the selective deoxygenation of polyfunctional mole-

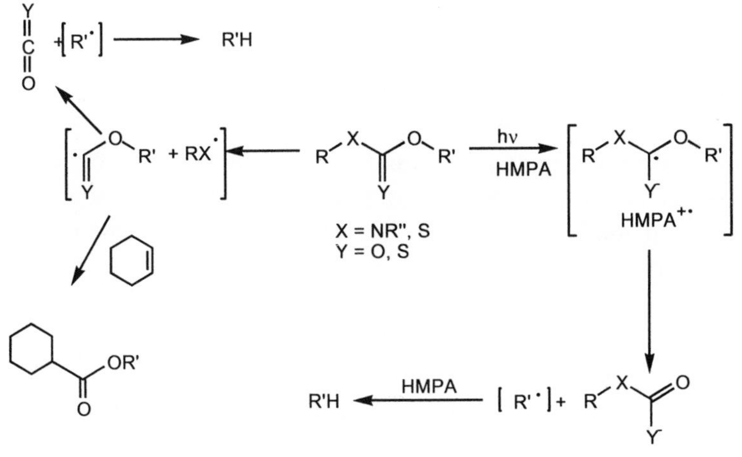

Scheme 13.

Table 3. Photoreduction of Carbonic Acid Derivatives

X	Y	R	Conditions	Conversion %	R'–H (%)[b]	R'OH (%)[a]	HCO_2R (%)
N–C_6H_5	O	CH_3	i-PrOH	55	20	5	25
			HMPA	77	47	2	14
			HMPA H_2O (95-5)	57	37	5	15
N–C_6H_5	S	H	i-PrOH	21	2	2	6
			HMPA	78	71	10	1
			HMPA H_2O (95-5)	48	52	15	12
N–CH_3	S	CH_3	HMPA H_2O (95-5)	66	65	12	4
S	S	CH_3	HMPA H_2O (95-5)	48	18	51	1
O	O	CH_3	HMPA H_2O (95-5)	59	6	14	—

Notes: [a]Starting material (R = 3β-Cholestanyl) (2×10^{-2} M $\times$ L^{-1}) was irradiated for 12 h in all cases.
[b]Isolated yields from transformed material.

cules, especially when molecular rearrangements and side reactions can be expected under polar conditions.

Although photoreduction of esters in HMPA is compatible with
many functional groups such as alcohols, ethers, ketals, or alkenes,
it cannot be carried out in the presence of the more readily reduced carbonyl and enone groups or chloro, bromo, and iodo
compounds.[27b] Under these conditions, the PET approach has
been shown to be particularly appropriate for the production of
deoxysugars present in many natural products of great biological
interest, as summarized in Table 4.[51]

The deoxygenation is general and proceeds at every position
of hexoses except at the anomeric carbon where a hydrolytic
process is favored over the expected reduction. It should also
be noted that satisfactory yields can be obtained when unpro-
tected alcohols, silylethers, or ketal groups are present. Furthermore, the deoxygenation of diesters is still of preparative value
even if small amounts of monoesters arise from the deoxygenation of either of the ester groups.

The nonionic nature of the process, and the very mild conditions of the reaction, make the photoreduction in HMPA very
useful, especially when epimerization of vicinal centers or re-

Table 4.

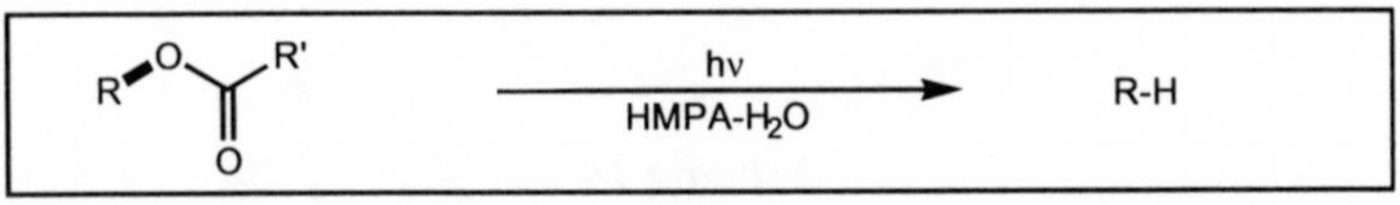

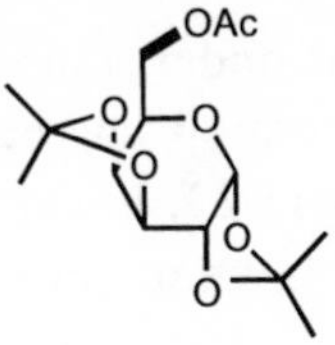

R-O-C(=O)-R' →(hv / HMPA-H₂O)→ R-H

85% [51a]

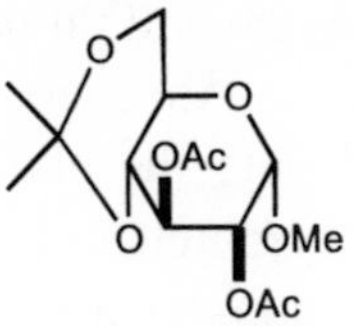

50% [51b]

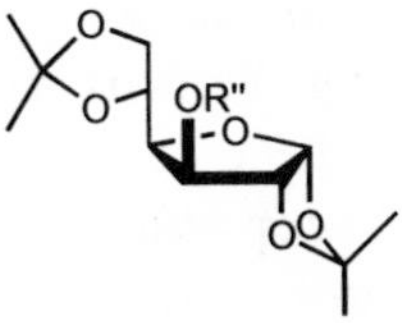

R"O = OAc   65 % [a] [51a]
Pivaloyl   75 % [51b]

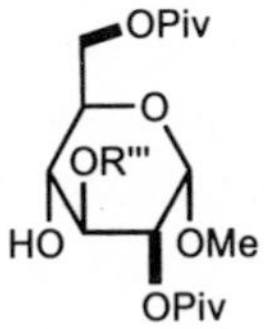

R''' = H   25 % [30]
Si(tBu)Me₂   42 % [51e]

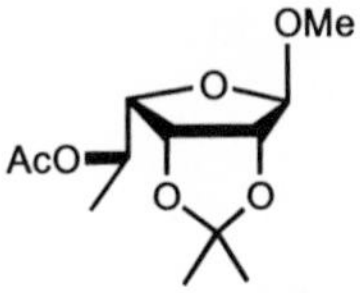

78% [51a]

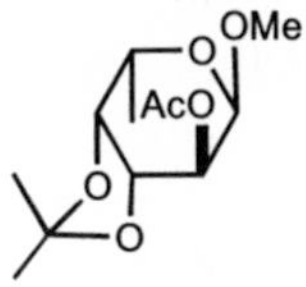

60% [51a]

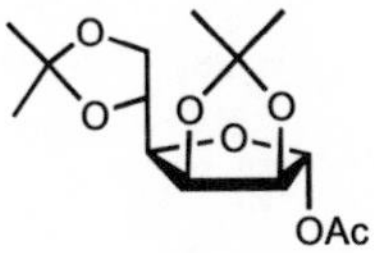

(b)

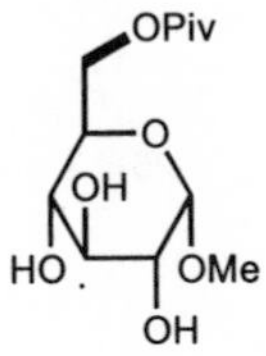

47% [51d]

Notes: [a]The corresponding alcohol is isolated (yield = 30%).
[b]The only product (yield = 30%) has a hydroxyl group on the anomeric carbon.

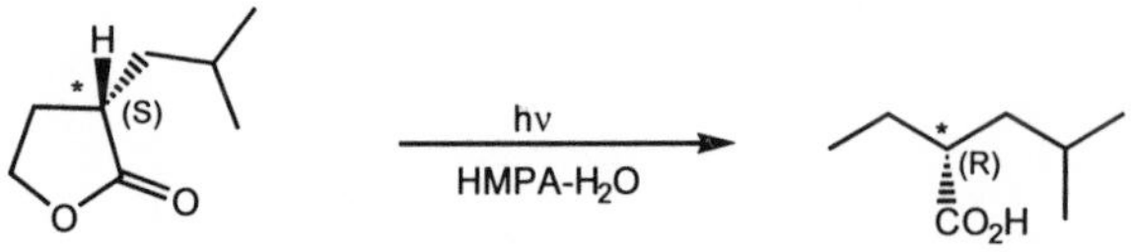

23 24

Scheme 14.

arrangements might be expected as side reactions under standard conditions. Absence of enolization and epimerization has been noted during the photoreduction of chiral lactone **23**, having a single asymmetric center in the α-position. As shown in Scheme 14, this conservation of the configuration during the reduction process was used to establish an absolute configuration by a chemical correlation with a known chiral compound **24**.[52]

The radical nature of the intermediate during the deoxygenation of alcohols, through the photoreduction of the corresponding esters, can also be advantageous in multistep syntheses of polyfunctional or bridge molecules. To prevent cationic rearrangements very common in bicyclic systems, the photoreduction of esters in HMPA was used with success for an unambiguous synthesis of tricyclic alkanes **28–30** from the corresponding acetates **25–27**, respectively (Scheme 15).[53]

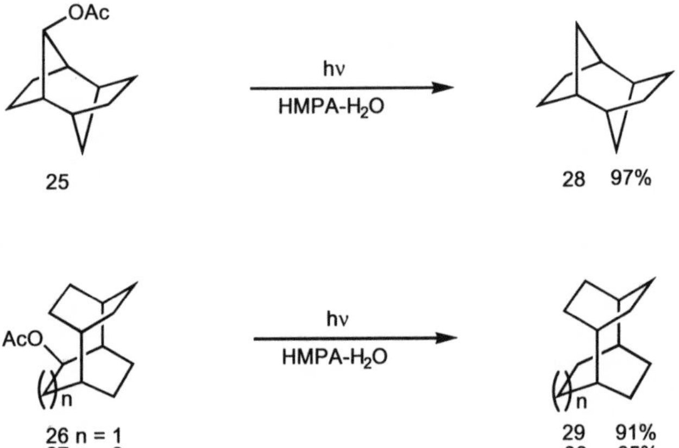

25 28 97%

26 n = 1
27 n = 2

29 91%
30 65%

Scheme 15.

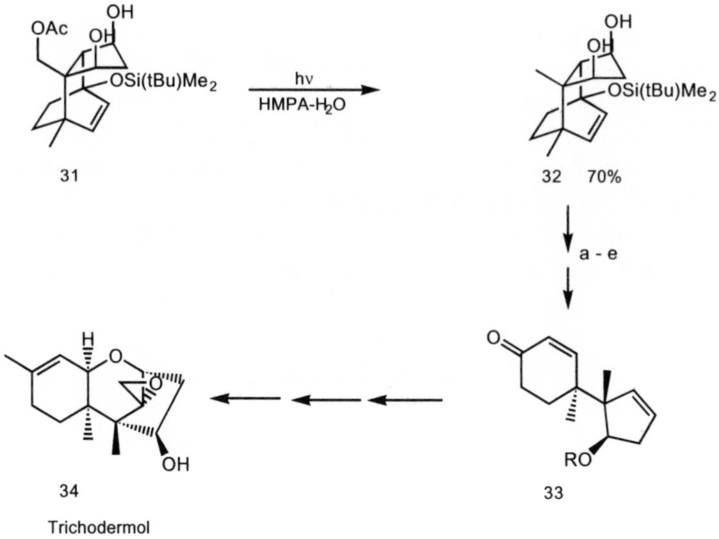

Scheme 16.

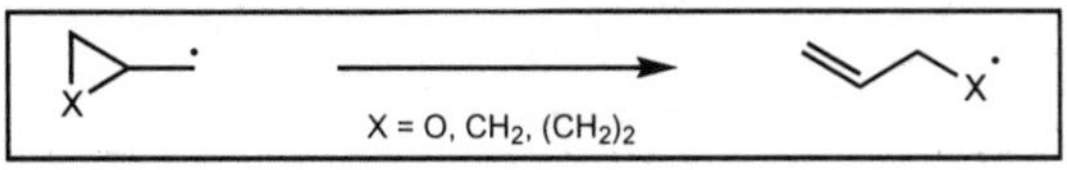

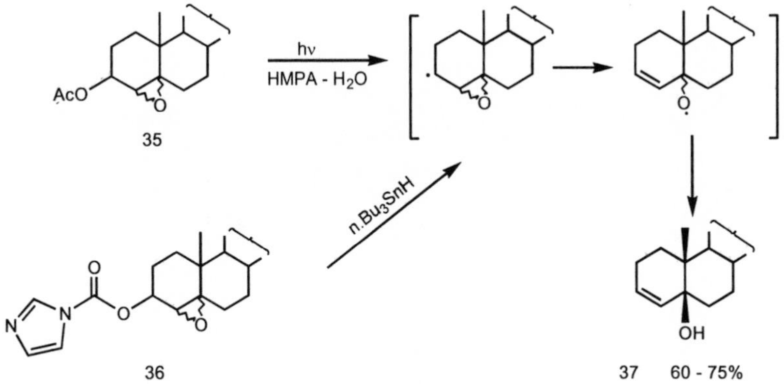

Scheme 17.

For the same reason, photoreduction of acetate **31** was similarly used as a strategic step in the total synthesis of (±) trichodermol **34** (Scheme 16).[54]

Finally, the proximity of a small ring system such as a cyclopropane, cyclobutane, or an oxirane might induce a rearrangement of the radical intermediate. This reaction, which was initially used to prove the mechanism of the photoreduction of acetates,[27] was also applied successfully to α-epoxyacetates (Scheme 17).[55]

4. PHOTOREDUCTION OF KETONES

As already indicated, carbonyl compounds such as ketones, aldehydes, enones, and quinones possess the property to act as effective electron acceptors in the excited state for generating radical anions in the presence of electron-donating partners such as alkenes, aromatics, ruthenium complexes, amines, and alcohols. We will not consider the reactivity of enones and quinones, but we will focus our attention on the behavior of the radical anions formed from ketones and aldehydes. Four different processes can occur from these radical anions including coupling of two radical anions and/or coupling of the radical anion with the radical cation formed from the donor, abstraction of hydrogen from the reaction media to produce alcohols, cyclization, in the case of ω-unsaturated radical anions, and fragmentation when a C_α–X bond (X=O, C) is present (Scheme 18).

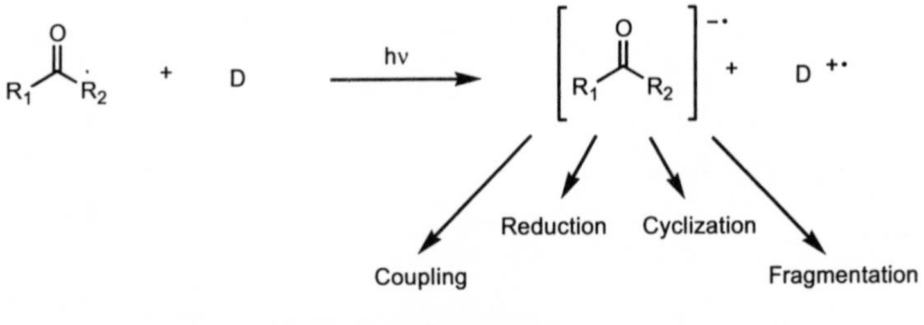

Scheme 18.

4.1. Coupling Reactions

Coupling reactions between a radical cation and a radical anion or between two radical anions can occur. The proportion of the different products is very sensitive to the solvent and additives.

In the presence of alkenes, the oxidizing properties of an excited ketone can become sufficiently strong to abstract an electron from an alkene, leading to a radical ion pair in polar solvents. Direct coupling of the radical ion pair can be observed. In nonpolar solvents, only complexes can be formed and oxetanes are favored (Scheme 19).

A typical example of ketone–olefin photoreaction involving a photoinduced electron transfer is represented by the system comprised of biacetyl and 1,1-diethoxyethene, where one simple isomeric oxetane **40** is obtained (Scheme 20).[56] This can be explained by "polarity reversal" of the reactivity of the ketone through PET.[57]

Similarly, the reaction of benzophenone in its triplet excited state with the electron-rich 1,3-dioxolene **42** in benzene yields only the corresponding oxetanes (Scheme 21). However, when

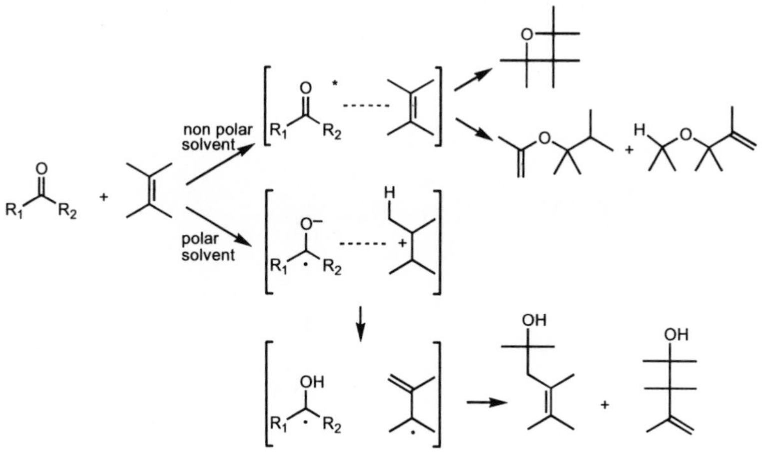

Scheme 19.

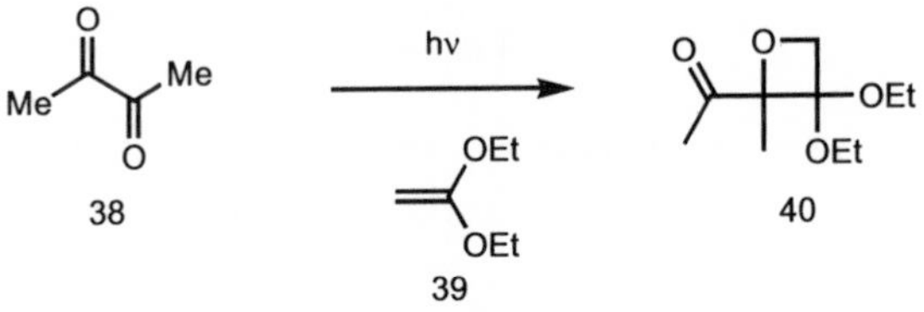

Scheme 20.

the polarity of the solvent increases, the yield of oxetane decreases. This is attributed to a larger extent to the dissociation
of the exciplex intermediate into a radical ion pair.

Interestingly, the irradiation of biacetyl with strong donating
1,3-dioxolenes produces coupling products 46 and 47[57] in acetonitrile. Formation of 46 and 47 can be explained according
to Scheme 22. In the radical cation, the acidity of the methyl
hydrogen allows a fast proton transfer to the radical anion with
formation of a radical pair and consecutively 46 and 47.

Photoinduced electron transfer from β,β-dimethyl-substituted
silyl acetal 49 to the triplet excited state of 1-naphthaldehyde
48 is energetically feasible, and radical coupling to adduct 50[59]
is observed (Scheme 23).

When 49 is replaced by allyltrimethylsilane 51, no reaction
with 48 occurs under similar irradiation conditions. However,
it was observed that the addition of $Mg(ClO_4)_2$ renders PET
possible between 48 and 51 as the result of a coordination of

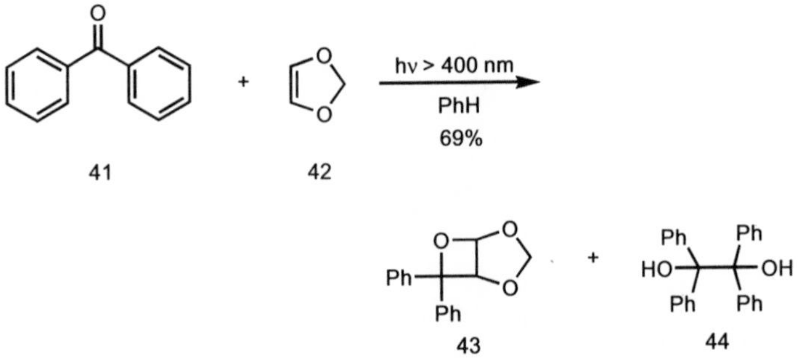

Scheme 21.

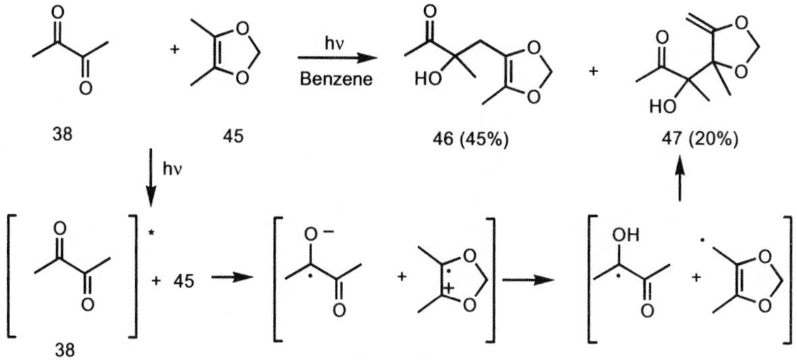

Scheme 22.

the aldehyde **48** with the magnesium ion, which increases its electron affinity (Scheme 24).

Irradiation of ketones in the presence of alkylbenzenes can produce coupling products. For example, irradiation of benzophenone **41** in toluene produced coupling products such as 1,2-diphenyl ethane **54**, the pinacol **55**, and 1,1,2-triphenyl ethanol **56** in modest yields (Scheme 25). Hydrogen transfer from toluene to the triplet state of benzophenone was shown to compete with a charge transfer complex intermediate of type **A**.[60–62]

Photoreaction of ketones and aldehydes in the presence of amines involves charge transfer interactions between amines and

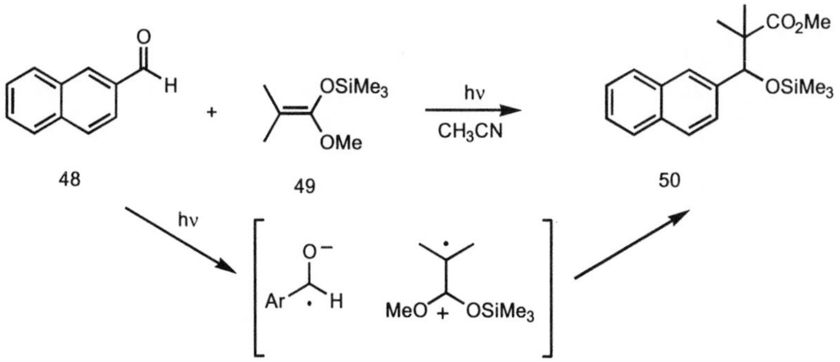

Scheme 23.

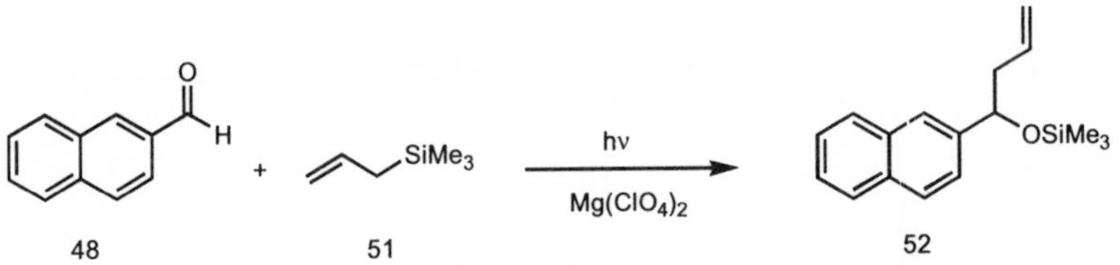

Scheme 24.

carbonyl excited states.[4] Kinetic studies indicate that for a given ketone, the rate constants increase when the oxidation potential of the amine is lowered (DABCO > $R^1R^2R^3N$ > R^1R^2NH > RNH_2) and that the products derive from an initial electron transfer rather than from a direct hydrogen atom transfer (Scheme 26).[63]

Depending on the nature of the amine, either a C–H or an N–H bond intervenes in the hydrogen atom transfer with the formation of a hemipinacol radical and an aminyl or α-amino radical.

In the intermolecular photoreductions of ketones by amines,[64,65] coupling of the radicals formed by PET and proton transfer terminates the process, and acyclic α-aminoalcohols, pinacols, alcohols, or diamines are isolated. As an example of the method, quenching of the excited triplet state of acetophenone by α-

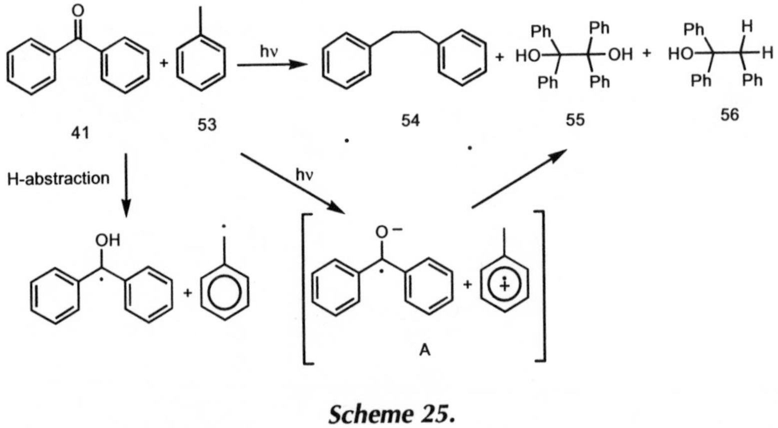

Scheme 25.

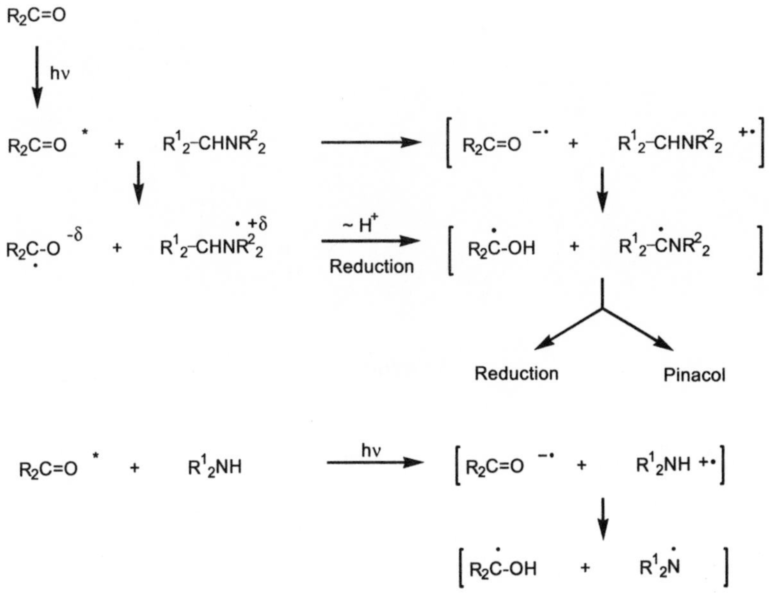

R$_2$C=O

$\downarrow$ hv

R$_2$C=O * + R$^1_2$-CHNR$^2_2$ $\longrightarrow$ $\left[\text{R}_2\text{C=O}^{-\cdot} + \text{R}^1_2\text{-CHNR}^2_2{}^{+\cdot}\right]$

$\downarrow$

R$_2$C-O$^{-\delta}$ + R$^1_2$-CHNR$^2_2{}^{\cdot\,+\delta}$ $\xrightarrow[\text{Reduction}]{\sim\text{H}^+}$ $\left[\text{R}_2\overset{\cdot}{\text{C}}\text{-OH} + \text{R}^1_2\text{-}\overset{\cdot}{\text{C}}\text{NR}^2_2\right]$

Reduction   Pinacol

R$_2$C=O * + R$^1_2$NH $\xrightarrow{\text{hv}}$ $\left[\text{R}_2\text{C=O}^{-\cdot} + \text{R}^1_2\text{NH}^{+\cdot}\right]$

$\downarrow$

$\left[\text{R}_2\overset{\cdot}{\text{C}}\text{-OH} + \text{R}^1_2\overset{\cdot}{\text{N}}\right]$

Scheme 26.

methylbenzylamine led to the formation of coupling products **58–60** (Scheme 27).[4]

The quenching of excited benzophenone by triethylamine leads to radical intermediates that can initiate the polymerization

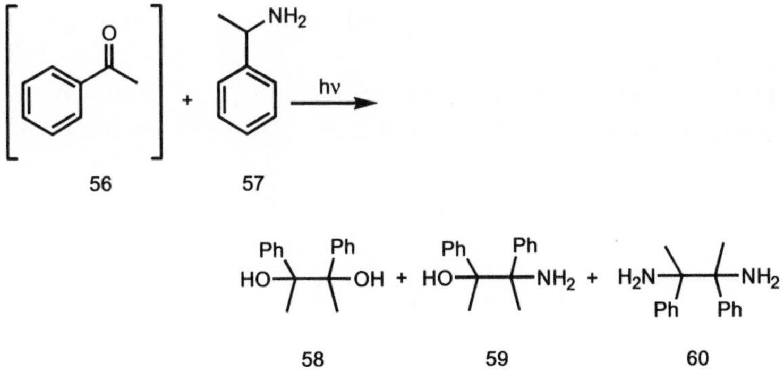

Scheme 27.

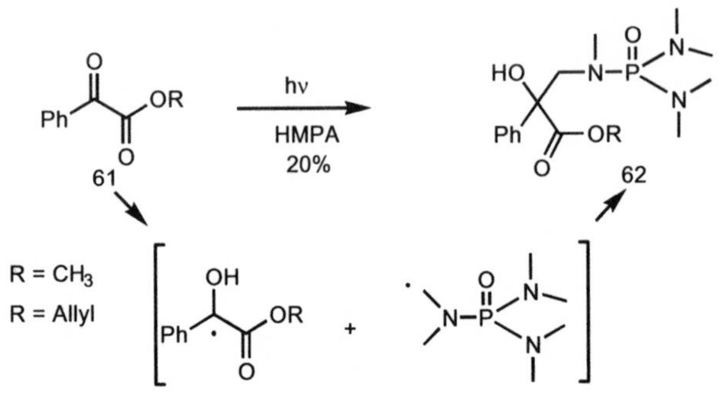

Scheme 28.

of monomers such as acrylonitrile.[66] The amine radicals formed
are the initiators of the polymerization.

Finally, irradiation of aromatic α-ketoesters[67] in HMPA re-
sulted in the cross-coupling of ketyl radicals with the generation
of a HMPA-derived radical according to Scheme 28.

4.2. Reduction Reactions

In aqueous media, the coupling of the radical anion can be
avoided. In water, it was found that reduction of aromatic ketones by amines proceeded rapidly to form a secondary alcohol
rather than a pinacol (Scheme 29).[4,68]

Alcohols are also obtained when solvated electrons are produced by irradiation.[69] For example, γ-radiolysis of ketones in
2-propanol gives the corresponding alcohols according to
Scheme 30.

It has also been demonstrated that Ru(bpy)$_3^{2+}$ can photosensitize
reduction of ketones in the presence of 1,4-dihydropyridine com-

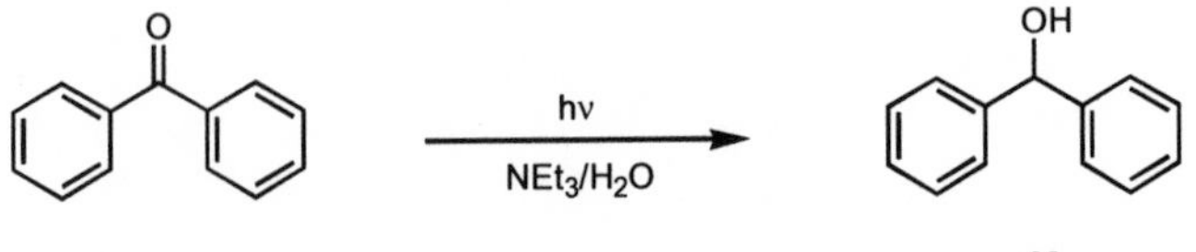

Scheme 29.

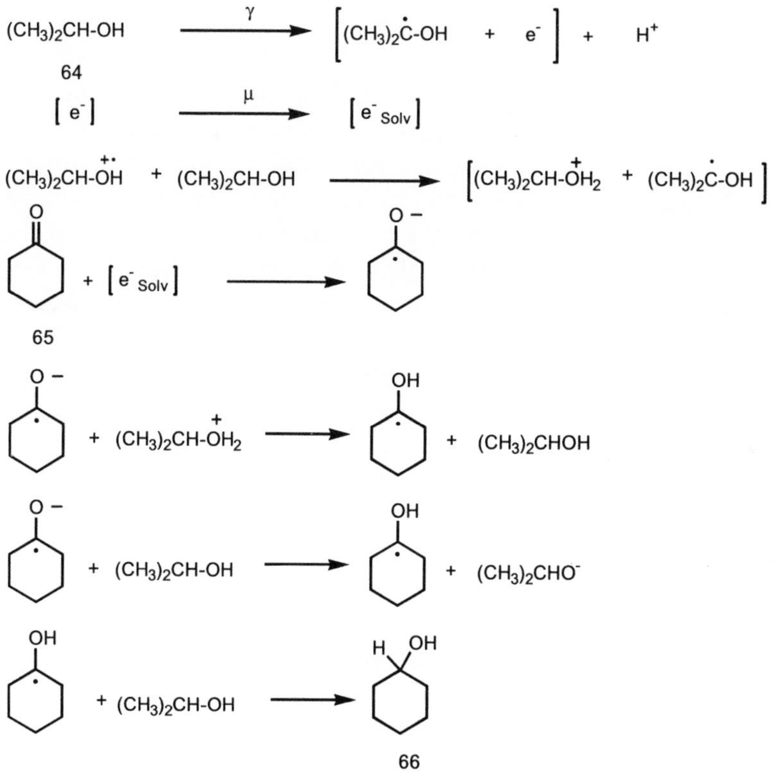
(CH3)2CH-OH
γ
(CH3)2C-OH + e-
H+
64
[e-]
μ
[e- Solv]
(CH3)2CH-OH + (CH3)2CH-OH
(CH3)2CH-OH2 + (CH3)2C-OH
O
O −
+ [e- Solv]
65
OH
+ (CH3)2CH-OH2
+ (CH3)2CHOH
+ (CH3)2CH-OH
+ (CH3)2CHO-
H OH
66

Scheme 30.

pounds.[61] Strategies to reduce ketones using enzyme catalysis coupled with photosensitization have also been investigated extensively.[70] The reduction of 2-butanone **67** takes place within a multicomponent system consisting of $Ru(bpy)_3^{2+}$, $NADP^+$, methyl viologen (MV^{2+}), $(NH_4)_3EDTA$ as an electron donor, and ferredoxin/$NADP^+$/reductase (FDR) coupled with an alcohol dehydrogenase (Scheme 31).

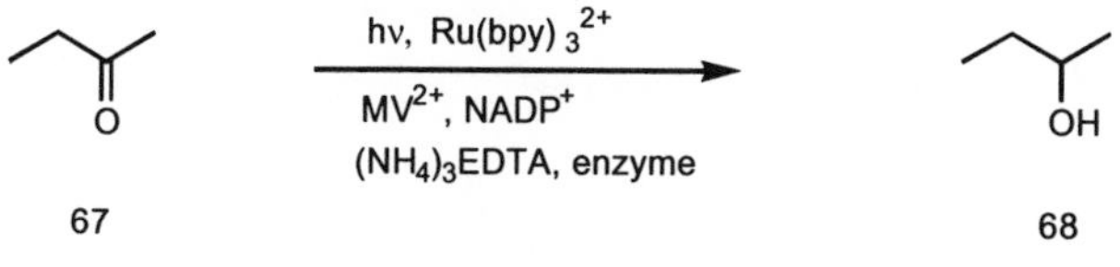
hν, Ru(bpy)3 2+
MV2+, NADP+
(NH4)3EDTA, enzyme
O
OH
67
68

Scheme 31.

4.3. Cyclization Reactions

Until recently, intermolecular photoreduction of ketones by amines has not provided much synthetic utility except for the production of aminoalcohols, alcohols, pinacols, and polymers. More interestingly the amino and the carbonyl groups can belong to the same molecule, without disturbing the change transfer process, and produce intramolecular coupling products.[60b] Depending on the structure of the starting aminoketones, α-aminocyclopropanols, α-aminocyclopentanols, or hydroxy-azetidines can be obtained in high yields (Scheme 32).

An intramolecular PET process in α-ketoazetidines induces an interesting rearrangement and formation of bicyclic hydroxy azetidines. These hydroxyaziridines rearrange quickly into 2-hydroxy-3,4-dihydroxypyrrole derivatives that aromatize through water elimination (Scheme 33).[74]

An interesting example of a photoreductive reaction of a δ,ε-unsaturated ketone in the presence of hexamethylphosphoric triamide (HMPA, neat) or triethylamine in acetonitrile has been

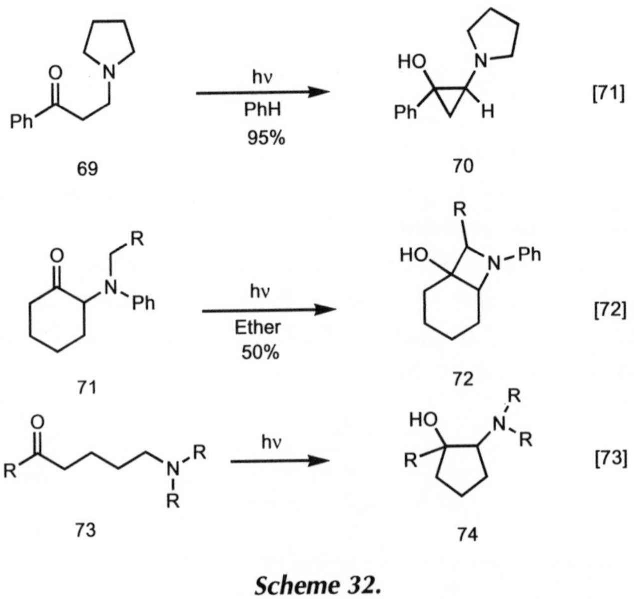

Scheme 32.

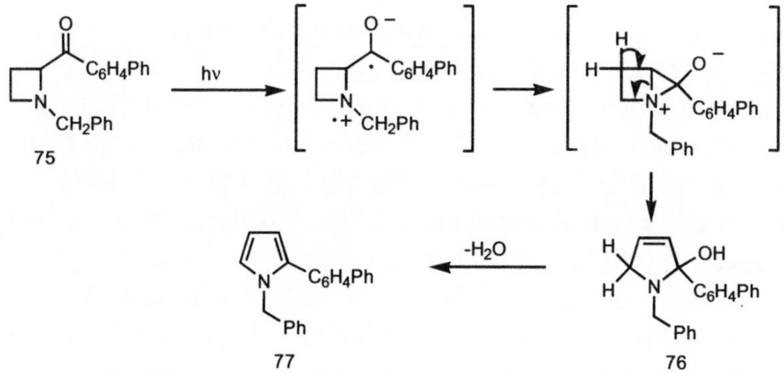

Scheme 33.

reported.[75] The thus formed δ,ε-unsaturated ketyl radicals have the same behavior as δ,ε-unsaturated carbon radicals[76] and they cyclize to produce cyclopentanols and cyclohexanols. A typical example is provided in Scheme 34.

The reaction proceeds by electron donation from excited HMPA to the ground state of the ketone, or by reduction of the excited ketone by ground state Et_3N. Good yields and stereoselectivity are observed under these mild reaction conditions. If HMPA gives better yields in the cyclization of unsaturated ketones, the two solvent systems, however, are equally effective in the case of acetylenic ketones. However, for photoreduction with Et_3N or HMPA, Et_3N is preferable since this compound is less hazardous, more volatile, and allows a simpler reaction work-up (only requiring evaporation of the solvent). From a

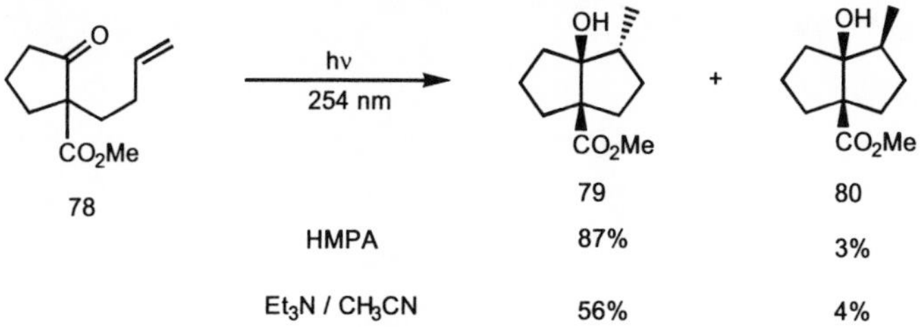

Scheme 34.

preparative point of view, it was found that the procedure using Et_3N tolerates various substituents such as carbonitriles, esters, ethers, alkenes, and alkynes. Furthermore, good regio- and stereoselectivities have been observed in most cases. The stereoselectivities observed can be explained by a repulsive electrostatic interaction which can take place between the negatively charged oxygen center and the terminal sp^2 carbon atom in one of the two diastereoisomeric cyclic and polar transition states.

The highly stereoselective production of alcohols **79** and **80** from δ,ε-unsaturated ketone **78** is consistent with the mechanism of electroreductive cyclization of such compounds (Scheme 35).[77] Although the high stereoselectivity observed in the photoreductive cyclization of the ketoester **78** (79/80 = 14/1) is better than that observed under chemical conditions using Zn/Me_3SiCl (79/80 = 3/1),[78] or Na/NH_3,[79] it remains lower than that observed when using SmI_2 as reducing agent.[80] The behavior of the intermediate radical formed from δ,ε-unsaturated ketones does not depend strongly on the method used to produce it: chemical reduction, electroreduction, or photoreduction. The latter, however, presents the advantage of being càrried out under very mild and homogeneous conditions with few problems of reproducibility constituting a complementary and advantageous approach to cyclic compounds.[81] For this reason, photoreductive

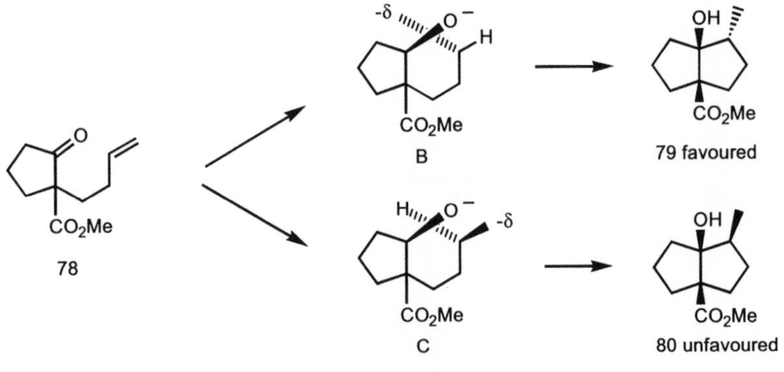

Scheme 35.

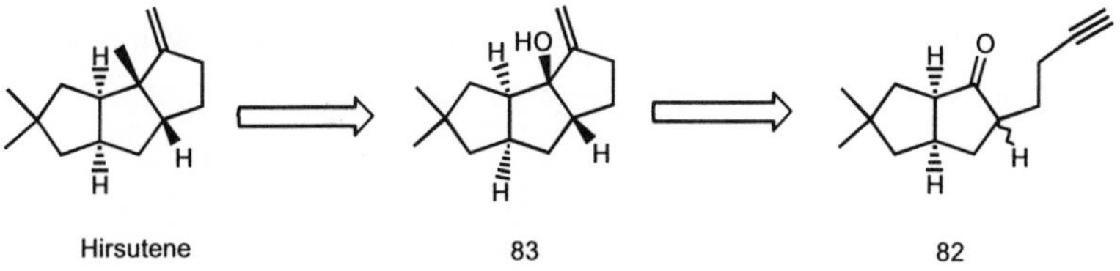

Hirsutene   83   82

Scheme 36.

cyclization has been applied successfully to the synthesis of cyclopentanoids, alkaloids, iridoids, and sesquiterpenes.

One of the first achievements based on this method was a short synthesis of (±)-hirsutene.[82] Retrosynthetic analysis initially called for the replacement of an angular methyl group by a hydroxyl group. Following this, the allylic alcohol was planned to be produced by a ketyl acetylene cyclization. Thus the photochemical reduction applied to compound **82** which was obtained as a mixture of two isomers (*exo/endo* = 2.9/1) by alkylation of the bicyclic ketone **81** afforded **83** as the only tricyclic product which possesses the desired *cis-anti-cis* stereochemistry (Scheme 36). Cyclization under these conditions of the *endo* isomer was so slow (for steric reasons) that it could not compete with hydrogen atom abstraction to form **84**. The highly regio-, stereo-, and chimioselective replacement of the tertiary allylic alcohol of **83** with methylmagnesium bromide in the presence of a Ni(II) catalyst[83] completed the synthesis of (±)-hirsutene (Scheme 37).

Straightforward access to heterocyclic compounds can be obtained using the photoreductive cyclization of ω-unsaturated ketones. When *N,N'*-dialkyloxoamides are irradiated under reducing conditions, competition between PET and γ-hydrogen abstraction products can be observed.[84] Surprisingly, α-oxoesters do not give coupling products under the same conditions (see Scheme 38 and Table 5).

The complexity of the reaction mixture does not allow an easy explanation for the difference of reactivity in HMPA and in CH_3CN in the presence of Et_3N. However, it indicates that in α-ketoamides an intramolecular γ-H abstraction competes

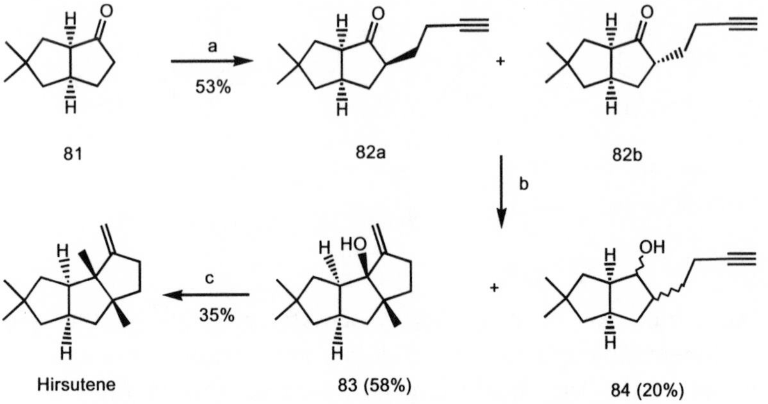
a
53%
81
82a
82b
b
c
35%
Hirsutene
83 (58%)
84 (20%)

a) i- KH-DME, $ICH_2CH=C(CH_3)Cl$, -78°C; ii- $LiAlH_4$, ether, 0° C; iii- KAPA, APA, 0° C; iv- PCC, MS 3A; b) hν, 254 nm, Et_3N, CH_3CN; c) $NiCl_2(PPh_3)_2$, MeMgBr, benzene, reflux.

Scheme 37.

with bimolecular PET processes. On the contrary, the photoreduction of *N*,*N'*-unsaturated diakyl β-oxamides **91** and **92** afforded only substituted 3-azabicyclo|4.3.0|nonanes (Scheme 39).[85]

This photoreductive cyclization is of great synthetic utility as illustrated below in the synthesis of actinidine[86,87] and isooxyskytanthine,[87,88] two rare monoterpenic alkaloids which

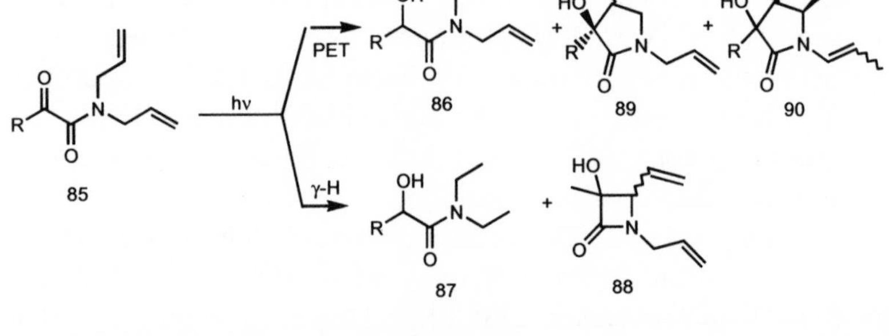
85
hν
PET
γ-H
86
89
90
87
88

Scheme 38.

Table 5.   Irradiation of Compound **85** in HMPA or in Acetonitrile in the Presence of NEt$_3$

Solvent	R	86	87	88	89	90
HMPA	Ph	18%	—	30%	—	—
Et$_3$N–MeCN	Ph	—	20%	22%	20%	10%
Et$_3$N–HMPA	Ph	—	20%	9%	25%	—
Et$_3$N–MeCN	Me	—	—	—	11%	4%
Et$_3$N–MeCN	H	—	—	—	11%	4%

contain a 3-azabicyclo $\lfloor 4.3.0 \rfloor$ nonane skeleton substituted by methyl groups at C4 and C8 (Scheme 40).

The synthesis of the skeleton of these two monoterpenic alkaloids and the control of the relative stereochemistry at C4, C5, and C6 was achieved using a Wolff rearrangement followed by a photoreductive cyclization of unsaturated *N*-alkyl-2-oxo-cyclopentane carboxamides of type **D** (Scheme 40).

A Wolff rearrangement[89] applied to the diazodiketone **96** in the presence of diallylamine gave a 1.6/1 mixture of two regioisomeric amides **97a** and **97b** (Scheme 41). The major product **97a**, which is the precursor of actinidine, was isolated in 56% yield. Similarly, photolysis of **96** in the presence of *N*-methyl propargylamine gave almost quantitatively a mixture **99a** and **99b** (1.5/1). The photoreductive cyclization of **97a** carried out in the presence of Et$_3$N led to a 1.7/1 mixture of **98a** and **98b** which was transformed to actinidine. Irradiation of **99a** under the same conditions led to a single product **100**, which could be converted to isooxyskytanthine (Scheme 41).

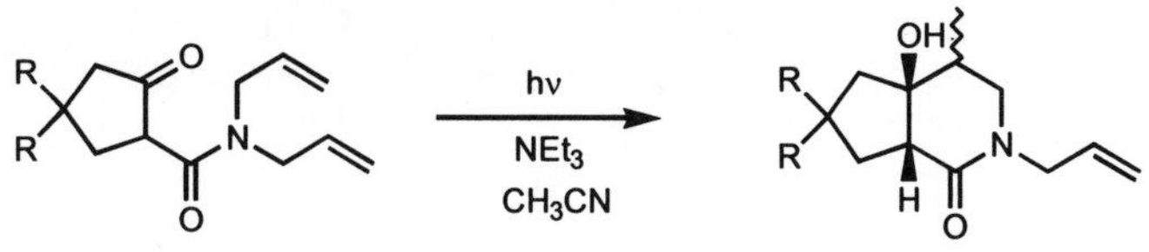

91 R = H
92 R = CH$_3$

93 (59%)
94 (52%)

Scheme 39.

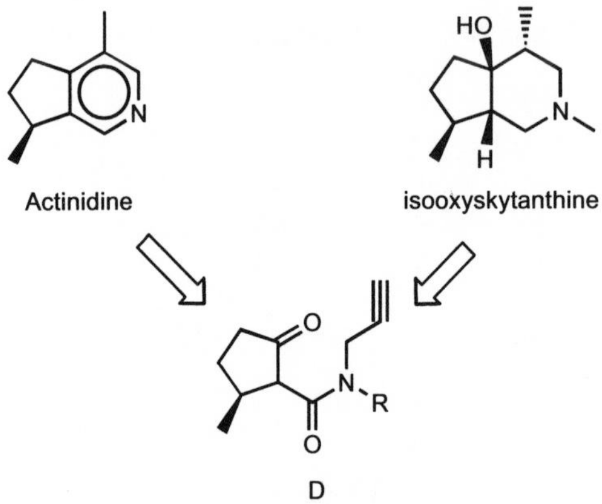

Actinidine   isooxyskytanthine

D

Scheme 40.

Iridoids represent a class of highly oxygenated monoterpenes characterized by a *cis*-fused cyclopentapyran ring system. In principle, synthesis of such systems could be achieved by a photoreductive cyclization of δ,ε-unsaturated β-ketoesters. Unfortunately, unsaturated β-ketoester **101** did not lead to the ex-

Synthesis of Actinidine

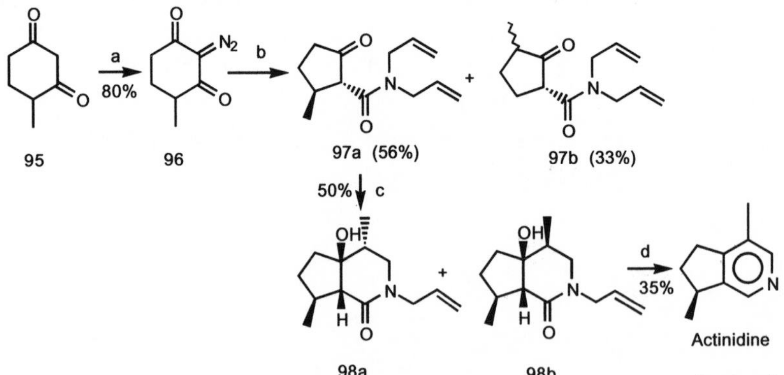

a) TsN₃, NEt₃; b) hv, 254 nm, N,N-diallylamine, CH₃CN; c) hv, 254 nm, CH₃CN;
d) i- LiAlH₄; ii- 10% Pd/C, xylene, nitrobenzene, MS 3A

(continued)

Scheme 41.

Synthesis of Isooxyskytanthine

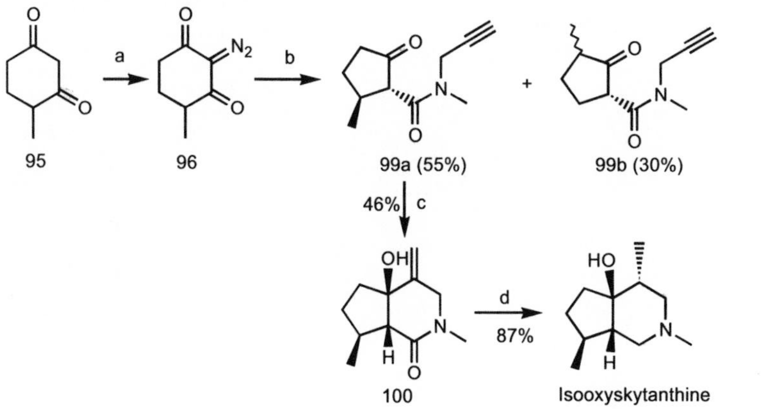

a) TsN$_3$, NEt$_3$; b) hv, 254nm, N-methyl, N-propargylamine, CH$_3$CN; c) hv, 254 nm, CH$_3$CN; d) i- LiAlH$_4$; ii- 10% Pd/C, H$_2$, MeOH

Scheme 41. (Continued)

pected bicyclic compound **102** because of an unfavorable conformation of the ester group of **101** (Scheme 42).[90] In order to overcome this conformational effect, annulation of the unsaturated β-ketoacetal **104** was investigated as a model for the synthesis of C5 oxygenated iridoids.[91]

The β-ketoester, readily available from the irradiation of the diazodiketone **96** in the presence of MeOH through a Wolff rearrangement, was transformed into the ketoketal **104** in a few steps. As expected, irradiation of **104** at 254 nm in acetonitrile with Et$_3$N led to the formation of the desired bicyclic compound **105** with a yield of 80% (Scheme 43).

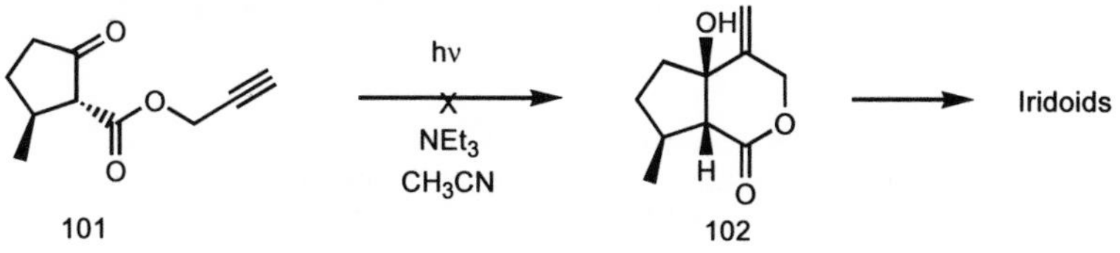

Scheme 42.

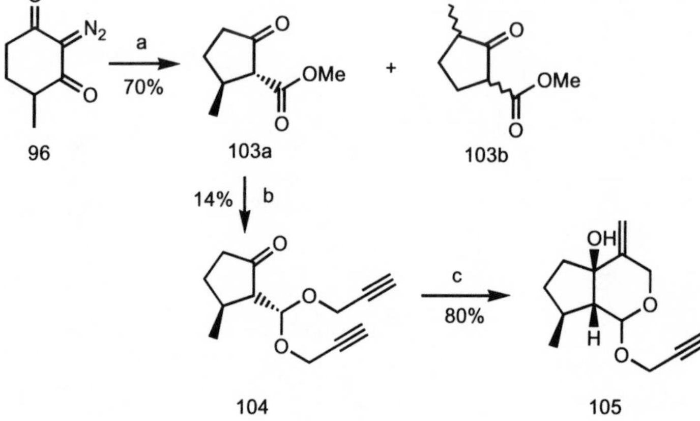

a) hv, CH$_3$CN, MeOH; b) i- LiAlH$_4$, ether, 0°C; ii- HMDS, TMSCl, CH$_2$Cl$_2$, 0°C;
iii- CrO$_3$, pyridine, CH$_2$Cl$_2$; iv- TMSCl, propargylic alcohol, CH$_2$Cl$_2$; v- PCC, MS 4A,
CH$_2$Cl$_2$; c) hv, Et$_3$N, CH$_3$CN

Scheme 43.

The photoreductive cyclization process has been extended to unsaturated alkoxyketones to attain the furofuranic system present in antifeedant substances such as azadirachtin.[92] Ketone **107** obtained from dihydrofuran **106** was irradiated in the presence of triethylamine to furnish the bicyclic compound **108**. Its

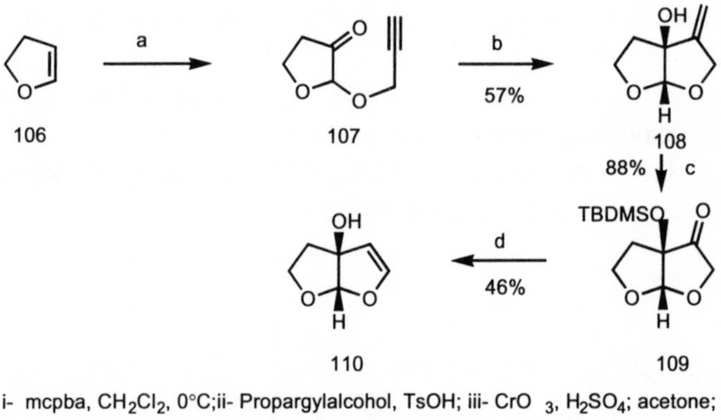

a) i- mcpba, CH$_2$Cl$_2$, 0°C; ii- Propargylalcohol, TsOH; iii- CrO$_3$, H$_2$SO$_4$; acetone;
b) hv, NEt$_3$; 254 nm; c) i- t-BuMe$_2$SiCl, imidazole; ii- O$_3$; d) i- H$_2$NNHTs, MeOH, H$_2$O; ii-
ethyleneglycol, Na, 140°C; iii- Bu$_4$NF, THF

Scheme 44.

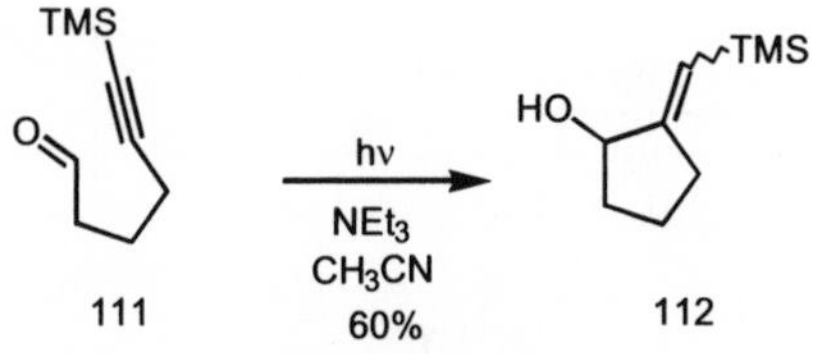

Scheme 45.

transformation to **110** was then achieved in 5 steps by using a Bamford–Stevens reaction[93,94] as the key step (Scheme 44).

ω-Unsaturated aldehydes which are more readily reduced than ketones can also be used to build up cyclopentanols and cyclohexanols,[95] as illustrated in Scheme 45. The synthetic utility of this process is exemplified by an improved synthesis of (–)-isocarbacyclin.[96] The photoreductive cyclization of the γ-ethynyl

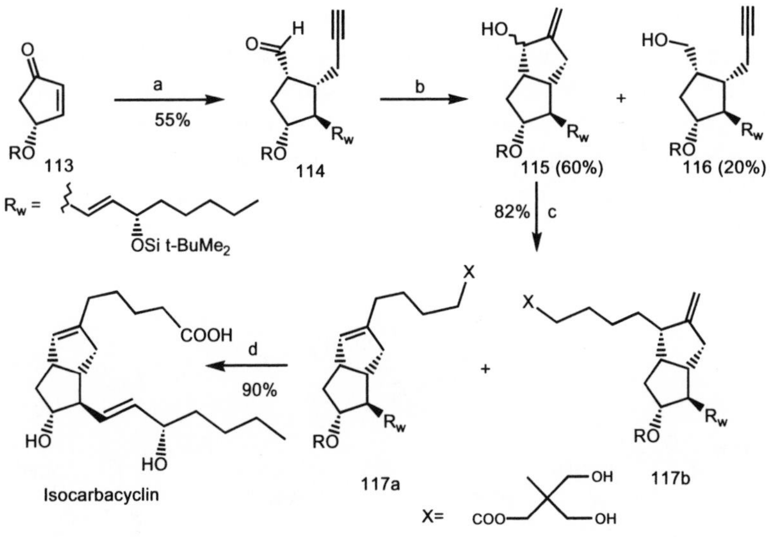

a) i- LiR$_w$/Cu-=-C$_4$H$_9$; ii- Ph$_3$SnCl; iii- ICH$_2$-=-SiMe$_3$; iv- Zn/CH$_2$Br$_2$/TiCl$_4$; v- 9-BBN, H$_2$O$_2$, NaOH; vi- NaOMe, MeOH; vii- Swern; b) hv, 254 nm, E$_3$N, CH$_3$CN; c) n-BuLi, CuI, LiR, R'$_3$P-NMePh$^+$ I$^-$, PPTS, H$_2$O/MeOH d) LiOH, Bu$_4$NF

Scheme 46.

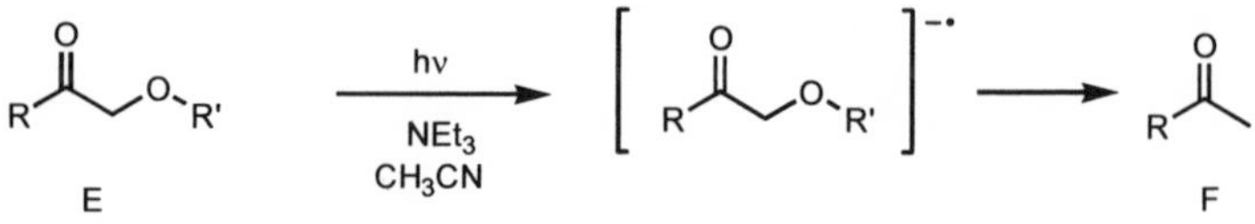

Scheme 47.

aldehyde **114**, which was synthesized from (*R*)-4-hydroxy-2-cy-clopentenone derivative **113** in 7 steps, gave the allylic alcohol **115** (60%) (Scheme 46). This allylic alcohol **115** is a very useful synthon in the isocarbacyclin synthesis since the regioselective introduction of the butanoic acid moiety in the α-side chain and formation of the double bond has been achieved by using known procedures[97] to give **117a**.

While most of the work related to PET reactions has focused on the formation of C–C bonds, the cleavage of C–O and C–C bonds has recently gained interest. One synthetic application of the cleavage of a C–O bond is the elimination of an allyl protection at the anomeric position of a carbohydrate (Scheme 47).[98] Allyl protection at the anomeric position is common in carbohydrate chemistry. The deprotection may be achieved by a number of methods.[99] However, serious problems can be encountered depending on the molecule. In the case of compound **118** the deprotection problem was solved by using a Wacker

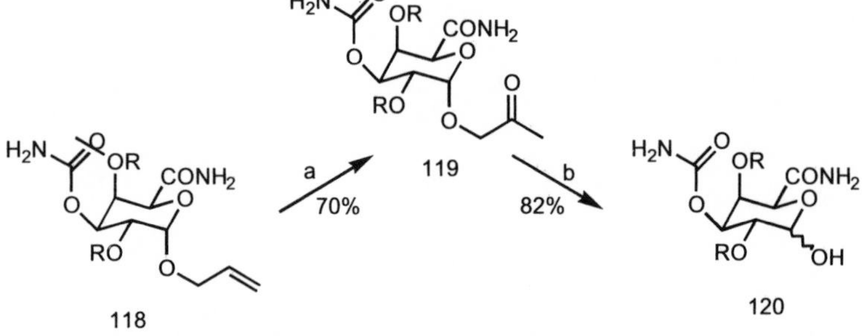

a) PdCl$_2$, CuCl, O$_2$, DMF/H$_2$O; b) hv, Et$_3$N, CH$_3$CN, 254 nm

Scheme 48.

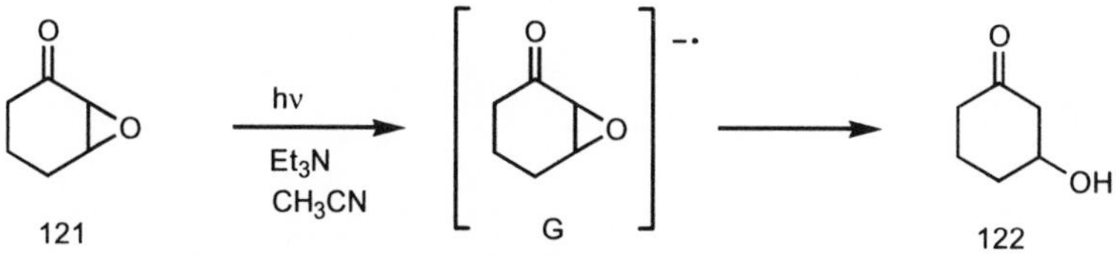

Scheme 49.

oxidation[100] followed by photolysis of **119** in the presence of triethylamine (Scheme 48: yield = 82%).

The cleavage of heterocyclic strained rings can also be achieved using the PET process. Cleavage of the epoxide ring of an α-epoxyketone leads to a 3-hydroxyketone (Scheme 49).[101] Although the exact mechanism of the epoxide ring opening from intermediate **G** has not yet been determined, a PET process seems to be involved. The observed cleavage of the C_α–O bond of an epoxyketone is similar to the reductive cleavage of the same bond using lithium in liquid ammonia,[102] Bu_3SnH under pressure,[103] or by cathodic reduction.[104] Surprisingly, SmI_2 did not cleave the epoxide ring of carvone oxide (Scheme 50).[105]

The photoinduced epoxy ring opening of an α-epoxyketone, allowing stereospecific formation of a β-hydroxy ketone, has also been used in the synthesis of the methyl glycoside of cinerulose B **128**, a rare sugar present in the antibiotic cinerubine B.[106] Irradiation of the epoxyketone **127** prepared from the commercially available di-O-acetyl-L-rhammal, affords the methyl glycoside **128** (Scheme 51). The transformation of **127** to **128**

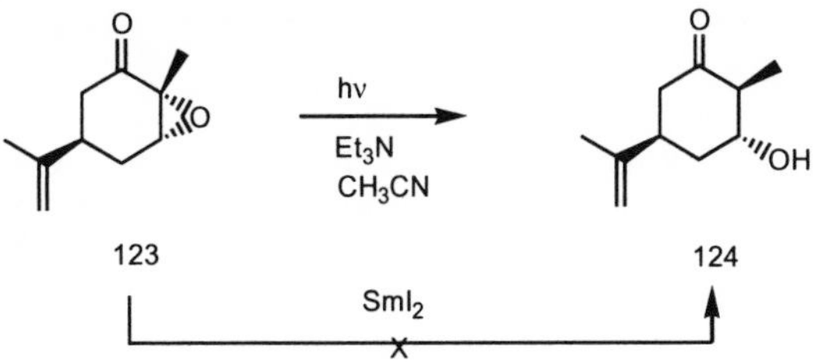

Scheme 50.

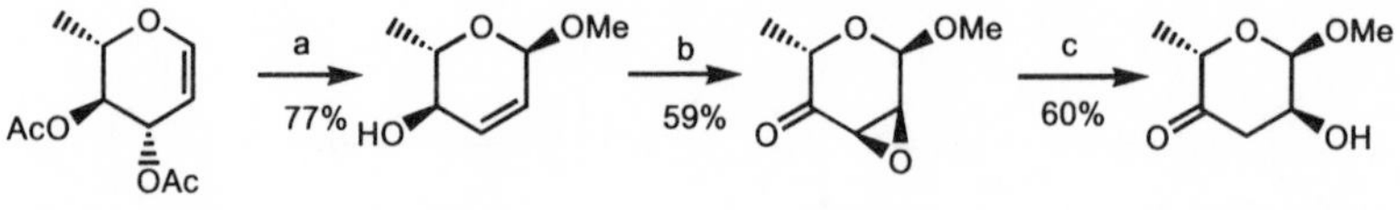

125 126 127 128

a) i- BF_3OEt, MeOH; ii- Resin HO^-; b) i- mCPBA CH_2Cl_2; ii- PCC, CH_2Cl_2, MS 3A; c) hν, Et_3N, CH_3CN, 254 nm

Scheme 51.

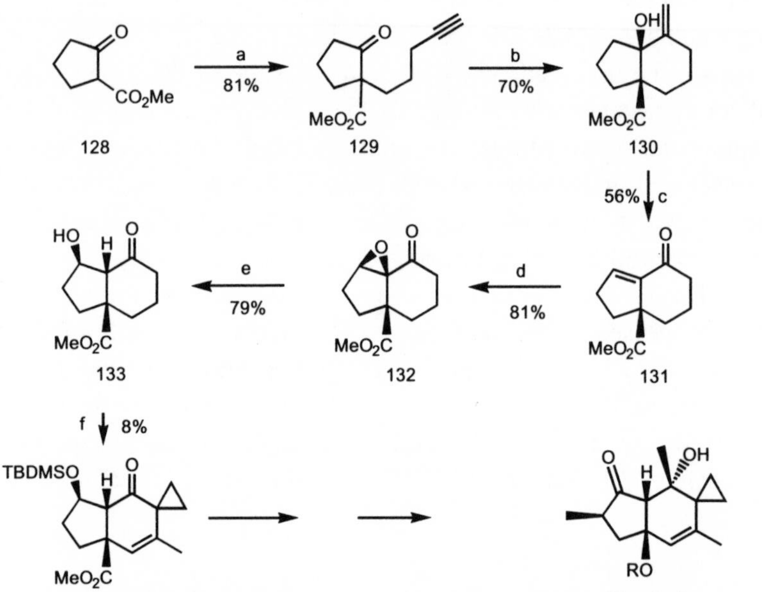

128 129 130 131 132 133 134 Ptaquilosin

a) KOH, EtOH, 1-iodopent-4-yne; b) hν, Et_3N, CH_3CN, 254 nm; c) i-O_3, MeOH, Me_2S; ii- Ac_2O, H_3PO_4 cat; iii- Resin OH^-, MeOH; d) H_2O_2, K_2CO_3; e) hν, Et_3N, CH_3CN, 254 nm; f) TBDMSCl, imidazole; ii- TMSOTf, 2,6-lutidine; iii- $Pd(OAc)_2$, p-benzoquinone, CH_3CN; iv- $CuBr,Me_2S$, CH_3Li, TMSCl; v- $Pd(OAc)_2$, p-benzoquinone; vi- t-BuOK / t-BuOH, $ClCHCH_2SMe_2I$, KI.

Scheme 52.

considerably shortens the synthesis of this rare sugar as compared with a previous synthesis.[107]

Ptaquilosin is the aglycone of ptaquilosine, which has been evaluated for its antitumor activity at the National Cancer Institute.[108] The photoreductive cyclization and photoreductive opening of an epoxide, which are two highly chemio-, regio-, and stereoselective processes, were used to control the configurations at C5 and C9 and consequently at C1 and C7 in a total synthesis of ptaquilosin (Scheme 52).[109] The photoreductive cyclization applied to compound **129** allows the formation of the bicyclic compound **130** (70%) in which the ester group is the precursor of the C5 hydroxy group present in ptaquilosin. Compound **130** was transformed to the enone **131** and this was epoxidized in a very stereoselective way using H_2O_2 in a methanolic potassium carbonate solution. The thus formed epoxide **132** was transformed under photoreductive conditions and hydroxy ketone **133** was isolated with a yield of 79%. In this compound all the functionalities needed are present to complete the synthesis of ptaquilosin. Since compound **129** can be prepared in its two enantiomeric forms,[110,111] both (+)-ptaquilosin and (−)-ptaquilosin have been synthesized using this approach.

Oxonorbornanones, which possess a strained oxabridge can be cleaved under PET conditions.[101,112] When these compounds are indeed irradiated in the presence of triethylamine, 3-hydroxycyclohexanones are obtained in moderate to good yields,

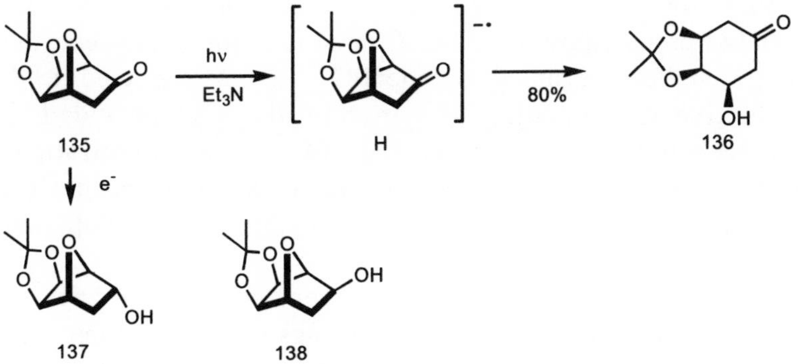

Scheme 53.

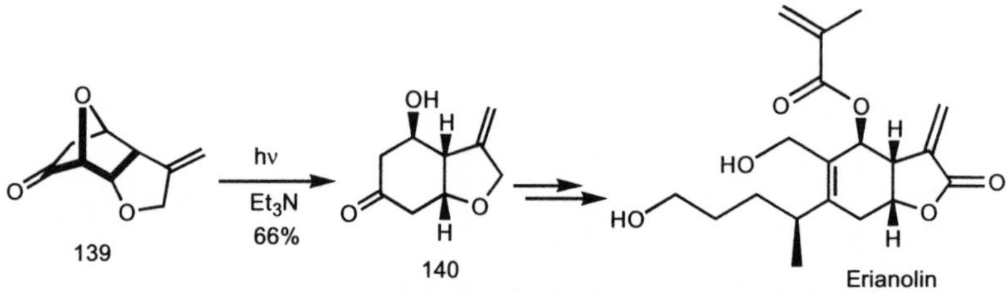

Scheme 54.

depending on the nature of the substituents at C5 and C6. This reaction was applied to the synthesis of 3-hydroxy-cyclohex-anones with excellent stereocontrol (Scheme 53).

Interestingly, the treatment of **135** with Na in liquid NH_3 (−78%) did not induce the required C–O bond cleavage but gave a 10/1 mixture of the *endo* and *exo* alcohols **137** and **138**, respectively.[112] Similarly treatment of **136** with 3 mol equivalents of SmI_2 in THF led to the exclusive formation of the *endo* alcohol **137**. These experiments show the difference in reactivity of intermediates produced by photochemistry and ground state chemistry.

The photoreductive 7-oxa ring opening method has allowed the synthesis of the erianolin skeleton from ketone **140** (Scheme 54).[113] A new class of disaccharide mimics[114] that are α-*C*-galac-topyranosides of carbopentopyranols[115] have been synthesized using the same approach.

PET from Et_3N to the all-*endo*-7-oxanorbornanone derivative (+)-**143** prepared by radical C–C bond formation between enone **141**[116] and acetobromogalactone **142**[117] led, as expected, to the reductive ring opening of the oxabridge and provided the tetrasubstituted cyclohexanone (+)-**144** without epimerization α to the ketone. Compound (+)-**144** was then converted into **145**, a dicarba analog of 2-*O*-(α-*O*-galactopyranosyl)-*O*-xylopyrano-dialdehyde (Scheme 55).

The PET-induced opening of oxygenated strained rings can be extended to carbocyclic strained rings such as cyclopropanes or cyclobutanes. One of the first examples of a PET-induced cleavage of a cyclobutane was reported in 1990.[118]

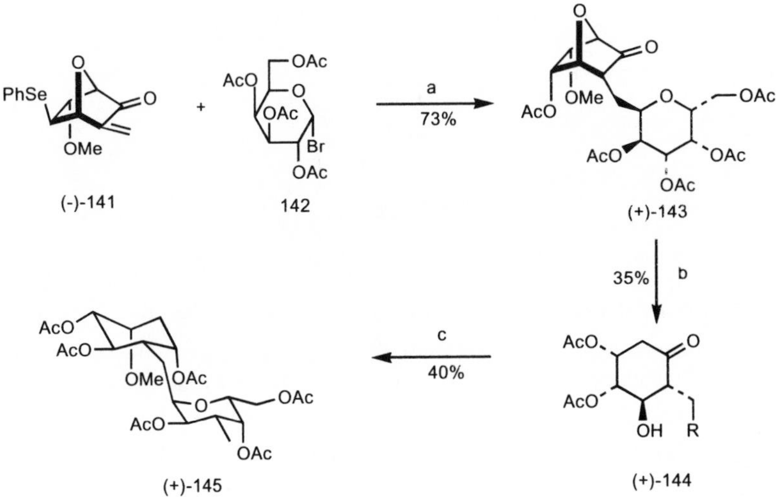

(-)-141   142   (+)-143

(+)-145   (+)-144

a) i- Bu₃Sn, AIBN, PhH; ii- m-CPBA, -78°C; iii- Ac₂O/AcOH; iv- Bu₃SnH; AIBN; b) Et₃N, CH₃CN, 254 nm; c) i- NaBH₄, MeOH; ii- Ac₂O, pyridine, DMAP

Scheme 55.

Irradiation of compound **146** in the presence of triethylamine results in spiroproduct **147** formation (Scheme 56).[119] A PET

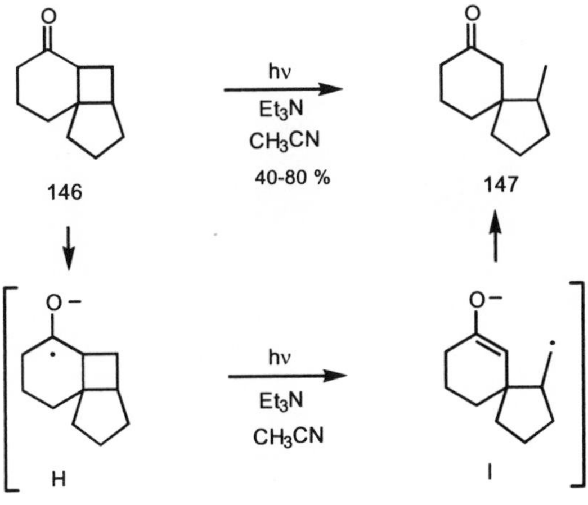

146   147

Scheme 56.

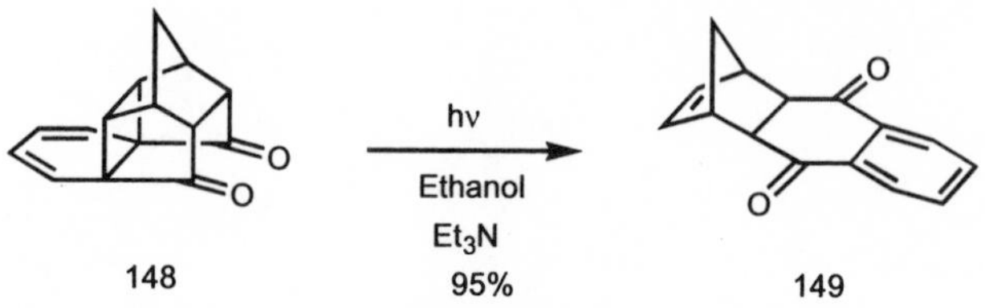

Scheme 57.

mechanism was postulated for this reaction, since the cleavage of cyclobutane is not observed in the absence of triethylamine. Similarly, various cyclobutyl ketones have been subjected to PET conditions with triethylamine. For example, the irradiation of an ethanolic solution of **148** in the presence of Et_3N led to its quantitative conversion to *exo*-8 **149** (Scheme 57).[120]

The skeleton of linear triquinane is easily accessible from the methyl 8-oxotricyclo|5.4.0.0|²,⁶undecan-1-carboxylate **150**.[119] Photoreduction of **150** implied the formation of a ring-expanded intermediate **K** which cyclized to produce the linearly fused triquinane **151** (Scheme 58). An extension of this reaction to heterocyclic angular tricyclic compounds has also been achieved (Scheme 59).[121] This photofragmentation method has been ex-

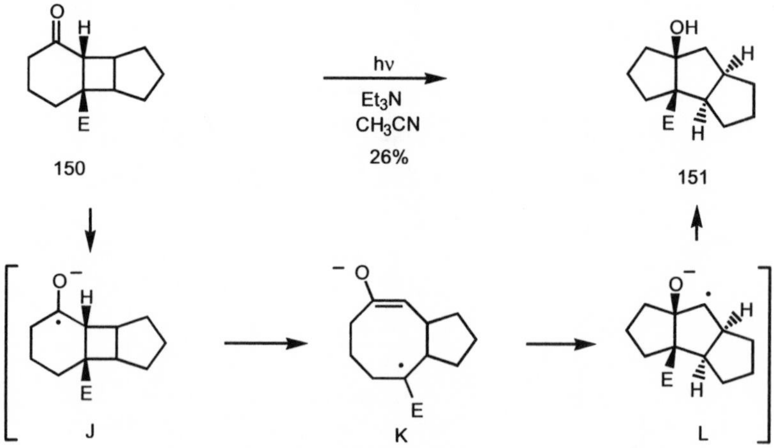

Scheme 58.

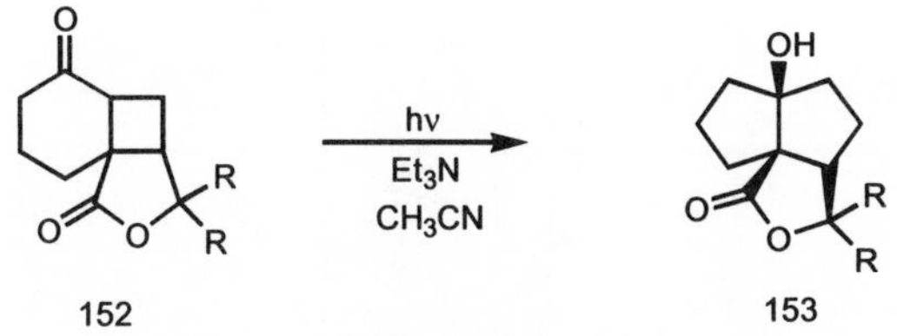

Scheme 59.

tended to the cleavage of the cyclopropyl moiety of cyclo-propylketones.[101,122] Irradiation of bicyclo|4.1.0|heptanone **154** at 254 nm in acetonitrile in the presence of Et_3N led to cyclohexanone **155** according to Scheme 60.[123]

Interestingly, the addition of $LiClO_4$ avoids further reduction of the ketone **155** to the alcohol **156** (Scheme 61). The preferred regioselectivity of the ring opening (*exo* versus *endo*) depends on the substitution pattern of the bicycloalkanones and on their ring size.[124]

When bicyclo|3.1.0|hexanone and bicyclo|4.1.0|heptanone are substituted by electron-withdrawing groups at C(β) a ring-expanded product is formed. Similarly, the irradiation of bicy-clo|5.1.0|octanone and bicyclo|6.1.0|nonanone in the presence of Et_3N led to the ring-expanded products (Scheme 62).

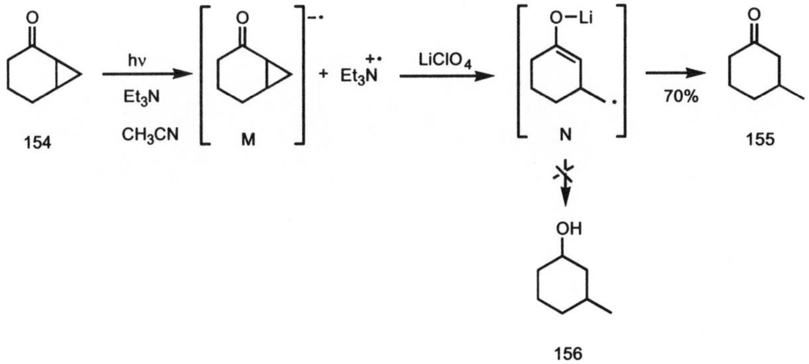

Scheme 60.

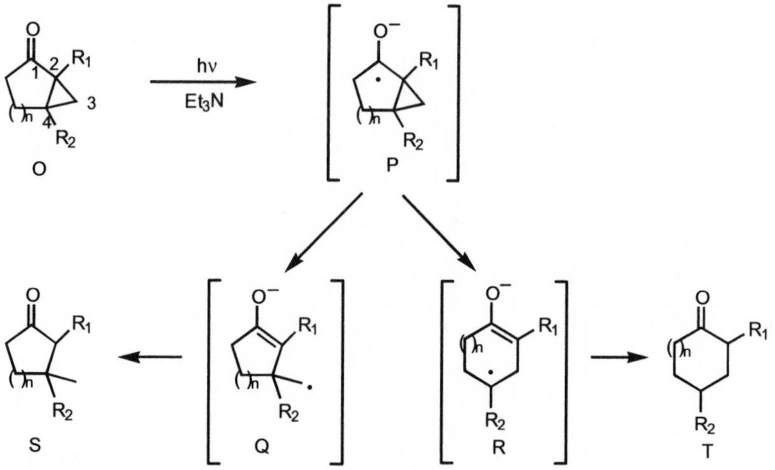

Scheme 61.

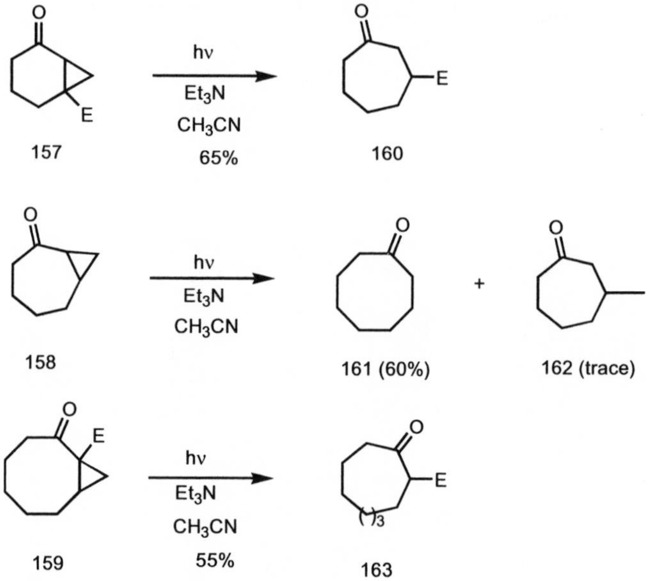

Scheme 62.

The radical enolate intermediates of type **R** arising from the cleavage of bond C2–C4 (ring-enlargement process) are more stable (3.4 kcal/mole if R_2 = H and 11–14 kcal/mole if R_2 = CO_2Me)[124] than the corresponding intermediate **Q** (Scheme 61). The former intermediate is a secondary radical either substituted or not by an ester moiety; the latter is a primary radical. The ring enlargement can be explained by the fact that the C2–C'4 bond of the bicyclo⌐n.1.0⌐alkan-2-ones is weaker than that of bond C2–C3. In the case of **154** the C2–C3 bond is cleaved preferentially due to stereoelectronic factors, the latter bond being better aligned with the π-system of the ketone radical anion than bond C2–C4. In the case of compounds **157–159** the kinetic stereoelectronic factor does not compete with the highly favorable factor which makes the ring enlarged radical anion intermediates highly stabilized by the carbonyl group. In compound **158**, the flexibility of the bicyclic carbon skeleton makes both the C2–C3 and C2–C4 bonds capable of proper alignment with the π-system of the ketone radical anion, thus leading to mixtures of the corresponding methylcycloheptanones and ring-enlarged cyclooctanones.

The radical intermediate **Q** induced by the PET fragmentation of bicyclo⌐n.1.0⌐alkanones can be trapped intramolecularly as shown by irradiation of the bicycloalkanone **164** (Scheme 63).[122b,124]

Furthermore, the ring cleavage of the cyclopropane ring of a chiral bicyclo⌐4.1.0⌐heptanone has been used as the key step in the synthesis of an antifungal agent, (+)-Ptilocaulin.[126] Thus the chiral 2-butylbicyclo⌐4.1.0⌐heptanone **167** was obtained by the cyclopropanation[127] of the chiral unsaturated ketal **166**[128] with high enantiomeric excess (99%). Its irradiation in the presence of Et_3N and $LiClO_4$ gave the desired ketone **169** which is the key molecule in the synthesis of (+)-Ptilocaulin (Scheme 64). The stereocontrol at C3 using this ring opening of a bicycloalkanone is much better than the addition of Me_2CuLi in the presence of a chiral inductor to the corresponding cyclohexenone.[129] Intermediate **169** was then transformed to ptilocaulin using a Sakuraï reaction,[130] a hydroboration,[131] an aldolization, and a treatment of **170** by guanidine.[132]

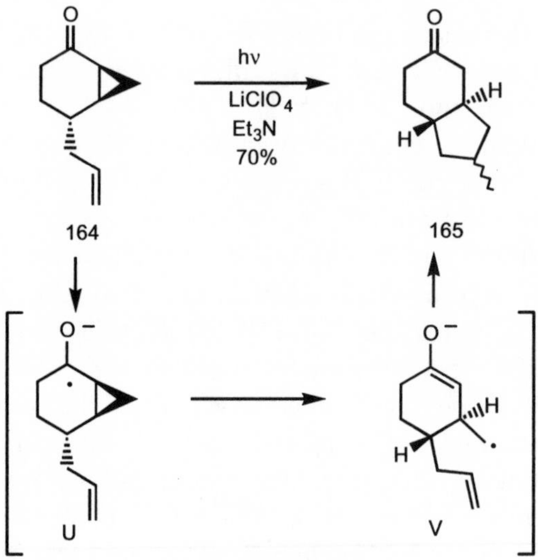

Scheme 63.

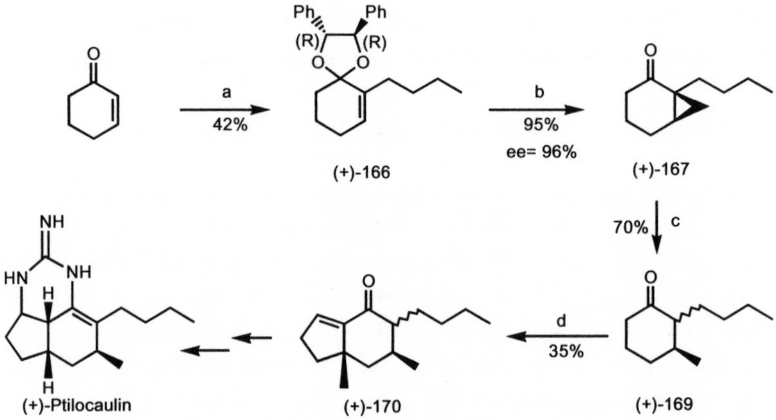

a) i- KF, Al$_2$O$_3$, t-BuOOH; ii- LDA, n-BuLi, TsOH; iii- Chiral diol, TsOH; b) i- CH$_2$I$_2$, ZnEt$_2$; ii- TsOH; c) hv, Et$_3$N, LiClO$_4$, CH$_3$CN, 254 nm; d) i- LDA, NBS; ii- NaOH,; iii- allylsilane, TiCl$_4$; iv- RhCl$_3$, catecholborane; v- PCC, CH$_2$Cl$_2$, MS 4A; vi- HCl, 2N

Scheme 64.

5. SUMMARY

Reactions involving PET processes are usually chemio-, regio-, and diastereoselective. For this reason, numerous synthetic developments have appeared during the last 20 years. For example, in the field of photodegradable protective groups, photoreduction of arenesulfonates and arenesulfonamides has been used for the regeneration of alcohols and amines. Transformation of alcohols into alkanes, via the photoreduction of the corresponding acetates and triflates, is easily carried out in HMPA due to the reducing character of the reaction mixture under UV irradiation.

At present and in spite of the interest of these reactions, the photoreduction of ketones by tertiary amines is probably one of the most useful processes from a synthetic point of view. In the field of natural products, carbocyclic and heterocyclic molecules can be easily prepared from unsaturated ketones and PET processes cannot be neglected in synthetic schemes. The mild conditions and the high selectivity involving PET processes make these reactions very attractive for further synthetic applications.

ACKNOWLEDGMENT

We would like to thank Dr. T. G. Bird for his particular assistance in the preparation of the manuscript.

REFERENCES AND NOTES

1. (a) Fox, M. A.; Chanon, M. *Photoinduced Electron Transfer*; Elsevier: Amsterdam, 1988; (b) Julliard, M.; Chanon, M. *Chem. Rev.* **1983**, *83*, 425.
2. (a) Mattay, J. *Synthesis* **1989**, 233; (b) Cossy, J. *Bull. Soc. Chim. Fr.* **1994**, *131*, 344; (c) Eberson, L. In *Electron Transfer Reactions in Organic Chemistry*; Springer Verlag: Berlin, 1987.
3. Rehm, D.; Weller, A. *Isr. J. Chem.* **1970**, *8*, 259.
4. Cohen, S. G.; Parola, A.; Parsons, G. H. *Chem. Rev.* **1973**, *73*, 141.
5. (a) Mc Omie, J. F. W. In *Advances in Organic Chemistry*; Interscience: New York, 1962, Vol. 3, p. 191; (b) Binkley, R. W.; Flechtner, T. W. In *Synthetic Organic Photochemistry*; Horspool, W. M., Ed.; Plenum: New York, 1984, p. 377.

6. (a) Zen, S.; Tashima, S.; Koto, S. *Bull. Chem. Soc. Japan* **1968**, *41*, 3025; (b) D'Souza, L.; Day, R. A. *Science* **1968**, *160*, 882.

7. (a) Hoshino, O.; Sawaki, S.; Umezawa, B. *Chem. Pharm. Bull.* **1970**, *18*, 182; (b) Kondo, Y.; Hosoyama, K.; Takemoto, T. *Chem. Pharm. Bull.* **1975**, *23*, 2167.

8. Portella, C.; Pete, J. P. *Bull. Soc. Chim. Fr.* **1980**, *II*, 275.

9. (a) Hamada, T.; Nishida, A.; Yonemitsu, O. *Heterocycles* **1979**, *12*, 647; (b) Nakamura, K.; Yasui, S.; Ohno, A.; Oka, S. *Tetrahedron Lett.* **1983**, *24*, 2001.

10. Hamada, T.; Nishida, A.; Matsumoto, Y.; Yonemitsu, O. *J. Am. Chem. Soc.* **1980**, *102*, 3978.

11. (a) Masnovi, J.; Koholic, D. J.; Berki, R. J.; Binkley, R. W. *J. Am. Chem. Soc.* **1987**, *109*, 2851; (b) Binkley, R. W.; Koholic, D. J. *J. Org. Chem.* **1989**, *54*, 3577.

12. Hamada, T.; Nishida, A.; Yonemitsu, O. *J. Am. Chem. Soc.* **1986**, *108*, 140.

13. (a) Denney, D. B.; Golstein, B. *J. Org. Chem.* **1956**, *21*, 479; (b) Cuvigny, T.; Larchevêque, M. *J. Organomet. Chem.* **1974**, *64*, 315.

14. (a) Horner, L.; Singer, R. J. *Chem. Ber.* **1968**, *101*, 3329; (b) Closson, W. D.; Ji, S.; Schulenberg, S. *J. Am. Chem. Soc.* **1970**, *92*, 650; (c) Cottrell, P. T.; Mann, C. K. *J. Am. Chem. Soc.* **1971**, *93*, 3579; (d) Mairanovsky, V. G. *Angew. Chem. Int. Ed. Engl.* **1976**, *15*, 281.

15. Pete, J. P.; Portella, C. *Bull. Soc. Chim. Fr.* **1985**, 195.

16. Tsuchiya, T.; Nakamura, F.; Umezawa, S. *Tetrahedron Lett.* **1979**, *20*, 2805.

17. (a) Shono, T.; Matsumura, Y.; Tsubata, K.; Sugihara, Y. *Tetrahedron Lett.* **1979**, *20*, 2157; (b) See also Ganson, J. R.; Schulenberg; Closson, W. D. *Tetrahedron Lett.* **1970**, 4397.

18. (a) Abad, A.; Mellier, D.; Pete, J. P.; Portella, C. *Tetrahedron Lett.* **1971**, 4555; (b) Mellier, D.; Pete, J. P.; Portella, C. *Tetrahedron Lett.* **1971**, 4559; (c) Umezawa, B.; Hoshimo, O.; Sawaki, S. *Chem. Pharm. Bull.* **1969**, *17*, 1115, 1120; (d) Graftiaux, A.; Gardent, J. *Tetrahedron Lett.* **1972**, 3321.

19. (a) Isawa, Y.; Kuromiya, N. *Bull. Chem. Soc. Japan* **1975**, *48*, 3197; (b) Weiss, B.; Dürr, H.; Haas, H. J. *Angew. Chem. Int. Ed. Engl.* **1980**, *19*, 648; (c) Pete, J. P.; Portella, C. *J. Chem. Res.(S)* **1979**, 20; *J. Chem. Res.(S)* **1979**, 209.

20. Nishida, A.; Hamada, T.; Yonemitsu, O. *J. Org. Chem.* **1988**, *53*, 3386.

21. Art, J. F.; Kestemont, J. P.; Soumillon, J. P. *Tetrahedron Lett.* **1991**, *32*, 1425.

22. Hamada, T.; Nishida, A.; Yonemitsu, *Tetrahedron Lett.* **1989**, *30*, 4241.

23. (a) Pfau, M.; Julliard, M. *Bull. Soc. Chim. Fr.* **1977**, 785; (b) Coyle, J. D. *Chem. Rev.* **1978**, *78*, 97.

24. Normant, H. *Bull. Soc. Chim. Fr.* **1968**, 791.

25. Beugelmans, R.; Le Goffand, M. T.; Compaignon de Marcheville, H. C. *R. Acad. Sc. Fr.* **1969**, *269*, 1309.

26. Deshayes, H.; Pete, J. P.; Portella, C.; Scholler, D. *J. Chem. Soc., Chem. Commun.* **1975**, 439.

27. (a) Deshayes, H.; Pete, J. P.; Portella, C. *Tetrahedron Lett.* **1976**, *17*, 2019; (b) Portella, C.; Deshayes, H.; Pete, J. P.; Scholler, D. *Tetrahedron* **1984**, *40*, 3635.

28. Klausener, A.; Beyer, G. H.; Leismann, H.; Scharf, H. D.; Müller, H.; Runsink, J.; Görner, H. *Tetrahedron* **1989**, *45*, 4989.

29. Rao, K. V. S.; Symons, M. C. R. *J. Chem. Soc., Faraday Trans. 2* **1972**, *68*, 2081.

30. Klausener, A.; Müller, E.; Runsink, J.; Scharf, H. D. *Carbohydrate Res.* **1983**, *116*, 295.

31. Prof. H. D. Scharf, personal communication.

32. (a) Pacifici, J. G.; Zannucci, J. S.; Lappin, G. R.; Ownby, J. C.; Kelly, C. A. *Molecular Photochem.* **1971**, *3*, 175; (b) Lappin, G. R.; Zannucci, J. S. *J. Org. Chem.* **1971**, *35*, 3679; (c) Anderson, J. C.; Reese, C. B. *J. Chem. Soc.* **1963**, 1781.

33. (a) Sevilla, M. D.; Morehouse, K. M.; Swarts, S. *J. Phys. Chem.* **1981**, *85*, 923; (b) Sevilla, C. L.; Swarts, S.; Sevilla, M. D. *J. A. O. C. S.* **1983**, *60*, 950.

34. (a) Portella, C.; Pete, J. P. *Tetrahedron Lett.* **1985**, *26*, 211; (b) Portella, C.; Iznaden, M. *Tetrahedron* **1989**, *45*, 6467.

35. Saito, I.; Ihehira, H.; Kasatani, R.; Watanabe, M.; Matsuura, T. *J. Am. Chem. Soc.* **1986**, *108*, 3115.

36. Lin, C. I.; Singh, P.; Ullmann, E. F. *J. Am. Chem. Soc.* **1976**, *98*, 7848.

37. Bouveault, L.; Blanc, G. *Bull. Soc. Chim. Fr.* **1903**, *29*, 787; **1904**, *31*, 666 and 672.

38. (a) Bouveault, L.; Locquin, R. C. *R. Acad. Sci. Paris* **1905**, *140*, 1593; (b) Bouveault, L.; Locquin, R. *Bull. Soc. Chim. Fr.* **1906**, *35*, 629; (c) McElvain, S. M. *Org. React.* **1948**, *4*, 256; (d) Finley, K. T. *Chem. Rev.* **1964**, *64*, 573; (e) Bloomfield, J. J.; Owsley, D. C.; Ainworth, C.; Robertson, R. E. *J. Org. Chem.* **1975**, *40*, 393.

39. Hartwig, W. *Tetrahedron Report* **1983**, *39*, N° 151, 2609.

40. (a) Boar, R. B.; Joukhadar, L.; Mc.Ghie, J. F.; Misra, S. C.; Barrett, A. G. M.; Barton, D. H. R.; Prokopiou, P. A. *J. Chem. Soc., Chem. Commun.* **1978**, 68; (b) Barrett, A. G. M.; Prokopiou, P. A.; Barton, D. H. R.; Boar, R. B.; Mc.Ghie, J. F. *J. Chem. Soc., Chem. Commun.* **1979**, 1173; (c) Barrett, A. G. M.; Prokopiou, P. A.; Barton, D. H. R. *J. Chem. Soc., Chem. Commun.* **1979**, 1175; (d) Barrett, A. G. M.; Godfrey, C. R. A.; Hollmshead, D. M.; Prokopiou, P. A.; Barton, D. H. R.; Boar, R. B.; Joukhadar, L.; Mc.Ghie, J. F.; Misra, S. C. *J. Chem. Soc., Perkin Trans. 1* **1981**, 1501.

41. (a) Deshayes, H.; Pete, J. P. *J. Chem. Soc., Chem. Commun.* **1978**, 568; (b) Deshayes, H.; Pete, J. P. *Can. J. Chem.* **1984**, *62*, 2063; (c) Mukhopadhyaha, J. K.; Mukhopadhyaha (née Ray), C.; Gjatak, U. R. *Indian J. Chem.* **1994**, 132.

42. Gremaschi, P.; Morosi, G.; Simonetta, M. *Angew. Chem. Int. Ed. Engl.* **1981**, *20*, 673.

43. Hayon, E.; Sisnic, M. *Acc. Chem. Res.* **1974**, *7*, 114.

44. Simon, J. D.; Peters, K. S. *J. Am. Chem. Soc.* **1982**, *104*, 6542.

45. (a) Stevenson, G. R.; Fraticelli, Y.; Concepcion, R. *J. Am. Chem. Soc.* **1976**, *98*, 3410; (b) Stevenson, G. R.; Castillo, C. A. *J. Am. Chem. Soc.* **1976**, *98*, 7950.

46. (a) Masnovi, J.; Maticic, J. *J. Am. Chem. Soc.* **1988**, *110*, 5189; (b) Masnovi, J. *J. Am. Chem. Soc.* **1989**, *111*, 9081.

47. (a) Mc Omie, J. F. In *Protective Groups*; Plenum Press: New York, 1973; (b) Greene, T. W.; Wuts, P. G. In *Protecting Groups*, 2nd Edition; J. Wiley: New York, 1991.

48. Bell, R. H.; Horton, D.; Williams, D. M. *J. Chem. Soc., Chem. Commun.* **1968**, 323.

49. Barton, D. H. R.; Mc Combie, S. W. *J. Chem. Soc., Perkin Trans. 1* **1975**, 1574.

50. (a) Dembele, A.; Deshayes, H.; Pete, J. P. *Tetrahedron Lett.* **1982**, *23*, 3489; (b) Dembele, A.; Deshayes, H.; Pete, J. P. *Bull. Soc. Chim. Fr.* **1988**, 671.

51. (a) Pete, J. P.; Portella, C.; Monneret, C.; Florent, J. C.; Khuong-Huu, Q. *Synthesis* **1977**, 774; (b) Collins, P. M.; Munasinghe, V. R. *J. Chem. Soc., Chem. Commun.* **1977**, 927; (c) Pete, J. P.; Portella, C.; Scholler, D. *J. Photochem.* **1984**, *27*, 128; (d) Klausener, A.; Runsink, J.; Scharf, H. D. *Liebigs Ann. Chem.* **1984**, 783; (e) Dornhagen, J.; Klausener, A.; Runsink, J.; Scharf, H. D. *Ann. Chem.* **1985**, 1838; (f) Dornhagen, J.; Scharf, H. D. *J. Carbohydrate Chem.* **1986**, *5*, 115.

52. Henin, F.; Mortezaei, R.; Muzart, J.; Pete, J. P.; Piva, O. *Tetrahedron* **1989**, *45*, 6171.

53. Ernst, B.; Ganter, C. *Helv. Chim. Acta* **1978**, *61*, 1107, 1775.

54. Still, W. C.; Yan-Tsaï, M. *J. Am. Chem. Soc.* **1980**, *102*, 3654.

55. Russel-Bournan, W.; Marples, B. A.; Zaïdi, N. A. *Tetrahedron Lett.* **1989**, *30*, 3343.

56. (a) Mattay, J.; Gersdorf, J.; Leismann, J.; Steenken, S. *Angew. Chem., Int. Ed. Engl.* **1984**, *23*, 249; (b) Mattay, J.; Gersdorf, J.; Buchkremer, K. *Chem. Ber.* **1987**, *120*, 307.

57. Mattay, J.; Gersdorf, J.; Freudensberf, U. *Tetrahedron Lett.* **1984**, *25*, 817.

58. Gersdorf, J.; Mattay, J.; Görner, H. *J. Am. Chem. Soc.* **1987**, *109*, 1203.

59. Fukuzumi, S.; Okamoto, T. *J. Am. Chem. Soc.* **1994**, *116*, 5503.

60. (a) Wagner, P. J.; Truman, R. J.; Puchalski, A. E.; Wake, R. *J. Am. Chem. Soc.* **1986**, *108*, 7727; (b) Wagner, P. J.; Park, B. S. *Organic Photochemistry*; Padwa, A., Ed.; Dekker, M.: New York, 1991, Vol. 11, p. 227.

61. (a) Ishitani, O.; Pac, C.; Sakurai, H. *J. Org. Chem.* **1983**, *48*, 2941; (b) Ishitani, O.; Yanagida, S.; Takamuku, S.; Pac, C. *J. Org. Chem.* **1987**, *52*, 2790.

62. Mandler, D.; Willner, I. *J. Chem. Soc., Perkin Trans. 2* **1985**, 1527.

63. Simon, J. D.; Peters, K. S. *J. Am. Chem. Soc.* **1983**, *105*, 4875.

64. Pac, C.; Sakurai, H.; Tosa, T. *J. Chem. Soc., Chem. Commun.* **1970**, 1311.

65. Davidson, R. S. *J. Chem. Soc., Chem. Commun.* **1966**, 575.

66. Kubota, H.; Ogiwara, Y. *J. Appl. Polym. Sci.* **1982**, *27*, 2683.

67. Kohmoto, S.; Kreber, T.; Yamamoto, H.; Yamada, K. *Bull. Chem. Soc. Jap.* **1990**, *63*, 3698.

68. Cohen, S. G.; Stein, N. M. *J. Am. Chem. Soc.* **1971**, *93*, 6542.

69. (a) Alipour, E.; Micheau, J. C.; Paillous, N.; Mathieu, J.; Lattes, A. *Tetrahedron Lett.* **1976**, 2833; (b) Alipour, E.; Vidril, D.; Micheau, J. C.; Paillous, M.; Lattes, A.; Gilles, L. *Tetrahedron* **1983**, *39*, 2807.

70. Mandler, D.; Willner, I. *J. Chem. Soc., Perkin Trans. 2* **1986**, 805.

71. (a) Roth, H. J.; El Raie, M. H. *Tetrahedron Lett.* **1970**, 2445; (b) Roth, H. J.; El Raie, M. H. *Arch. Pharm.* **1972**, *305*, 209; (c) Abdul-Baki, A.; Rotter, F.; Schrauth, T.; Roth, H. J. *Arch. Pharm.* **1978**, *311*, 341; (d) Cossy, J.; Guha, M., unpublished results; (e) Kraus, G. A.; Chen, L. *Tetrahedron Lett.* **1991**, *32*, 7151.

72. (a) Ailworth, K. L.; El-Hamamy, A. A.; Hesab, M. M.; Hill, J. *J. Chem. Soc., Perkin Trans. 1* **1980**, 1671; (b) Hesab, M. M.; Hill, J.; El-Hamamy, A. A. *J. Chem. Soc., Perkin Trans. 1* **1980**, 2371; (c) Gold, E. H. *J. Am. Chem. Soc.* **1971**, *93*, 2793; (d) Clasen, R. A.; Searles, S., Jr. *J. Chem. Soc., Chem. Commun.* **1966**, 289.

73. Wagner, P. J.; Scheve, B. J. *J. Am. Chem. Soc.* **1977**, *99*, 1858.

74. Padwa, A.; Albrecht, F.; Singh, P.; Vega, E. *J. Am. Chem. Soc.* **1971**, *93*, 2928.

75. (a) Belotti, D.; Cossy, J.; Pete, J. P.; Portella, C. *Tetrahedron Lett.* 198; (b) Belotti, D.; Cossy, J.; Pete, J. P.; Portella, C. *J. Org. Chem.* **1986**, *51*, 4196.

76. Giese, B. *Radicals in Organic Synthesis: Formation of Carbon-Carbon Bonds*; Baldwin, J. E., Ed.; Pergamon Press, 1986.

77. Shono, T.; Nishigushi, I.; Ohmizu, H.; Mitami, M. J. *J. Am. Chem. Soc.* **1978**, *100*, 545.

78. Corey, E. J.; Pyne, S. G. *Tetrahedron Lett.* **1983**, *24*, 2821.

79. (a) Pradhan, S. K.; Radhakrishnan, T. V.; Subramanian, R. *J. Org. Chem.* **1976**, *41*, 1943; (b) Stork; G.; Malhotra, S.; Thomson, H.; Uchibayashi, M. *J. Am. Chem. Soc.* **1965**, *87*, 1148.

80. Molander, G. A.; Etter, J. B.; Zinke, P. W. *J. Am. Chem. Soc.* **1987**, *109*, 453.

81. Typical procedure: A solution of ketone (5×10^{-2} M) in acetonitrile in the presence of Et_3N (5 equiv) was irradiated at 254 nm by using a 12 TUV 15 Philips lamps merry-go-round system.

82. (a) Cossy, J.; Belotti, D.; Pete, J. P. *Tetrahedron Lett.* **1987**, *28*, 4547; (b) Cossy, J.; Belotti, D.; Pete, J. P. *Tetrahedron* **1990**, *46*, 1859.

83. Cherest, M.; Felkin, H.; Umpleby, J. D. *J. Chem. Soc., Chem. Commun.* **1981**, 681.

84. (a) Cossy, J.; Madaci, A.; Pete, J. P. *Tetrahedron Lett.* **1994**, *35*, 1541; (b) Chesta, C. A.; Whitten, D. G. *J. Am. Chem. Soc.* **1992**, *114*, 2188.

85. Cossy, J.; Belotti, D.; Pete, J. P. *Tetrahedron Lett.* **1987**, *28*, 4545.

86. Cossy, J.; Belotti, D. *Tetrahedron Lett.* **1988**, *29*, 6113.

87. Cossy, J.; Belotti, D.; Leblanc, C. *J. Org. Chem.* **1993**, *58*, 2351.

88. Cossy, J.; Leblanc, C. *Tetrahedron Lett.* **1991**, *32*, 3051.

89. (a) Wittaker, B. *The Chemistry of Diazonium and Diazo Groups*; Wiley-Interscience: New York, 1978, p. 593; (b) Froborg, J.; Magnusson, G. *J. Am. Chem. Soc.* **1978**, *100*, 6728; (c) Kunish, F.; Hobert, K.; Welzel, P. *Tetrahedron Lett.* **1985**, 5433; (d) Cossy, J.; Bouzide, A.; Thellend, A.; Belotti, D. *Bull. Soc. Chim. Fr.* **1994**, 723.

90. (a) Oppolzer, W.; Robbiani, C.; Bättig, K. *Helv. Chim. Acta* **1980**, *63*, 2015; (b) Oppolzer, W.; Kurth, M.; Reichlin, D.; Chapuis, C.; Mohnhaupt, M.; Moffat, F. *Helv. Chim. Acta* **1981**, *64*, 2803.

91. Cossy, J. *Tetrahedron Lett.* **1989**, *30*, 4113.

92. Brunetière, A. P.; Leclaire, M.; Bhatnagar, S.; Lallemand, J. M.; Cossy, J. *Tetrahedron Lett.* **1989**, *30*, 341.

93. (a) Bamford, W. R.; Stevens, T. S. *J. Chem. Soc.* **1952**, 4735; (b) Shapiro, R. H. *Organic Reactions* **1976**, *23*, 405.

94. Gianturco, M. A.; Friedel, D.; Flanagan, V. *Tetrahedron Lett.* **1965**, 1847.

95. Cossy, J.; Pete, J. P.; Portella, C. *Tetrahedron Lett.* **1989**, *30*, 7361.
96. Bannai, K.; Tanaka, T.; Okamura, N.; Hazato, A.; Sugiura, S.; Manabe, K.; Tominori, K.; Kato, Y.; Kurozumi, S.; Noyori, R. *Tetrahedron* **1990**, *46*, 6689.
97. Tanigwa, Y.; Ohta, H.; Sonoda, A.; Murahashi, S. *J. Am. Chem. Soc.* **1978**, *100*, 4610.
98. Lüning, J.; Möller, U.; Debski, N.; Welzel, P. *Tetrahedron Lett.* **1993**, *34*, 5871.
99. (a) Prosser, T. *J. Am. Chem. Soc.* **1961**, *83*, 1701; (b) Price, C. C.; Snyder, W. H. *J. Am. Chem. Soc.* **1961**, *83*, 1773; (c) Corey, E. J.; Suggs, J. W. *J. Org. Chem.* **1973**, *38*, 3224; (d) Baudry, D.; Ephritikhine, M.; Felkin, H. *Nouveau J. Chem.* **1978**, *2*, 355; (e) Baudry, D.; Ephritikhine, M.; Felkin, H. *J. Chem. Soc., Chem. Commun.* **1978**, 694; (f) Oltvoort, J. J.; Van Boeckel, C. A. A.; De Koning, J. H.; Van Boom, J. H. *Synthesis* **1981**, 305; (g) Boss, R.; Scheffold, R. *Angew. Chem.* **1976**, *88*, 578–579; *Angew. Chem., Int. Ed. Engl.* **1976**, *15*, 588; (h) Cleavage of an allyl ether: Nicolaou, K. C.; Hummel, C. W.; Bockovich, N. J.; Wong, C.-H. *J. Chem. Soc., Chem. Commun.* **1991**, 870; (i) Gigg, J.; Gigg, R. *J. Chem. Soc. (C)* **1966**, 82; (j) Reagents: α) Mild acid: Dreef, C. E.; Jansze, J.-P.; Elie, C. J. J.; Van Der Marel, G. A.; Van Boom, J. H. *Carbohydrate Res.* **1992**, *234*, 37; β) HgO/HgCl$_2$: Gigg, R.; Warren, C. D. *J. Chem. Soc. (C)* **1968**, 1903; γ) NBS in water: Hébert, N.; Just, G. *J. Chem. Soc., Chem. Commun.* **1990**, 1497; δ) I$_2$ in water: Nashed, M. A.; Anderson, L. *J. Chem. Soc., Chem. Commun.* **1982**, 1274; ε) OsO$_4$ in CH$_2$Cl$_2$: Lamberth, C.; Bednarski, M. D. *Tetrahedron Lett.* **1991**, *32*, 7369; (k) Kariyone, K.; Yazawa, H. *Tetrahedron Lett.* **1970**, 2885; Nishizawa, M.; Imagawa, H.; Kan, Y.; Yamada, H. *Tetrahedron Lett.* **1991**, *32*, 5551; (l) Ito, H.; Taguchi, T.; Hanzawa, Y. *J. Org. Chem.* **1993**, *58*, 774; (m) Espanet, B.; Dunach, E.; Périchon, J. *Tetrahedron Lett.* **1992**, *33*, 2485; (n) Nakayama, K.; Uoto, K.; Higashi, K.; Soga, T.; Kusama, K. *Chem. Pharm. Bull.* **1992**, *40*, 1718; (o) Akiyama, T.; Hirofuji, H.; Ozaki, S. *Tetrahedron Lett.* **1991**, *32*, 1321 and references therein; (p) Ogawa, T.; Nakabayashi, S.; Kitajima, T. *Carbohydrate Res.* **1983**, *114*, 225.
100. Tsuji, J. *Synthesis* **1984**, 369 and references therein; Goudedard, M. *Bull. Soc. Chim. Fr.* **1973**, 577.
101. Cossy, J.; Aclinou, P.; Bellosta, V.; Furet, N.; Baranne-Lafont, J.; Sparfel, D.; Souchaud, C. *Tetrahedron Lett.* **1991**, *32*, 1315.
102. (a) Caine, D. *Organic Reaction*; Dauben, W. G., Ed.; John Wiley: New York, 1976; (b) Mc Chesney, J. D.; Thompson, T. N. *J. Org. Chem.* **1985**, *50*, 3473.
103. Hasegawa, E.; Ishiyama, K.; Kato, T.; Horaguchi, T.; Shimizu, T. *J. Org. Chem.* **1992**, *57*, 5352.
104. Shapiro, E. L.; Gentles, M. J. *J. Org. Chem.* **1981**, *46*, 5017.
105. Molander, G. A.; Hahn, G. *J. Org. Chem.* **1986**, *51*, 1135.
106. Cossy, J.; Ibhi, S. *Carbohydrate Res.* **1994**, *259*, 141.
107. Stevens, C. L.; Schultz, K. W.; Smith, D. J.; Pillai, P. M.; Rubenstein, P.; Strominger, J. L. *J. Am. Chem. Soc.* **1973**, *95*, 5767.
108. Hirono, I.; Ogino, H.; Fujimoto, M.; Yamada, K. J.; Yoshida, Y.; Ikagawa, M.; Okumura, M. *J. Natl. Cancer. Inst.* **1987**, *79*, 1143.
109. Cossy, J.; Ibhi, S.; Tacchini, L.; Kahn, P. *Tetrahedron Lett.* **1995**,

110. (a) Buisson, D.; Azerad, R. *Tetrahedron Lett.* **1986**, *23*, 2631; (b) Genêt, J. P.; Pfister, X.; Ratovelomanana-Vidal, V.; Pinel, C.; Laffitte, J. A. *Tetrahedron Asymmetry* **1994**, *5*, 4559.

111. (a) Frater, G. *Helv. Chim. Acta* **1979**, *62*, 2825; (b) Frater, G. *Helv. Chim. Acta* **1980**, *63*, 1383.

112. Cossy, J.; Ranaivosata, J. L.; Bellosta, V.; Ancerewicz, J.; Ferritto, R.; Vogel, P. *J. Org. Chem.* **1995**, in press.

113. Cossy, J.; Ranaivosata, J. L.; Bellosta, V. *Tetrahedron Lett.* **1995**, *36*, 2067.

114. Postema, M. H. D. *Tetrahedron* **1992**, *48*, 8545.

115. Ferrito, R.; Vogel, P. *Tetrahedron Lett.* **1995**, *36*, 3517.

116. Arval, G.; Fattori, D.; Vogel, P. *Tetrahedron* **1992**, *48*, 10621.

117. (a) Martin, O. R.; Lai, W. *J. Org. Chem.* **1990**, *55*, 5188; (b) Martin, O. R.; Lai, W. *J. Org. Chem.* **1993**, *58*, 176; (c) Lopez-Herrera, F. J.; Pino-Gonzalez, M. S.; Planas-Ruiz, F. *Tetrahedron Asymmetry* **1990**, *1*, 465.

118. Bischof, E. W.; Mattay, J. *Tetrahedron Lett.* **1990**, *31*, 7137.

119. Mattay, J.; Banning, A.; Bischof, E. W.; Heibreder, A.; Runsink, J. *Chem. Ber.* **1992**, *125*, 2119.

120. Pandey, B.; Rao, A. T.; Dalvi, P. V.; Kumar, P. *Tetrahedron* **1994**, *50*, 3835.

121. Le Blanc-Piva, S.; Piva, O.; Pete, J. P., unpublished results.

122. (a) Pandey, B.; Rao, A. T.; Dalvi, P. V., Kumar, P. *Tetrahedron* **1994**, *50*, 3835; (b) Kirschberg, T.; Mattay, J. *Tetrahedron Lett.* **1994**, *35*, 7217.

123. Cossy, J.; Furet, N. *Tetrahedron Lett.* **1993**, *34*, 8107.

124. Cossy, J.; Furet, N.; Bouzbouz, S. *Tetrahedron* **1995**, *51*, 11751.

125. Mc Millen, D. F.; Golden, D. M. *Ann. Rev. Phys. Chem.* **1982**, *33*, 493.

126. Cossy, J.; Bouzbouz, S., unpublished results.

127. Sugimura, T.; Yoshikawa, M.; Furagawa, T. *Tetrahedron* **1990**, *46*, 5955.

128. Mash, E. A.; Torok, D. S. *J. Org. Chem.* **1989**, *54*, 250.

129. Corey, E. J.; Naef, R.; Hannon, F. J. *J. Am. Chem. Soc.* **1986**, *108*, 7115.

130. Hosomi, A.; Sakurai, H. *J. Am. Chem. Soc.* **1977**, *99*, 1673.

131. Männig, D.; Nöth, H. *Angew. Chem. Int. Ed. Engl.* **1985**, 879.

132. Snider, B. B.; Faith, W. C. *J. Am. Chem. Soc.* **1984**, *106*, 1443.

INDEX

Advances in Electron Transfer Chemistry

Edited by **Patrick S. Mariano,** *Department of Chemistry and Biochemistry, University of Maryland, College Park*

J
A
I

P
R
E
S
S

Advances in Cycloaddition

Edited by **Dennis P. Curran**, *Department of Chemistry, University of Pittsburgh*

Volume 1, 1988, 208 pp. $109.50
ISBN 0-89232-861-4

CONTENTS: Introduction to the Series: An Editor's Foreword, *Albert Padwa, Emory University*. Preface, *Dennis P. Curran*. Steric Course and Mechanism of 1,3-Dipolar Cycloadditions, *Rolf Huisgen*. Nonstabilized Azomethine Ylides, *Edwin Vedejs*. Molecular Rearrangements Occurring from Products of Intramolecular 1,3 Dipolar Cycloadditions: Synthetic and Mechanistic Aspects, *Arthur G. Schultz*. Dipolar Cycloadditions of Nitrones with Vinyl Ethers and Silane Derivatives, *Philip DeShong, Stephen W. Lander, Jr., Joseph M. Leginus and C. Michael Dickson*. The Cycloaddition Approach to β-Hydroxy Carbonyls: An Emerging Alternative to the Aldol Strategy, *Dennis P. Curran*.

Volume 2, 1990, 220 pp. $109.50
ISBN 0-89232-951-3

CONTENTS: Introduction to the Series: An Editor's Foreword, *Albert Padwa*. Preface, *Dennis P. Curran*. Intramolecular 1,3-Dipolar Cycloaddition Chemistry, *Albert Padwa and Allen M. Schoffstall*. Stereochemical and Synthetic Studies of the Intramolecular Diels-Alder Reaction, *William R. Roush*. Thermal Reaction of Cyclopropenone Ketals, Key Mechanistic Features, Scope and Application of the Cycloaddition Reactions of Cyclopropenone Ketals and π - Delocalized Singlet Vinyl Carbenes; Three Carbon I,I-/1,3-Dipoles, *Dale L. Boger and Christine E. Brotherton-Pleiss*.

Volume 3, 1993, 210 pp. $109.50
ISBN 1-55938-319-4

CONTENTS: Facial Diastereoselection in Diels-Alder Cycloadditions and Related Reactions: Understanding Planar Interactions and Establishing Synthetic Potential, *A. G. Fallis and Yee-Fung Lu*. Substituent and Structural Effects in the Ozonolysis of Cyclic Vinylogous Esters, *W. H. Bunnelle*. N-Metalated Azomethine Ylides, *S. Kanemasa and Otohiko Tsuge*. Azomethine Ylide Cycloadditions via 1,2- Prototropy and Metallo-Dipole Formation from Imines, *R. Grigg and V. Sridharan*. Index.

Advances in Nitrogen Heterocycles

Edited by **Chris Moody,** *Department of Chemistry, Loughborough University of Technology, England*

Volume 1, 1994, 257 pp. $109.50
ISBN 0-89232-864-9

CONTENTS: Reaction of Metal Stabilized Carbenoids with Pyrroles, *H.M.L. Davies.* Synthesis of Porphyrins with Exocyclic Rings from Cycloalkenopyrroles, *T.D. Lash.* Palladium-Catalyzed Coupling Reactions of Indoles, *A.R. Martin and Q. Zheng.* Cycloaddition Reactions of Indole Derivatives, *U. Pindur.* Transition-Metal Mediated Synthesis of Carbazole Derivatives, *H. J. Knolker.* Synthesis of [b]-Annelated Indoles by Thermal Electrocyclic Reactions, *S. Hibino and E. Sugino.* Total Synthesis of (-) and ent(-) Duocarmycin SA, *D.L. Boger.*

Volume 2, 1996, 300 pp. $109.50
ISBN 0-7623-0056-6

CONTENTS: Nucleophilic Addition to the α–Carbon of β-Lactams, *P. R. Guzzo and M. J. Miller.* Chemical Synthesis of Porphobilinogen and Studies of Its Biosynthesis, *R. Neier.* Synthesis and Cycloaddition Reactions of Iso-Condensed Heteroaromatic Pyrroles, *C. K. Sha.* Azacyclopentadienyl Metal Compounds; Historical Background and Recent Advances, *C. Janiak and N. Kuhn.* Recent Developments in the Synthesis of Marine Pyridoacridine Alkaloids, *A. M. Echavarren.* Alkaloid Synthesis Using 1-Acylpyridinium Salts as Intermediates, *D. L. Comins and S. P. Joseph.* Index.

FACULTY/PROFESSIONAL discounts are available in the U.S. and Canada at a rate of 40% off the list price when prepaid by personal check or credit card and ordered directly from the publisher.

JAI PRESS INC.
55 Old Post Road No. 2 - P.O. Box 1678
Greenwich, Connecticut 06836-1678
Tel: (203) 661- 7602   Fax: (203) 661-0792

J A I   P R E S S

J A I   P R E S S

Organic Synthesis:
Theory and Applications

Edited by **Tomas Hudlicky,** *Department of Chemistry, University of Florida*

These volumes will cover areas of organic synthesis ranging from the latest developments in enantioselective methodologies to reviews of updated chemical methods. They are written by experts in the respective fields who will describe their own area of expertise as well as those of their peers.

Volume 1, 1989, 242 pp. $109.50
ISBN 0-89232-865-7

CONTENTS: Introduction to the Series: An Editor's Foreword, *Albert Padwa.* Preface, *Tomas Hudlicky.* Asymmetric Diels-Alder Reactions, *Michael J. Tasihner.* Nonconventional Reaction Conditions: Ultrasound, High Pressure, and Microwave Heating in Organic Synthesis, *Raymond J. Giguere.* Allylsilanes in Organic Synthesis, *George Majetich.*

Volume 2, 1993, 188 pp. $109.50
ISBN 1-55938-185-X

CONTENTS: Preface, *Tomas Hudlicky.* Modern Synthetic Design: Symmetry, Simplicity, Efficiency and Art, *Tomas Hudlicky and Michael Natchus.* Toward the Ideal Synthesis: Connectivity Analysis, *Paul Wender and Benjamin L. Miller.* Application of Graph Theory to Synthesis Planning: Complexity, Reflexivity and Vulnerability, *Steven H. Bertz and Toby J. Sommer.* Asymmetric Reactions Promoted by Titanium Reagents, *Koichi Narasaka and Nobuharu Iwasawa.* The Use of Arene Cis-diols in Synthesis, *Stephen M. Brown*

FACULTY/PROFESSIONAL discounts are available in the U.S. and Canada at a rate of 40% off the list price when prepaid by personal check or credit card and ordered directly from the publisher.

JAI PRESS INC.
55 Old Post Road No. 2 - P.O. Box 1678
Greenwich, Connecticut 06836-1678
Tel: (203) 661- 7602   Fax: (203) 661-0792